Introduction to Geological Microbiology

International Series in the Earth Sciences
ROBERT R. SHROCK, *Consulting Editor*

Kenneth O. Emery, *Woods Hole Oceanographic Institution*
Fritz Koczy, *Institute of Marine Science, University of Miami*
Konrad Krauskopf, *Stanford University*
Walter Monk, *University of California, La Jolla Laboratories*
Sverre Petterssen, *University of Chicago*

INTRODUCTION TO
GEOLOGICAL
MICROBIOLOGY

Sergey Ivanovich Kuznetsov

Institute of Microbiology
Corresponding Member, Academy of Sciences, USSR

Mikhail Vladimirovich Ivanov

Institute of Microbiology
Academy of Sciences, USSR

Natal'ya Nikolayevna Lyalikova

Institute of Microbiology
Academy of Sciences, USSR

translator
Paul T. Broneer
Senior Geologist
Scripta Technica, Inc.

editor of English edition
Carl H. Oppenheimer
Institute of Marine Science
University of Miami

McGRAW-HILL *Book Company, Inc.*
New York   San Francisco   Toronto   London

Introduction to Geological Microbiology

35700

Translated from Vvedeniye v Geologicheskuyu Mikrobiologiyu, Academy of Sciences,
USSR Press, Moscow, 1962.

212673
Geology

Editor's Preface

It can be presumed that much of the transition or diagenesis of inorganic elements and organic compounds in water and sedimentary environments takes place directly or indirectly through the activities of living microorganisms. These microorganisms are indigenous to all environments except volcanic high-temperature sites, and their abundance throughout the hydrosphere and surface of the lithosphere is evidence of their activity. They can withstand and be active at pressures up to 25,000 psi, pH from 1 to 10, temperatures from 0 to 75°C, and salinities up to saturation. Some grow in the absence of gaseous oxygen, using combined oxygen sources. They can migrate through interstitial spaces in sediments, and in unfavorable environments can evolve into resistant bodies which may be activated at some later time when the environment changes.

Our Soviet colleagues have produced a large part of the literature on fundamental aspects of microbial ecology and the influence of microorganisms as geological agents. The present book provides a very good review of the past history and the current thinking of the Soviet scientists in this field. The reference to the older Soviet literature is of considerable value. The subjects covered include: fossil fuels, iron, sulfur, certain trace elements and an outline of the effects of microorganisms in the weathering of surface rocks.

Although the book emphasizes the role of Soviet scientists, the pertinent literature of other countries is included. The student of microbiology, geology and geochemistry will be interested in this compilation of the role of the ubiquitous microorganism in certain of its natural habitats.

The illustrations and original photographs, as well as some additional text, were kindly supplied by the Soviet authors. My compliments to Mr. Paul T. Broneer, Senior Geologist at Scripta Technica, Inc., who has done an excellent piece of work in translating the Russian, making the editing a pleasure.

Carl H. Oppenheimer

Virginia Key, Florida
July, 1963

Contents

Authors' Preface to the
American Edition

The idea that microorganisms were important in the cycles of the various elements in nature was expressed by S. N. Vinogradskiy in his discovery of the process of chemosynthesis. He first formulated this idea in 1897, in a speech delivered at a general meeting of the Russian Academy of Sciences. Somewhat later a great step forward in developing the concept of the participation of microorganisms in geologic processes was made by V. I. Vernadskiy, who, in his "Descriptive Mineralogy" and "History of the Minerals in the Earth's Crust," discussed geochemical processes that could not have taken place in the absence of living matter.

Factual data on the geochemical activities of microorganisms, however, began to be collected only much later. The first fundamental advance in this new science was represented by S. A. Waksman's outstanding book, "Principles of Soil Microbiology," which even thirty-five years after its first publication has still not lost its value. Various aspects of oil microbiology were later extensively developed by ZoBell and some of his co-workers, and the results of their work summarized in a monograph by Beerstecher (1954). The study of the role played by microorganisms in oxidizing sulfide ores was initiated by the brilliant work of A. R. Colmer and M. E. Hinkle, and further developed by W. W. Leathen, S. Braley and J. Beck. During the same period the study of the theoretical aspects of the physiology of chemoautotrophic microorganisms was being widely carried forward by Starkey, Barker, Van Niel, Umbreit and others. In the past few years, finally, L. D. M. Baas Becking and W. Schwartz have published generalizing works on the geological activities of microorganisms. Many studies of the role of microorganisms in deposits of oil, sulfur and sulfide ores have also been made in the Soviet Union.

The present book is in no sense an exhaustive presentation of the principles of geomicrobiology; it is, rather, merely a first attempt to generalize some of the existing information on the role of microorganisms in the formation and alteration of economic mineral deposits. For this reason it might perhaps be more accurately titled "The Microbiology of Economic Mineral Deposits."

The authors will be extremely gratified if the present book has succeeded in acquainting its readers with some of the most important aspects of the work on geomicrobiology that has been done in the USSR.

S. I. Kuznetsov

M. V. Ivanov

Introduction

In studying the processes involved in the formation of the earth's crust and sedimentary rocks, the weathering of rocks, and the formation and destruction of economic mineral deposits, the investigator constantly encounters the effects of powerful physical and chemical agents. Until recently, however, the role played by living organisms in the history of the earth has been recognized only in connection with the carbon cycle. According to the available calculations, the total quantity of organic matter produced each year upon our planet amounts to 50-100 billion tons. The annual mineralization of organic matter and its transformation into carbon dioxide is of approximately the same order of magnitude. Although the leading role in the first part of the carbon cycle—the formation of organic matter—is played by the green plants, the processes of mineralization take place mainly through the action of microorganisms, which are biochemically the most active of all living organisms and are, moreover, the most widespread organisms in nature.

However, the activity of microorganisms in nature is not limited only to the transformation and destruction of organic substances. From the time of S. N. Vinogradskiy's classic investigations (1888) to the present writing, microbiologists have been studying many microorganisms whose life activities do not require the presence of preexisting organic matter.

These so-called chemosynthetic autotrophic microorganisms grow and reproduce by using inorganic food and the energy from the oxidation of inorganic compounds such as molecular hydrogen, methane and reduced compounds of nitrogen, sulfur and iron.

Of particular interest to the deciphering of history of the geochemical processes that have taken place on the earth are the anaerobic organisms, which are able to grow by using both organic and mineral substances (hydrogen, hydrogen sulfide) in the absence of oxygen. Evidently such organisms must have been the ancestors of life on the earth, since oxygen was lacking on this planet in the first stages of the development of life (Fig. 1).

However, it is presently impossible to define the first forms of life in detail because of the lack of sufficient data. Nevertheless, this has become an object of intensive study in one of the youngest branches of microbiology—geomicrobiology. As an experimental science, geomicrobiology is the study of microbial processes currently taking place in the modern sediments of various bodies of water, in ground waters circulating through sedimentary and igneous rocks, and in the weathered earth crust. In addition, the scope of this science also encompasses the physiology of specific microorganisms taking part in presently occurring geochemical processes.

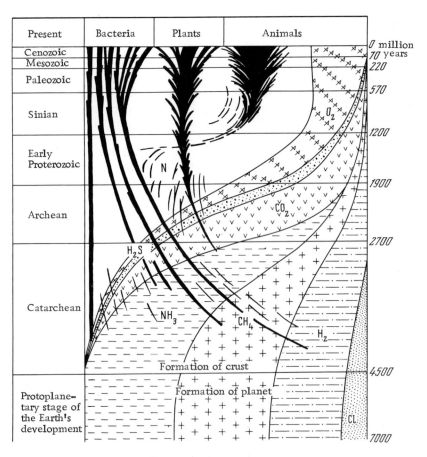

Fig. 1. Evolution of life and its environment on the earth (after A. G. Vologdin).

Investigations of the activities of microorganisms which are now observed to be taking place in various stages of sedimentation, diagenesis and metamorphism, in combination with the paleogeographic analysis of sedimentary rocks, and of the direct indications of the presence of microorganisms and the products of their activities in the rocks of ancient geologic periods, should provide an answer to the question of the extent and scale of the geological activity of microorganisms in the past (Isachenko, 1951; Kuznetsov, 1959a, 1961; Baas Becking, 1959).

In concluding this brief introduction, it must be stressed that the development of geomicrobiology as a science has been closely associated with the discovery of the role played by microorganisms in the genesis of the various species of economic minerals.

The discovery of the geological role of microorganisms began with the study of the microflora in mineral springs and saltpeter mines (Vinogradskiy). This was followed by the discovery of the part played by microorganisms in the formation of medicinal muds (Nadson, Verigo, Isachenko), and the parallel study of the microbiological processes taking place in ooze deposits (Isachenko, Perfil'yev, ZoBell, Pel'sh, Kuznetsov). The next stage was the investigation of the role of microorganisms in the formation of iron and manganese ores (Butkevich, Perfil'yev, Kholodnyy and others) and the explanation of their presence in oil deposits (Bastin, Ginzburg-Karagicheva and others).

These investigators emphasized the general problems in geomicrobiology, such as the distribution of the individual groups of microorganisms in the lithosphere and hydrosphere and adaptation of microorganisms to the specific environments in rocks and ground waters, as well as a number of others, and partially solved them by studying specific phenomena found associated with certain economic mineral deposits. For this reason most of the material presented in the present book is arranged by chapters, each characterizing the microflora in fossil fuels, in sulfur or iron deposits and so forth.

The authors of this book believe that the study of microbiological processes occurring primarily in deposits of economic minerals is justified from both the theoretical and the practical standpoints. The specific role of the microbiological processes in changing the nature of sulfur or iron compounds, for example, is far easier to determine in areas of large accumulations of the compound in question, inasmuch as these will reveal not only that certain particular microbiological processes can, in principle, take place, but also the true geological scale in which they occur.

Introduction to Geological Microbiology

CHAPTER I

The Geological Environment of Microorganisms

The activities of microorganisms contributing to the formation and the destruction of rocks take place in the surface layers of the lithosphere and at its boundary with the atmosphere and hydrosphere. The most important factors controlling the development of microorganisms in nature are light, temperature, pressure, moisture, the presence of organic matter and biogenic elements, oxidation-reduction conditions and salinity.

Thus environments in which microorganisms may be active can differ sharply both in geological regions and in various kinds of rocks which have different ages and are characterized by different lithologic, chemical and particle size compositions. For these reasons it will be necessary to present some elementary information on geology, so that the reader who lacks a background in geology may gain a better understanding of the environments in which microorganisms take part in geologic processes.

1. THE ELEMENTS OF HISTORICAL GEOLOGY

The surface of the earth is undergoing constant change and may, according to A. D. Arkhangel'skiy, be divided into areas in which the mobility of the earth's crust is manifested by different degrees of intensity.

The most highly mobile parts of the earth's crust are the geosynclinal regions. Here the vertical oscillatory movements have the greatest velocity and amplitude. The uplift and subsidence of the entire geosyncline are accompanied by its breaking up into separate blocks, which move at very different velocities and in different directions. Such is the genesis of the individual basins and mountains, and of the folds in the rocks that compose them. Extensive manifestations of volcanic activity also resulting in the formation of extrusive and intrusive rocks. Sedimentary rocks accumulate in the marine basins that form in the depressions in geosynclinal regions. Later on, with the upwarping of that part of the earth's crust, the sea disappears and the region is gradually transformed into land.

Soviet geologists believe that in the early eras of geologic history, geosynclinal regions covered the whole of the earth's surface—that is, that the earth's crust was mobile everywhere. Thereafter more stable areas began to form on the surface of the earth—these are the platforms, whose area has been increasing continually up to the present. On the platforms there are accumulations of relatively thin strata of sedimentary rocks. The development of the earth's crust in the transition from geosynclinal regions to platforms is an intermittent process. In the earth's history, from the beginning of the Paleozoic Era to the present time, there have been three such cycles: the Caledonian, which corresponds in time to the Cambrian and Silurian periods of geologic history; the Hercynian, which occurred from the Devonian through the Permian; and the Alpine cycle, which lasted from the beginning of the Mesozoic Era to the present. After each cycle, a considerable part of the geosynclinal regions became platform areas, thus losing their mobility. The causes that produce these movements and deformations of the earth's crust, however, remain unknown to the present time.

All the changes that have taken place on the earth's surface, such as the formation of the seas and continents, have led to changes in the physical and geographic environment in which organisms exist. Thus, the organic world has also changed along with the inorganic. Among the great variety of past forms of life, it is possible to distinguish so-called index fossils—the remains of organisms which lived for a comparatively short time and as a species were widely distributed during the time of their existence. The brief period of their existence, as V. A. Varsonof'yeva (1945) has written, makes it possible to assign deposits containing guide fossils to a definite and limited interval of geologic history. Moreover, the widespread occurrence of a given organism in a particular epoch makes it possible to correlate chronologically different sediments which have been deposited in localities far distant from each other.

Each geologic period has been characterized by a corresponding predominance of definite groups of both animals and plants (see Fig. 19, p. 80). It is commonly known, for instance, that the formation of coal, lignite, peat and other caustobioliths began with the accumulation of great amounts of dead plants.

From a study of the distribution of the fossil remains of plants and animals in rocks, geologists have been able to subdivide the entire history of the earth into six major chapters, or Eras, and each Era again into Periods. The latter are, in turn, subdivided into Epochs.

Table 1 presents a graphic picture of the basic geochronological subdivisions.

Table 1

Geochronology

(after B. A. Trofimov, 1954, and A. G. Vologdin)

Era	Period (System)	Epoch (Series)
Cenozoic	Quaternary, or Anthropogene	Holocene (Recent)
		Pleistocene (Ice ages)
	Neogene	Pliocene
		Miocene
	Paleogene	Oligocene
		Eocene
		Paleocene
Mesozoic	Cretaceous	Upper Cretaceous
		Lower Cretaceous
	Jurassic	Upper Jurassic
		Middle Jurassic
		Lower Jurassic
	Triassic	Upper Triassic
		Middle Triassic
		Lower Triassic
Paleozoic	Permian	Upper Permian
		Lower Permian
	Carboniferous	Upper Carboniferous
		Middle Carboniferous
		Lower Carboniferous
	Devonian	Upper Devonian
		Middle Devonian
		Lower Devonian
	Silurian	Upper Silurian (Gotlandian)
		Lower Silurian (Ordovician)
	Cambrian	Upper Cambrian
		Middle Cambrian
		Lower Cambrian
Proterozoic	Sinian	
	Middle Proterozoic	
	Lower Proterozoic	
Archean	Not subdivided	
Catarchean	Not subdivided	

2. SEDIMENTARY ROCKS AND THE CONDITIONS OF THEIR FORMATION

The rocks which form the surface layers of the earth's crust may be classed as sedimentary, igneous and metamorphic. The sedimentary rocks were formed principally in marine or fresh-water basins under conditions more or less closely approximating those existing in present bodies of water. Microorganisms, although not directly involved in sediment formation, have evidently been able to take part in the decomposition of the organic substances that entered into the composition of the sedimentary rocks during their deposition in the bodies of water.

The primary formation of the igneous rocks, of course, has in no way been associated with microbial activity; nevertheless in becoming exposed at the earth's surface, from their location deep within the earth's crust, these rocks are subjected to a considerable degree of alteration. Here the microorganisms are active and have played a role in the weathering of igneous rocks in the geologic past.

Microorganisms have played a great part in the transformation of enormous amounts of organic matter, and have thus been the primary source of many fossil fuels such as oil and coal. The sulfide compounds of metals, such as pyrite, chalcopyrite and others, are very readily weathered and oxidized. For these and other reasons the conditions governing the formation of sedimentary and igneous rocks, and the genesis of ore-forming fluids and sulfide ores, will be briefly characterized below.

Conclusions regarding the participation of microorganisms in the genesis of economic minerals or commercially useful substances in rocks, however, may be drawn only on the basis of a study of analogous processes taking place at the present time.

The problems associated with the formation of sedimentary rocks are discussed in detail in the classic work by N. M. Strakhov (1960). Sedimentary rocks were formed mainly in bodies of water. The time when these processes of sedimentation and lithogenesis occurred may be approximately determined by studying the stratigraphy of the particular deposits in question. The external environment as it existed at that time can to some degree be ascertained from a study of the lithology of the surrounding rocks, or the "facies of the deposits." Huxley defines "facies" as a sediment (or rock) which maintains the same lithologic composition and contains the same fauna and flora throughout its extent.

The conditions governing the formation of particular facies of marine deposits have been examined in detail by D. V. Nalivkin (1956). After analyzing the formation of modern marine and continental sediments, Nalivkin classifies them according to individual facies; he also presents a number of examples of the reconstruction of ancient bodies of water in which an accumulation of similar sediments might have occured. He divides the entire region of formation of marine sediments genetically into three zones:

1) the littoral zone of the sea, with depths of water from 0 to 400 m;

2) the zone of continental slope deposits, with depths from 200 to 3000 m. Both these zones are greatly affected by the influx of terigenous material;

3) the zone of the world's oceanic deposits.

A classification of marine sediments according to Murray and Renard (1891) is presented in Table 2.

Table 2

Classification of marine sediments

Depth of basin in which sediments formed, m	Lithologic composition of deposits	Origin of deposits (after Murray)	Place of formation (after Nalivkin)
Tidal zone	Boulders Pebbles Sand Ooze	Shallow-water deposits of terrigenous origin	Littoral zone of sea
0—200	Pebbles Sand Ooze Limestones Brackish lagoonal deposits	Shallow-water deposits of terrigenous and chemogenic origin	Littoral region of sea
200—3000	Ooze: blue-gray blue red green volcanic coral	Deep-water deposits of terrigenous origin	Area of continental slope
3000—10,000	Red deep-water clay Ooze: radiolarian diatom globigerina pteropod	Pelagic deposits	Area of deposits of the world's ocean

Along with the increasing depth of water in the littoral zone of the sea from the shore seaward, there is a regular replacement of one facies by another. Beginning at the shoreline, there is a zone of sand, which in places contains pebbles. Sand is deposited where the speed of the current exceeds 1 meter per second. As the water becomes deeper this is followed by a zone of silts, or of sand composed of particles ranging from 0.1 to 0.01 mm in diameter. This is sometimes also called the zone of clayey sand. Still deeper is the most extensive zone, that of ooze deposits. Farther out from the shore, where the influx of terrigenous material decreases, the oozes are enriched in lime and grade into highly calcareous oozes. In their lithified state, such oozes become marls, or clayey limestones.* In elevated areas in the relief of the sea bottom, where the water's depth is no more than 60–80 m, so that light is able to penetrate, calcareous algae and bryozoa may develop.

Isolated bodies of water may be present in the littoral region of the sea as currents or in basins from river flow or evaporation, or within enclosed bays. The main feature which distinguishes these bodies from the open sea is the higher or lower salinity of their water.

Throughout the open ocean the salt content of the water is quite constant at about 3.5%. Thus even fairly small changes in the salinity can bring about radical transformations of the communities of organisms inhabiting the sea. A change in salinity may easily occur in an isolated body of water such as a bay or lagoon caused by a flow of fresh river water or, in the absence of any streams, by intensified evaporation of the water. The latter process leads to the formation of hypersaline evaporite basins. In hypersaline lagoons the leading factor in the formation of mineral deposits is the chemical differentiation of the salts. Nalivkin (1956) has stated that as the salinity increases to a density of 1.05, carbonates first begin to be precipitated in the lagoon: these are chiefly limestones, dolomitized limestones and dolomites.** When the specific gravity of the sea water rises to 1.12–1.20, anhydrite begins to separate out; then, as the density of the water is in the 1.21–1.26 range, anhydrite and halite are precipitated simultaneously; and finally, when the density reaches 1.23–1.31, pure halite is precipitated. Magnesium sulfate is precipitated at the same density of the water during winter, when the temperature is lower; this salt is deposited in the form of separate intercalated layers. These regularities characterizing the differential precipitation of salts are illustrated by a diagram taken from N. M. Strakhov (1960) (Fig. 2).

The limestones and dolomites precipitated in lagoons are of chemogenic origin, and are readily distinguishable from the limestones formed in the open sea by the absence of fauna in the former.***

---

*Translator's Note: This European usage of the term "marl" to refer to argillaceous limestone is not to be confused with the predominantly American use of the word "marl" to indicate a purely calcareous calcilutite; in any case, there is considerable inconsistency in the meanings given to this term. See the American Geological Institute's Glossary of Geology and Related Sciences.

**Editor's Note: Mason (Principles of Geochemistry, John Wiley and Sons, 1958), page 1975, states that there is no evidence that extensive deposits of dolomite have been formed in this way.

***Editor's Note: Deposited limestone could also come from broken-up calcareous algae or coral.

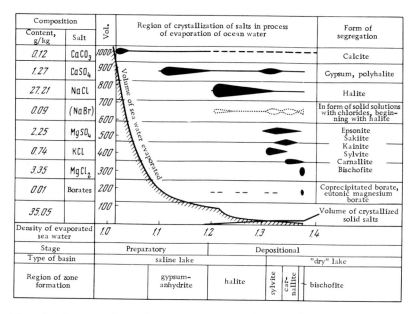

Composition		Vol.	Region of crystallization of salts in process of evaporation of ocean water	Form of segregation
Content, g/kg	Salt			
0.12	CaCO₃	1000		Calcite
1.27	CaSO₄	900		Gypsum, polyhalite
27.21	NaCl	800		Halite
0.09	(NaBr)	700 / 600		In form of solid solutions with chlorides, beginning with halite
2.25	MgSO₄	500		Epsonite / Sakiite
0.74	KCl	400		Kainite / Sylvite
3.35	MgCl₂	300		Carnallite / Bischofite
0.01	Borates	200		Coprecipitated borate, eutonic magnesium borate
35.05		100		Volume of crystallized solid salts
Density of evaporated sea water			1.0 1.1 1.2 1.3 1.4	
Stage			Preparatory Depositional	
Type of basin			saline lake "dry" lake	
Region of zone formation			gypsum-anhydrite	halite	sylvite	carnallite	bischofite

Fig. 2. Succession of precipitation of salts in the evaporation
of ocean water (after Strakhov, 1960).

The areas of marine basins that are farther out from the shore,
at depths of water to 2000 m, but are still affected by the importa-
tion of some amount of terrigenous sediments, may be characterized
by the following facies:

1) deep-water sands in areas with strong bottom currents, such
as those which lie along the coast of Norway at 800 m;

2) blue or gray-blue ooze. This is the most widespread type of
deposit on the continental slope; there is little calcareous material
here, and an admixture of pyrite appears. The color of the ooze
depends on the presence and content of iron sulfide, which has been
formed through microbial reduction of sulfates;

3) red ooze, which owes its color to the great quantity of lateritic
rock particles carried in by rivers;

4) green sand with grains of glauconite, which contains 50% of
the remains of organisms;

5) calcareous sand, occurring in areas where coral reefs
containing up to 85% of calcium carbonate are present.

The deposits of the open ocean bottom are characterized by
the data in Table 3.

Fossil deep-water oozes are known at the present time only in
the islands of the West Indies and the Indonesian Archipelago. This
is probably due to the fact that the rate of accumulation of these

Table 3

Chemical composition of deep-water oozes of Pacific Ocean
(percent of dry weight)
(after D. V. Nalivkin, 1956)

Ooze	Insoluble sediment				Calcium carbonate			
	Weight	Constituents			Weight	Constituents		
		Siliceous organisms	Mineral grains	Ooze particles		Planktonic forms	Benthic forms	Other organisms
Globigerina	35.53	1.64	3.33	30.65	64.47	53.1	2.13	9.24
Red deep-water clay	93.3	2.39	5.56	85.35	6.7	4.77	0.59	1.34
Radiolarian (at depth of more than 5500 m)	95.99	54.44	1.67	39.88	4.0	3.11	0.11	0.79

deposits is no more than 0.25-0.90 cm every 1000 years. A summary of work reported on deep-water oozes may be found in S. V. Bruyevich's monograph (1949).

On the basis of the characteristics of presently occurring sedimentation processes, it is possible, by analyzing the lithology of ancient deposits, to reconstruct the history of their formation. An illustration of this method is N. M. Strakhov's reconstruction (1947a) of the Southern Urals evaporite salt basin. The cross section through this basin shows that it contains three longitudinal zones: a dolomite-anhydrite zone in the west, a salt-bearing zone in the center and a zone of terrigenous-gypsiferous deposits in the east. The salt-bearing series in the center is divided into three suites. The lower salt-bearing suite fills the lower part of the basin. The gypsum-anhydrite suite in the middle is thinner but more widespread laterally. In some places the gypsiferous anhydrites are replaced by sulfate-bearing clays, marls* and sandstones; Strakhov (1947a) considers these to be a facies of delta deposits. The upper suite is composed almost entirely of these sulfate-containing deposits.

Strakhov relates the history of this basin as follows: at the end of the Late Artinskian age (Early Permian) the whole basin was uplifted. The sea retreated, remaining only in the very center where a lagoonal basin was formed in post-Artinskian (Permian)

---

*See Translator's Note on p. 6.

times. The upwarped parts of the former sea bottom in the west hindered the entrance of water from the sea and this was the reason for the transformation of the normal marine basin into a lagoon. The climate became more arid, and the lagoon very rapidly became salinified to a high degree. After a brief period of anhydrite deposition, halite and polyhalite began to be precipitated in the basin.

Subsequently, as the Urals foothills basin began its subsidence, the lagoon increased in size. The areas of dry land to the west began to sink into the sea, and the connection between the lagoon and the sea became stronger. Fresh sea water entered and the salt concentration decreased, while at the proper salinity the calcium sulfates from the fresh sea water were separated out, and anhydrite began to be deposited once more on top of the halite.

The third stage in the lagoon's history coincided with the beginning of mountain building processes on the western flank of the Urals. Thus a mass of clastic material began to be carried into the foothills basin and gradually filled up the lagoon.

3. THE FORMATION OF IGNEOUS ROCKS

Study of the geologic composition of the earth's crust has shown that considerable parts of the earth's surface are occupied by magmatic, or igneous, rocks. Magma, rising from great depths, may either pour out upon the earth's surface through volcanos or else solidify within the crust in the form of batholiths, stocks and other formations.

The magma that pours out on the surface of the earth cools rapidly, forming very small crystals, and produces the so-called extrusive rocks, which include tuffs, lavas, andesites, basalts, liparites and so forth.

Magmatic melts which harden at some depth form intrusive rocks. These rocks have a readily visible crystalline structure. Thus, when these rocks are freed of the overburden of rocks above them as a result of tectonic uplifts or through erosion, they are exposed at the surface as outcrops of granites, diorites, gabbros, peridotites and other such formations.

Igneous rocks consist of 98-99% silica, as well as oxides of iron, aluminum, alkali earths and alkalis, the SiO_2 amounting to some 45-65% of the total. The remaining 1-2% is made up of titanium, manganese, chromium, phosphorus, sulfur and the rare elements. In their mineral composition, igneous rocks consist primarily of quartz and the silicate minerals—silica and aluminosilicate salts. These compounds include the felspars, pyroxenes, amphiboles, micas, olivine, nepheline and others. The ore minerals are most commonly encountered in the ultrabasic rocks, which contain less than 45% SiO_2.

After comparing the various hypotheses of the origin of mineralizing fluids and solutions, A. S. Saakyan (1960) has prepared a diagram classifying them according to their principal types; he believes that the formation of sulfide ore deposits may have involved the action of magmatic fluids, metamorphic fluids and solutions infiltrating from the earth's surface. Their respective roles in the formation of mineral deposits may, in Saakyan's opinion, be represented by the diagram shown in Fig. 3.

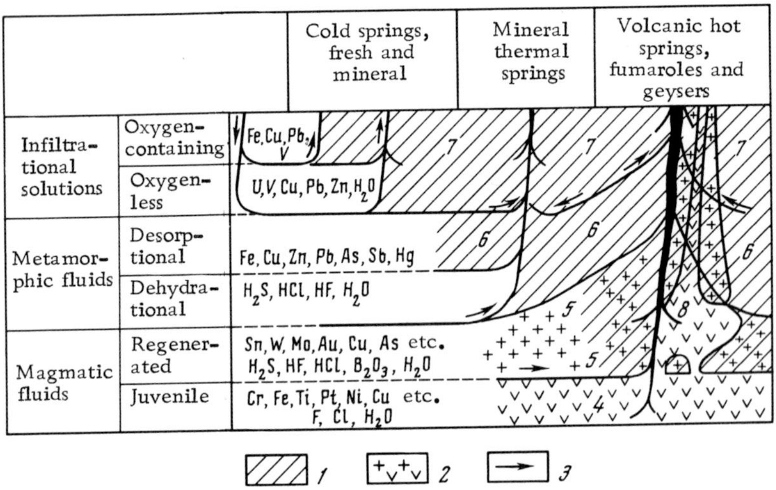

Fig. 3. Diagram illustrating the formation and migration of ore-bearing fluids and solutions (after Saakyan, 1960):
1—region of mixed fluids and solutions; 2—region of magmatic processes; 3—direction of movement of ore-forming fluids and solutions; 4—subcrustal basaltic layer; 5—ultrametamorphism and gravitization; 6—region of intensive metamorphism; 7—region of near-surface alteration; 8—dikes.

a) Magmatic Fluids

The primary or original magmas, in the course of their differentiation, yield certain highly volatile substances, or fluids, which are called magmatic fluids. Hydrothermal deposits formed through the action of juvenile fluids are rare. In the majority of cases, the sulfide ores of pyrrhotite-chalcopyrite-pentlandite composition bear traces of true magmatic origin.

When igneous rocks, after their primary formation, are later carried down and buried at great depths, they may be remelted, resulting in the formation of "regenerated" fluids representing the solutions and emanations from magmas. An example of a deposit formed in this manner is the Zangezur ore district in the Lesser Caucasus. This is also how the chalcopyrite disseminations in slightly altered granites and other rocks of many deposits have been formed.

Polymetallic sulfide deposits occur frequently under these conditions.

b) Metamorphic Fluids

Endogenic ore mineralization is to a great degree associated with the segregation of metal sulfides from the waters formed in the metamorphism of rocks.

According to V. I. Vernadskiy (1933), metamorphic fluids may be divided into two types: dehydrational and desorptional. By comparing the water content of sedimentary rocks and of similar rocks that have undergone metamorphism, it will be seen that water forms a considerably smaller part of the composition of the metamorphic minerals. Thus water must be given off during the metamorphism of sedimentary rocks; it is this water which forms the dehydrational fluids. This process involves not only the redeposition of ore materials, but also the formation of secondary minerals such as sericite, chlorite and others.

Such, in A. N. Zavaritskiy's opinion (1950), was the formation of the pyrite ores of the Urals. Zavaritskiy believes that the elements in the ore substances, particularly copper and zinc, entered into solution and were redeposited under the conditions of dynamic metamorphism. The vein ores in the disseminated mineralization of the Lesser Caucasus were, apparently, also formed in this way.

Part of the water occurs in an adsorbed state in rocks. This adsorbed water together with the constitutional water, according to V. I. Vernadskiy (1933), forms some 8% of the rocks in the earth's crust.

In the course of metamorphism, the adsorbed water is the first to be separated. Ore elements begin to be dissolved in it, so that the contents of metals in desorptional fluids may reach several percent. It is not always possible to distinguish between the roles of the hydrated and sorbed water released during formation of ore deposits.

c) The Role of Infiltrating Solutions in the Formation of Ore Deposits

Rainwater penetrates deep into the rocks at the earth's surface and may, in the presence of dispersed or disseminated ore minerals, come into contact with and dissolve the ore elements. Then, depending on the geologic structure and composition of the locality, the infiltered solutions may spread outward through fractures along the ore bed. Penetrating to great depths, these waters may lose all their dissolved oxygen by entering a zone of reducing conditions.

As the individual elements migrate and are concentrated by water in the oxygen-containing zone, they form deposits of limonite, copper carbonates and oxides, lead sulfates and so forth. The oxygen-lacking infiltering solutions usually remain rich in free carbon dioxide and nitrogen. They contain uranium, vanadium, copper, zinc and other metals and may reach the zone in which the metamorphic fluids occur. Very large deposits of infiltrational origin exist in the USA, in the state of Colorado. This is a vast province of sedimentary rocks composed of marine, lacustrine and river deposits of Paleozoic and Mesozoic age. The ores were formed by the infiltration of waters through the sandstones at various levels in the sedimentary series.

Saakyan (1960) considers that mixed ore-bearing fluids and solutions play an important role in ore mineralization. The course followed by the processes of oxidation of the sulfide ores is affected by the following factors: 1) the nature of the ore mass; 2) its mineral composition and structural peculiarities; 3) the general character of the host rocks; 4) the climate; 5) the relief; 6) the tectonics of the area; 7) the activities of microorganisms, and other features.

The chemistry of the main processes involved in the formation and oxidation of sulfide ores is discussed in detail in a paper by S. S. Smirnov (1955), and may be summarized by the following reactions.

In the precipitation of metals from sulfate solutions, the first event is the neutralization of H_2SO_4; then, in the neutral medium, the reversible reaction takes place:

$$RSO_4 + CaCO_3 \rightleftarrows RCO_3 + CaSO_4.$$

Thus calcite and dolomite are gradually replaced by carbonates of the heavy metals. This process is most important in the case of copper and zinc.

The reaction between the sulfates and sulfides goes according to the following general scheme:

$$RSO_4 + MS = MSO_4 + RS,$$

where R and M are metals.

Exchange reactions may also take place between the various sulfides, according to certain definite laws. Schuermann (cited in Smirnov, 1955) has composed the following series of metals in order of decreasing affinity for sulfur:

Hg, Ag, Cu, Bi, Cd, Pb, Zn, Ni, Co, Fe, Mn.

Each metal on the left in this series will remove the metal on the right from sulfide compounds. Thus various sulfide ores may be deposited and transformed.

In concluding this brief characterization of the chemistry of ore formation, something must be said about the tendency of metals to be released from rocks. For example, in weathering, and especially in an oxidizing zone, complex silicates break down into simple oxides, hydroxides and carbonates. Zinc and lead, which are unseparated in the hypogene process, may become separated in the oxide zone; thus the readily soluble zinc sulfates will be carried off, while the relatively insoluble lead sulfates remain. Similarly copper is separated from iron.

4. THE EFFECT OF THE CLIMATE ON THE FORMATION OF THE OXIDE ZONE AND ON THE SECONDARY ENRICHMENT OF SULFIDE ORES

The quantity of porous sediments and the temperature determine the amount of moisture in rocks, and thus also the concentration of the solutions which circulate through the saturated and discharge zones (see Chapter II).

Table 4 characterizes the intensity of the processes of formation of sulfide and oxide ores under different climatic conditions. The

Table 4

Characteristics of oxide zones and zones of sulfide enrichment
in different climatic environments
(after S. S. Smirnov, 1955)

Climate					
Tropical		Temperate		Polar	
Humid	Arid	Humid	Arid	Humid	Arid
Oxide zone					
Very distinct, often highly leached	Very distinct	Usually quite distinct	Often very distinct	Very slightly distinct	
Zone of sulfide enrichment					
Lacking or slightly distinct	Often very distinct	Most often poorly discernible	Often quite distinct	Lacking	

data here show that these processes take place most intensively in a dry tropical climate and are almost completely lacking in both polar and moist tropical climates. In the former instance the processes are hindered by low temperature, and in the latter all the ore elements are carried away along with large amounts of sediments by water movement.

CHAPTER II

The Elements of Hydrogeology

1. THE PRINCIPAL FACTORS GOVERNING THE DISTRIBUTION OF THE VARIOUS TYPES OF WATERS IN THE LITHOSPHERE

Water containing dissolved salts is one of the basic items necessary for the development of microorganisms. A region in which internal waters circulate may be divided into three zones. (1) The *zone of infiltration* (vadose zone) extends from the earth's surface to the water table; its waters are characterized by an abundance of dissolved oxygen and carbon dioxide. The waters of this zone also have a great dissolving power and move primarily in the vertical direction. (2) The lower boundary of the *zone of discharge* is determined by the level at which the ground waters intersect the surface of the drainage horizon. The movement of the waters in this zone is nearly horizontal. (3) In the *zone of stagnate waters*, the waters do not move about and contain no free oxygen in solution. The alternation of dry and humid periods during the year causes fluctuations in the depth of the water table, and consequently also causes the boundary between the two upper zones to fluctuate.

The ground-water circulation scheme as a whole can be applied only to those cases in which all the rocks have the same porosity. Even then, however, the water may infiltrate at very different rates. This results in different intensities of oxidation in different parts of the deposit.

As a rule, the zone of infiltration is the zone of oxide ores. The zone of discharge contains both oxide and sulfide ores, and the zone of stagnate waters is the zone of sulfide ores.

As V. A. Sulin has stated (1948), aquifer horizons are always in some manner directly connected with the surface of the earth. The rate of water circulation is a measure of the degree of hydrogeological openness, or fissuring of the stratum. The ease with which surface waters penetrate into the deeper layers of the crust depends on the permeability of the rocks, the amount of precipitates present in the rock, the inclination of the beds along their strike, the distance from the region of ground water source in the stratum to the region of discharge, and other factors.

15

On the basis of these hydrogeological characteristics, Sulin subdivides the waters in sedimentary strata into three zones: (1) The *zone of free water circulation.* The waters of this zone are usually only slightly mineralized, and are of the bicarbonate or sulfate type. They contain dissolved oxygen and carbon dioxide. In the sulfide facies of igneous and sedimentary rocks, the waters may be quite acid and contain high contents of iron salts. (2) The *zone of impeded water circulation.* This is a zone where waters circulate in strata characterized by poor filtration capacity and by their great distance from the outcrops at the earth's surface. The concentration of salts in the ground waters increases with an increase of depth of the rocks and degree of isolation from the surface of the earth. (3) The *zone of no water circulation.* Here the waters are located in hydrogeologically closed structures, so that any exchange between these and the surface waters is extremely difficult. The waters of this zone are characterized by high contents of sodium or calcium chloride.

2. THE SALT COMPOSITION OF GROUND WATERS

In comparing the variations in chemical composition of the ground waters of the Moscow Basin, Samar Luka, Dnepr-Donets Basin and the Caspian Depression, K. V. Filatov (1947) found that in any tectonically formed basin or depression, regardless of the geologic age or lithology of the rock formations filling it, the total mineral content of the ground waters increases with depth. The changes in the salt composition of the waters do not depend on the lithology of the surrounding aquifer rocks; as may be seen from Table 5, these characteristics may be summed up in the following general rule: from the shallower to the deeper strata, the ground waters change in mineral type from bicarbonate to sulfate and, finally, to chloride. The older the depression and the more water-permeable the rocks that fill it, the more distinct will be the hydrochemical zonal differentiation of the water.

At the present time the chief factor producing the layering of underground fluids is considered (Sulin, 1948; Filatov, 1947) to be the specific gravity of the principal anions and cations, among which are Cl^-, SO_4^{--}, HCO_3^-, Na^+, Ca^{++} and Mg^{++}.

Of extremely great importance in determining whether microorganisms have developed in the waters of oil, sulfide and other deposits is the possibility of contamination by intrusion of water into a "standing" zone. After analyzing the available data, Filatov (1947) came to the conclusion that crystalline rocks, except for the upper zone of weathering at depths of 60-100 m, may be considered impermeable to gravitational water. The situation is

Table 5

Hydrochemical characteristics of the ground waters in the
Moscow district
(after K. V. Filatov, 1947)

Type of water	Depth, m	Dry residue, g/liter	Content in %-eq.		
			HCO_3	SO_4	Cl
Calcium hydrocarbonate	50	0.30	46	2.5	1.5
Calcium sulfate-hydrocarbonate	250	0.5	23.5	24	2.5
Magnesium-calcium sulfate	450	4.57	5.7	38.0	6.3
Sodium chloride	775	80.6	0	1	49
Same	1350	274.1	0	1	49

different with regard to the sedimentary rocks that fill depressions in the earth's crust and carbonate rocks that have been deposited and later became fractured, as in the Moscow Basin. These rocks, although they attain thicknesses of several thousands of meters and have become compacted, nevertheless constitute a loose, inhomogeneous substratum, and their pore spaces are filled with atmospheric waters. Filatov believes, on the basis of experimental

Table 6

Salt content and composition of the waters in oil deposits
(after V. A. Sulin, 1948)

Province	District	Salt content		Per cent equivalents				
		°Be	meq.-eq.	Cl^-	SO_4^{--}	CO_3^{--}	Ca^{++} Mg^{++}	$K^+ + Na^+$
Azerbaijan	Balakhny	3	108.76	36.66		13.34	0.33 0.33	49.34
	"	12.8	422.60	49.10		0.83	4.68 5.31	40.01
	Vinagady	1		33.18	10.06	6.76	1.12 2.24	
	"	16.4		46.11	0.56	3.33	0.04 0.04	
	Neftechacla	19	597.48	49.74	0.23	0.03	11.02 4.70	34.28
Dagestan	Kayakent	0.1	4.23	9.92		40.08	4.75	45.24
	Berekest	30	1082.80	49.91		0.09	0.99	49.01
Groznyy	Novogroznen-skiy	1	35.4	44.8		5.2	0.8 1.3	47.9
	Groznyy	2	45.44	44.81		5.19	10.04 2.35	37.61
Turkmeni-stan	Neftedag	20.5	705.90	49.94	0.03	0.03	8.01 4.33	37.66
Emba region	Dossor	8.1	322.02	49.69		0.31	3.07 4.44	42.49
Pechora region	Ukhta			49.0		0.19	8.27 4.26	37.47
Sakhalin Is.	Okha	0.3	12.66	7.4	0.4	42.2	0.9 1.3	47.8

data obtained by Adamson and Bridgman in their studies of the effect of pressures of 6000-7000 atm on the water-permeability of rocks, that gravitational water under the conditions of nature is capable of moving through sedimentary rocks down to the depth of 4000 meters.

Various internal waters may differ sharply in their chemical composition. The total salt content may vary from 0.1 to 30.0°Be. Table 6 shows that great differences in the individual salt components have also been noted. All these factors have a strong influence on the character of the microflora inhabiting internal waters.

3. THE DISSOLVED ORGANIC MATTER IN GROUND WATERS

One of the factors promoting the growth of microorganisms in ground water is the presence of organic substances, especially those which can be assimilated by microorganisms. The total content of assimilable organic matter is, perhaps, most readily determined by the rate of biological consumption of oxygen (BOD), employing a method widely used in public health investigations. This method is based upon the fact that in a closed system microorganisms oxidize organic substances present in solution in the water, and consume dissolved oxygen. The greater the quantity of assimilable matter in the water, the more oxygen will be consumed, and the change in oxygen is measured.

No direct relationship exists, as a rule, between the total amount of dissolved organic matter and its readily assimilable portion (Novobrantsev, 1937; Kuznetsov, 1952). In surface and especially in dark-colored humic waters, the total content of organic matter may reach 200-300 mg/liter, while the quantity of assimilable substances remains small. A different situation is present in eutrophic lakes, although the magnitudes are almost the same.

The content of readily assimilable organic substances in internal waters has rarely been analyzed. The most systematic data on the total quantities of organic substances are to be found in a publication by M. Ye. Al'tovskiy, Z. I. Kuznetsova and V. M. Shvets (1958). Some of the results of their analyses are shown in Table 7, which indicates that the amount of organic matter in internal waters is determined, apparently, by numerous factors. In any case, analysis by the Datsko method reveals the presence of considerable quantities of organic carbon, up to 20-30 mg/liter.

Table 7

Content of organic carbon in ground waters
(after M. Ye. Al'tovskiy, Z. I. Kuznetsova and V. M. Shvets, 1958)

Area	Aquifer horizon	Depth of occurrence, m	Organic carbon, mg/liter
Moscow basin	Waters:		
	Cretaceous	6	0.3—0.6
	Jurassic		0.08—1.2
	Upper Carboniferous	80—260	0.64
	Middle Carboniferous	116	0.48
	Lower Carboniferous	54—227	0.3
	Devonian		0.32—0.6
Western Turkmenia (red bed series)	Upper strata	0—150	2.4—2.8
	Lower strata	512	4.2
Groznyy region	Middle strata	1040—1127	20.2—28.9
	Chakrak and Karagan source regions		3.4
	Area of oil deposits; gushers and high-discharge wells	300—1500	6.6
	Area of oil deposits; low-discharge wells	500—1500	34.7
	Unloaded region		3.4

4. THE CONTENT OF MOLECULAR HYDROGEN IN UNDERGROUND GASES

It is well known that microorganisms require for their development either available organic matter or a source of energy which they may use in photosynthetic or chemosynthetic formation of organic matter from carbon dioxide. Since photosynthesis does not take place in ground waters, because of the absence of light, autotrophic organisms may develop only by chemosynthesis.

The energy obtained from the oxidation of molecular hydrogen can be most fully utilized in the process of chemosynthesis. The hydrogen may be oxidized by molecular oxygen in the presence of hydrogen-oxidizing bacteria. These processes can take place, apparently, either in the region where internal waters are being replenished or in the upper layers of the lithosphere in the zone of more intensive water circulation.

Furthermore, molecular hydrogen may also be oxidized by bacteria under anaerobic conditions by the oxygen in sulfates or carbon dioxide. The first case involves the reduction of sulfate and the formation of hydrogen sulfide through the action of *Vibrio desulfuricans*. In the latter case, the hydrogen is oxidized by the oxygen in carbon dioxide, and methane is simultaneously formed.

Without dwelling on the genesis of the molecular hydrogen in the deeper layers of the lithosphere, it is enough to say that it is frequently present in petroleum gases, and sometimes emerges as streams of pure hydrogen. Summaries of the data on this subject may be found in Vernadskiy (1955) and ZoBell (1946c). At Reykjavik, Iceland, for example, the gas emerging from fumaroles contains 25.19% hydrogen. In the submarine eruptions at the island of Santorin (Thera), the hydrogen content of the gas reached 56.70%, and in the gases from the Mont Pelée volcano on Martinique Island it was as high as 22.3%. Hydrogen may be trapped in vesicles in igneous rocks, where it can amount to 33.8% of the total gas content, as has been noted in the serpentinites of Rumania. Hydrogen has often been noted in the gases from hot springs, forming jets of hydrogen and carbon dioxide. For example, in the gases of Namafjal in Iceland the hydrogen content reached 54%; in the gases from the mud volcanos of the Apsheron Peninsula it was 15.4%, and in Makaluba 85.4%.

In petroleum gases, as Vernadskiy (1957) writes, the hydrogen content is no less than that of nitrogen, and in a number of American deposits reaches 1.64-2.35% (up to 22.5% according to the old analyses). Vernadskiy also cites data to the effect that the natural gases in the former Novouzensk uyezd of the former Samara guberniya contained 3.4-10.6% hydrogen. In other regions the hydrogen content in the gases averaged 1%, in individual cases amounting to as much as 20%. The gases of salt mines are especially hydrogen-rich: at Neu-Strasfurt the gases extracted in 1879 contained 93.1% hydrogen.

5. THE OXIDATION-REDUCTION CONDITIONS IN GROUND WATERS

The redox conditions of the medium in which microorganisms develop may be ascertained by determining the amount of oxygen dissolved in the water, or by measuring the oxidation-reduction (redox) potential. It should be kept in mind, however, that the content of dissolved oxygen does not accurately reflect the oxidation-reduction conditions of the medium, inasmuch as the process of oxidation, as is well known (Uspenskiy, 1936; Nekrasov, 1934), consists of the loss of an electron by the atom of the substance being oxidized, regardless of whether or not oxygen takes part in the reaction. For this reason it is far more accurate to determine the redox potential. Measurement of the redox potential also provides a means of judging the intensity with which the medium is capable of reducing or oxidizing the material occurring within it.

The degree of intensity of the oxidation-reduction processes within the medium is determined by measuring the difference in potentials between the medium and the normal hydrogen electrode. The oxidation-reduction potential is designated by the symbol Eh and is expressed in volts:

$$Eh = 0.029 \, (rH_2 - 2pH).$$

As may be seen from the above formula, it depends on the concentration of the reducing agent or, in general form, on the concentration of molecular hydrogen and hydrogen ions.

The redox potential may be differently expressed in terms of the negative logarithm of the concentration of molecular hydrogen, for which the conventional designation is rH_2. From the preceding formula, the following relationship is easily derived:

$$rH_2 = \frac{Eh}{0.029} + 2pH.$$

The Eh does not of itself characterize the oxidation-reduction conditions. If the acidity of the medium and its redox potential change simultaneously, it is possible that in certain cases the Eh will remain constant. The changes in the oxidation-reduction environment of the surrounding medium may be judged directly from the magnitude of the Eh only if the pH remains unchanged. In contrast to this, the rH_2, which is the negative logarithm of the concentration of the reducing agent, reflects the oxidation-reduction conditions of the medium, regardless of the magnitude of the pH.

Few measurements have been made of the redox potential in internal waters, probably because of the considerable methodological difficulties involved. Such measurements are most easily made in water from flowing wells. Great care must be taken to prevent the water from coming into contact with oxygen during the analysis.

The distribution of hydrogen and of the redox potentials in soil and internal waters depends to a large degree on the nature of the source of water. As may be seen from the data cited in Table 8, the greatest amount of hydrogen in the waters of the mine workings and wells of the Groznyy oil district was found in the source region

Table 8

Oxidation-reduction potential and content of dissolved oxygen
in the internal waters of the Groznyy oil region
(after M. Ye. Al'tovskiy, Z. I. Kuznetsova and V. M. Shvets, 1958)

Region	Well heads			Wells		
	Examined	Dissolved O_2, mg/liter (average)	rH_2	Depth, m	Dissolved O_2, mg/liter	rH_2
Source region	11	6.66	24.8	100	0.0	
				249	10.6	22.9
				75	4.8	27.2
Oil deposits Unloaded region	0 15**	— 0.0	— 10.3	225—2097	0.0*	11.0 *
				600	0.0	10.27
				670	0.0	11.8
				20	0.0	14.34

*Average values for 18 wells.
**One well head, not included in this number, had a content of 1.68 mg/liter of dissolved oxygen and rH_2 = 17.8 in the water. It is likely that the well water somewhere was mixed with surface water.

of the aquifer strata. In some cases the content of dissolved hydrogen reached 10 mg/liter at a depth of 250 m. The opposite picture was observed in the internal waters of the oil deposit and in the region of discharge of the water-bearing strata: here there was no dissolved hydrogen.

A study of the values of the redox potential in the stratal waters of oil deposits has been made by V. A. Kuznetsov (1960). The determinations were made from samples of stratal waters in the various oil deposits of Samar Luka. The data from these analyses are presented in Table 9. This table shows that the stratal waters in the Carboniferous rocks, which contain sulfides, have a lower redox potential than the deeper sulfur-less waters in the underlying Devonian rocks.

A detailed study of the redox potential was made by M. V. Ivanov (1960b and c) in the stratal waters of a number of sulfur deposits in the Carpathian region. Figure 4 shows that the magnitude of the redox potential changes regularly along a single aquifer stratum. Beyond the deposit, the stratal waters contain dissolved oxygen; the value of the rH_2 = 20. The closer one moves toward the center of the deposit, the more sharply the rH_2 decreases; this is in accord with the intensity of sulfate reduction and with the presence of sulfate-reducing bacteria.

Table 9

Oxidation-reduction conditions in the stratal waters of the oil
deposits in the Kuybyshev region

Deposit	Stratigraphic level	Eh, mv	pH	rH$_2$	Fe^{3+}	Fe^{2+}	H$_2$S
					mg/liter		
Mukhanovskoye	Carbonif., stratum I	−202	6.2	5.5	—	—	308
	" " IV	−15	5.5	10.5	0.48	181.0	0
	Devonian, stratum II	+10	5.6	11.6	0.18	530.0	0
	" " III	−6	5.7	11.2	0.8	80.0	0
Zolnyy ovrag	Carbonif., coal-bearing formation	−118	6.7	9.4	—	—	Present
	Devonian, stratum I	+ 15	6.5	12.5	0.4	99.5	0
	" " II	+ 3	5.8	11.7	0.4	180.0	0
Zhigulevskoye	Devonian, stratum II	+ 20	5.6	11.9	0.25	92.0	0
Kalinovskoye	Permian, Kalinovskoye formation	−250	7.1	6.9	0	—	1975.6
	Same	−194	7.3	7.7	—	—	684.6

Thus the magnitude of the redox potential in the upper water-bearing layers of the rocks, in the zone of active water circulation, may reach high rH$_2$ values, and these waters may frequently be rich in dissolved oxygen. The waters in the zone of impeded water circulation, generally speaking, are characterized by lower rH$_2$ values, in the 15-18 range. But here, too, in the presence of active microbiological processes, the redox potential may drop to rH$_2$ = 9-11. In the zone of stagnate waters, dissolved oxygen is lacking, and the redox potential is characterized by still lower rH$_2$ values. No direct relationship has been established, however, between the magnitude of the rH$_2$ and the depth of the aquifer stratum. For example, the iron-containing waters in the Devonian rocks of Samar Luka usually have a higher redox potential than the overlying hydrogen sulfide waters in the coal-bearing formations of the Carboniferous (see Table 9).

6. THE TEMPERATURE REGIME OF GROUND WATERS

The seasonal fluctuations in temperature extend down approximately to a depth of 10 m. The ground water temperature at this depth corresponds to the mean annual temperature of the given locality.

With an increase in depth, the temperature of the rocks and their internal waters also increases. The thermal gradient depends

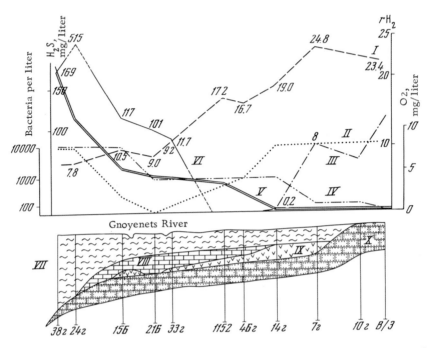

Fig. 4. The change in the chemical composition of the water and the microflora as the waters move from the source region to the Yazov sulfur deposit:
I—oxidation-reduction potential (rH₂); II—sulfur bacteria; III—oxygen content (mg/liter); IV—sulfate-reducing bacteria; V—total mineral content of water (mg/liter); VI—hydrogen sulfide; VII—Upper Tortonian-Sarmatian clayey marl series; VIII—Ratinskian sulfur-bearing limestones; IX—gypsum-anhydrite series; X—Lower Tortonian deposits.

on the geologic structure and the intensity of tectonic activity in the given region. V. D. Pokrovskiy (1961) has obtained more than 500 measurements of the temperature in boreholes in the European part of the Soviet Union, and has plotted the resulting data on a map (Fig. 5). On this basis he has divided the whole of European Russia into three geothermal provinces. The first province includes the Baltic and the Ukrainian crystalline shields, as well as the Kursk-Voronezh and the Belorussian-Lithuanian outcrops of the crystalline basement complex. In this geothermal province, even at depths of 1000 m or more below the earth's surface, the ground water temperature does not exceed 20°C. The second province encompasses the area of the Precambrian crystalline basement where it is covered by the mantle of Paleozoic and Mesozoic sedimentary rocks. Here, at a depth of 1000 m below the surface, the temperature fluctuates between 20° and 30°C. The third province, where the ground-water temperature exceeds 30°C at a

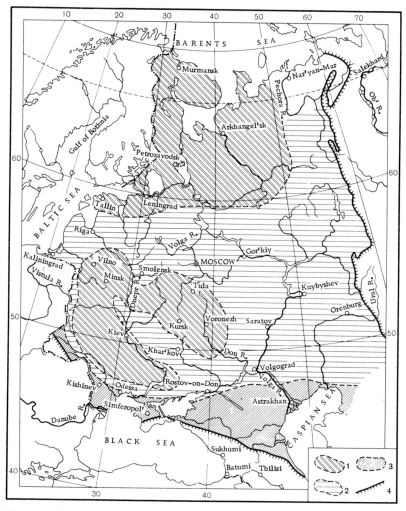

Fig. 5. Geothermal provinces within the European part of the USSR. Temperatures at the depth of 1000 m: 1—below 20°C; 2—from 20° to 30°C; 3—above 30°C (up to 100°C or higher); 4—boundaries of mountain structures (after Pokrovskiy, 1961).

depth of 1000 m, includes the territories of the young Alpine geosynclinal basins, where the Hercynian folded basement occurs at great depths.

In the first geothermal province, the 100°C isotherm lies between depths of 10 and 15 km below the earth's surface, in the second between depths of 2.9 and 5.5 km, and in the third it occurs at depths of 1.5–2.5 km from the surface. In certain localities, where hot springs emerge at the surface, as at Bragunakh in the Caucasus, the rocks are at a temperature of 100°C almost all the way to the earth's surface.

Assuming that 100°C is the limiting temperature for the existence of microorganisms, Pokrovskiy considers that, on the average, the lower boundary of the biosphere may be as deep as 4000 m.

CHAPTER III

The Problems and the Methods of Research

The task of studying any process in which, according to our assumptions, the activity of a particular microorganism or group of microorganisms may be significant, must begin with a literature search, a working hypothesis and a plan of investigation. Before setting out upon a microbiological investigation, one must first collect all the available information about the geologic structure of the locality and the hydrogeology and chemical composition of its waters and dissolved gases. All this is necessary to gain the fullest possible picture of the ecological environment in which the microorganisms may carry on their life processes. One must remember, however, that the presence of a given group of microorganisms testifies only to its *possible* role in the geologic process.

A definite conclusion that the activity of microorganisms has taken place is justified only after comparing the presence of the organisms with the ecological environment and with a substrate that may have supported the given process. For example, the presence of proteolytic bacteria in the Black Sea sediments, which contain practically no albumin, still does not permit the conclusion that the hydrogen sulfide in the Black Sea's deeper waters is of proteolytic origin. In fact, A. Ye. Kriss and Ye. A. Rukina (1949) compared the intensity of hydrogen sulfide formation by bacteria in ooze deposits in Baars medium and in a medium for proteolytic microorganisms which contained equal amounts of sulfur as sulfate and albumin respectively (26 g/liter albumin). The results showed that in every case the production of hydrogen sulfide was greater in the medium with albumin than in the Baars medium. From these experiments the authors conclude that the hydrogen sulfide in the Black Sea is formed by protein decomposition. In this case Bruyevich (1953) is quite correct in considering that the proper question is not which bacteria occur in latent state in the ground, but what are the functions that they can carry out under the actual given conditions? It means little to find microorganisms capable of decomposing albumin with the formation of hydrogen sulfide—one must also find the albumins themselves.

Another instructive example of erroneous conclusions may be seen in Kriss's arguments (1954) that the free nitrogen in the Black

27

Sea water owes its origin to denitrification processes. His reasoning is as follows: the water of the abyssal zone in the Black Sea contains free nitrogen, and analysis has revealed the presence of denitrifying bacteria. Since the nitrates they require for their vital activity do not exist in the water, Kriss supposes that nitrification must first take place, and that the resulting nitrates break down to free nitrogen immediately after their formation. Thus the author, in effect, comes to the absurd conclusion that nitrification can occur under anaerobic conditions.

Similar errors may also crop up in studying the internal waters of the lithosphere. For instance, the occurrence of denitrification is frequently concluded from the presence of denitrifiers in stratal waters, whereas nitrates as a rule are lacking in stratal waters. It must be kept in mind that the reduction of nitrates may occur through the action of a number of reducing agents, and not only through any specific fermenting agent. This is the source of the incorrect conclusions regarding the presence of active denitrification in these waters. The examples cited above show convincingly that the mere presence of microorganisms need not mean that they are active.

Geologists, in speaking of the geological activity of microorganisms, usually go to one of two extremes: either they completely deny the significance of microorganisms, as does N. M. Strakhov (1947b), or else they attribute all otherwise unexplained phenomena of the genesis of oil, hydrogen sulfide, etc., to the activity of microorganisms. It is widely believed among geologists that methane can be used by *Vibrio desulfuricans** as a source of organic matter for the reduction of sulfates and formation of hydrogen sulfide in the stratal waters of oil deposits. Nevertheless special investigations of the physiology of this organism, made by Yu. I. Sorokin (1957), have shown that desulfurizing bacteria do not assimilate methane.

Another method of estimating the activity of microorganisms in diagenesis is based on the ratios of stable isotopes in the initial substances and in the final products of the process under consideration. The reasoning is based on the assumption that in compounds such as sulfur with several isotopes the smaller mass isotope will be preferentially utilized in sulfate reduction. For example, the S^{32}/S^{34} ratio in the hydrogen sulfide formed by desulfurizing bacteria will be greater than the S^{32}/S^{34} ratio in the original sulfates. In the case of abiogenic processes, these quantities will be the same. This method has been used in Thode's investigations (Thode, Wanless and Wallouch, 1954) of the genesis of the sulfur in the Louisiana salt domes.

In some cases, chemical analysis may be used to solve analogous problems, such as that of the role of microorganisms in the anaerobic decomposition of oil. By analyzing the ratio of argon to

---

* Editor's Note: *Desulfovibrio desulfuricans.*

nitrogen in petroleum gases, one may, in the absence of argon, conclude that the nitrogen originated from decomposition of the oil, and not from the air. This reasoning also suggests that combustible gases may be formed in the decomposition of oil.

Finally, the rates of the individual cycles of various substances in nature may be determined by the use of radioactive isotopes, both directly in nature and in experiments with isolated samples of water under conditions most closely approaching those of nature. Experiments with models must be conducted under conditions as closely as possible reproducing those in nature. Conclusions regarding the intensity and rates of natural processes cannot be drawn on the basis of laboratory experiments alone.

Let us consider two examples of incorrect conclusions. Butlin and Postgate (1953b, 1954) investigated four lakes located in Cyrenaica, in North Africa. These lakes are fed by hydrogen sulfide waters from springs, and the content of molecular sulfur in the lake oozes is as much as 50% of the dry weight. Microbiological investigations showed that the water, and especially the oozes, contained large numbers of sulfate-reducing and colored sulfur bacteria, the latter spreading a continuous red mantle over the shallow-water areas of the lake bottoms. The authors concluded that the sulfur deposits were created by the combined activity of these groups of bacteria. Laboratory experiments in which the sulfate-reducing bacteria were grown in a medium to which 0.1% sodium malate had been added together with the cultures of *Chromatium* and *Chlorobium* supported the authors' conclusions: molecular sulfur was deposited upon the bottom and walls of the dishes containing the cultures. Thus Butlin and Postgate consider the chief source of sulfur to be due to the sulfate-reducing bacteria in the lake itself, using the organic matter produced by photosynthesis of the colored sulfur bacteria as an energy source, inasmuch as all other sources from which organic matter could enter the lake had been ruled out.

Simple calculations, however, based on the physiology of these organisms (Ivanov, 1957b), show that the organic matter synthesized by the colored sulfur bacteria is not enough for the process of sulfate reduction. Thus the hydrogen sulfide in the lake waters must be derived mainly from without, from the underground springs.

The application of data from laboratory experiments to an actual body of water has similarly led to wrong conclusions on the part of P. M. Murzayev (1937, 1950). His calculations proceeded from the initial fact that in van Delden medium, *Vibrio desulfuricans* formed 1900 mg/liter of hydrogen sulfide during the 19 days of the experiment. Then in a lake 3 km in diameter, with a hydrogen sulfide zone 10 m in depth, during 100 days of summer this bacterium should form 407 metric tons of sulfur, or 45 kg/m^2 of the lake bottom. On this subject A. S. Uklonskiy (1940) quite properly writes: "It is extremely precarious to draw conclusions regarding the amount of sulfur deposited on the bottom of a body of water on the basis of the van Delden experiments, which have nothing in common with natural conditions, since asparagine, sodium lactate, etc., were introduced into the medium."

On the basis of the examples cited here, the present writers believe that a reliable judgment of possible or actual geological activity by microorganisms must be founded upon the following:

1) quantitative, or at least qualitative, determination of the presence of the given group of organisms;

2) chemical analysis of the waters or rocks, taking account of the ingredients whose transformation is assumed to result from the activity of the microorganisms;

3) study of the ecological conditions (the rH_2, the concentration of salts, O_2, H_2S, biogenic elements, etc.) to find out to what degree these favor the development of the group of microorganisms in question;

4) the collection of all possible information on the geology and hydrogeology of the deposit in which the process in question supposedly takes place;

5) the exhaustive collection of information on the physiology of the given group of organisms and on the specific factors encountered by the microorganisms in their natural environment which influence their growth and life processes;

6) the performance of experiments under conditions most closely approaching those of nature, particularly with a high-sensitivity radioisotope method;

7) determination of the ratios of stable isotopes in the original substances and in the final products formed by the activity of the microorganisms. This is based on the supposition that isotopes with smaller mass play a greater part in metabolism than heavier isotopes of the same elements.

A clear statement of the question to be investigated, and a detailed treatment of the materials according to the methods prescribed above, will allow the researcher to draw correct conclusions regarding the geological activity of microorganisms. An example of the proper approach in determining the geological significance of the various groups of microorganisms is the work of Baas Becking, Kaplan and Moore (1960), who have generalized an enormous amount of material on the relationship between the propagation of certain physiological groups of microorganisms and the oxidation-reduction conditions of their enviroment. Other examples of the role played by microorganisms in certain geochemical processes, based on the natural conditions and the intensity of microbiological processes, will be presented in the following chapters of this monograph.

CHAPTER IV

Some Data on the Physiology and Ecology of Bacteria as Related to Their Development in the Lithosphere

The effect of the individual properties of the external medium upon the development of microorganisms is expressed within definite limits and has a specific optimum. For an understanding of the ecological conditions influencing the geological activity and the development of microorganisms it is worth while to present some data on their physiological reactions to high temperatures, hydrostatic pressures, salts, water and dissolved organic matter.

1. THE EFFECT OF TEMPERATURE

Temperature is one of the fundamental environmental properties limiting the penetration of bacteria into the interior of the lithosphere. Bacteria, like all living organisms, develop within specific limits of temperature, which may be very different for different species.

Table 10

Optimal temperatures for various life processes
of *Streptococcus lactis* and *Streptococcus thermophilis*
(after Porter, 1946)

Function of organism	Temperature, °C	
	S. lactis	*S. thermophilis*
Most intensive growth	34	37
Largest number of cells in culture	25—30	37
Most rapid fermentation	40	47
Formation of largest amount of acid in culture	30	37

Porter (1946) states that the minimum temperature at which marine bacteria have developed is 7.5°C, whereas the optimal temperature for their growth and intensive metabolic exchange may differ widely for the various species. As an example, data are cited for two species of streptococci (Table 10).

The maximum temperature of growth is understood to be that temperature at which organisms still grow and reproduce. Like minimum and optimal temperatures, the highest temperature at which growth takes place differs sharply for different species of bacteria. For instance, the majority of soil and water-dwelling bacteria have a maximum growth temperature of 30-35°C. Nevertheless some species may develop at temperatures of 70-75°C and even higher. Table 11 shows Porter's data on the maximum temperatures for certain spore-forming bacteria.

Table 11

Temperature maxima for certain spore-forming bacteria
(after Porter, 1946)

Organism	Maximum temperature for		
	Spore germination	Vegetative growth	Spore formation
Bacillus mycoides	30—35	30—35	30—35
" simplex	35—40	35—40	35—40
" asterosporus	40—45	35—40	35—40
" alvei	40—45	45—50	45—50
" megatherium	45—50	45—50	35—40
" subtilis	55—60	55—60	55—57
" robustus	65—67	65—67	65—67
" calidus	70—73	70—73	70—73
" cylindricus	73—74	73—74	70—73
" tostus	74—75	74—75	73—74

Porter (1946) also states that the maximum temperature for the growth of the bacteria (Table 12) frequently coincides with the minimum temperature at which there is decomposition of certain nutrients. This problem has been investigated in detail by Edwards and Rettder (1937).

Bacteria whose optimal growth takes place at temperatures above 55°C and whose lower limit of growth is 37°C are called strict thermophils. Facultative thermophils have their optimal growth in the 45-55°C range, and their maximum temperature of growth is 75°C. There are a number of reports of the occurrence of live bacteria at still higher temperatures. For example, L. Ye. Kramarenko (1956) has found thermophilic sulfate-reducing bacteria in 83°C water taken from the Omsk stratigraphic test well. M. Ye. Al'tovskiy (1958) mentions the occurrence of micro-organisms in the oil waters of the Terek-Dagestan province at a temperature of 89°C. Finally, ZoBell (1958) presents data on the occurrence of sulfate-reducing bacteria at a temperature of 104°C; the same paper mentions experiments by the author showing that at elevated pressures, up to 200–400 atm, the maximum temperature for the growth of bacteria is still higher.

Table 12

Comparison of maximum temperature of bacterial growth and minimum temperature at which decay of certain compounds takes place
(after Porter, 1946)

Organism	Maximum temperature of growth, °C	Minimum temperature of decomposition, °C		
		Indophenol-oxidases	Catalases	Succindehy-drogenases
Bacillus mycoides	40	41	41	40
" *prausnitzii*	40	44	40	40
" *simplex*	43	55	52	40
" *cereus*	45	48	46	50
" *megatherium*	46	48	50	47
" *subtilis*	54	60	56	51
" *vulgatus*	55	56	56	50
" *mesentericus*	58	60	63	53
Thermophils	76	65	67	59

The authors of the present volume consider that a distinction must be made between the mere presence of bacteria and the possible occurrence of their growth and reproduction. Even if ZoBell's data on the occurrence of thermophilic bacteria at 104°C are correct, this still does not mean that the organisms could have been active at that temperature. Numerous references indicating that the spores of thermophilic bacteria can withstand a temperature of 100°C for a long time are given by Porter (1946).

Considering the above data the present authors believe that the upper temperature limit at which the life processes of micro-organisms can still take place, although in weakened form, can be no higher than 75–80°C. Moreover, in all the literature mentioned above on the natural occurrence of bacteria at temperatures above 80°C, there has been no confirmation of the ability of any given group of microorganisms to develop under laboratory conditions at the high temperature at which they were found in nature.

2. THE EFFECT OF HYDROSTATIC PRESSURE ON THE GROWTH OF MICROORGANISMS

As one moves into the deeper layers of the earth, the pressure becomes greater. This increase is due not only to the weight of the overlying rocks and water, but also to the pressure of gas that may be formed by anaerobic decomposition of oil. If the sedimentary deposits consist of sand or plastic clay, then the pressure of the overlying strata will be transmitted to the entire depth of the deposits, as V. A. Sokolov has written (1948), and the magnitude of the hydrostatic pressure will correspond approximately to the weight of the deposits. If, however, the sedimentary rock has been consolidated and cemented into a massive, rigid body crumpled into folds, then in certain cases the surface pressure of the overlying strata is not transmitted to strata below, and the pressure will not correspond to the weight of the overlying rocks. This pressure will be determined mainly by the hydrostatic pressure of the water contained in the rock.

All that has been said so far applies to the particles of which the sedimentary and igneous rocks are composed where the material that occupies the pores in the rock, regardless of its composition, may not be subjected to any pressure from the rock itself. However, this will depend on the pore size. If the pores are open, more than 0.0002 mm in magnitude or if they are extensively interconnected, the pressure on the substance occupying the pores will be determined by hydrostatic and gas pressure.

Experiments by K. B. Ashirov and S. P. Maksimov (1958) have shown that the pressure on the sides of the deepest oil wells at Mukhanovo in some cases reaches 325 atm. Thus in the majority of strata where bacterial development has not been suppressed by high temperatures, the hydrostatic pressure should not exceed 300-400 atm, and will frequently be considerably smaller because of the folded structure and the rigidity of the surrounding rocks.

As ZoBell and Oppenheimer have shown (1950), the critical pressures for bacteria lie within the limits of 3000 to 12,000 atm. A number of bacteria subjected to pressure in the logarithmic phase of growth, however, according to data from ZoBell and Johnson (1949), died at pressures of 500-600 atm, and ceased to multiply at 300 atm. The most highly pressure resistant organisms are the endospores and resting cells of bacteria.

The effect of the hydrostatic pressure on the different species of bacteria varies widely. *Vibrio desulfuricans*, which occurs extensively in stratal waters, is the most resistant to high pressures. ZoBell (1958) gives the following data on the effect of pressure on the reduction of sulfate by *V. desulfuricans* during 18 hours at a temperature of 30°C (Table 13). This experiment was carried out with a washed culture of the microorganism in a mineral medium in the presence of hydrogen, at different hydrostatic pressures. The most intensive reduction of sulfate took place at 1000 atm.

ZoBell (1958) considers that when the pressure is increased, the temperature optimum and maximum for development of the microbes is increased. At 1000 atm, the organisms grew and reduced sulfate at 104°C. These experiments must be very thoroughly checked, and their results are to be used only with the greatest caution.

Table 13

Effect of hydrostatic pressure on intensity of
sulfate reduction
(after ZoBell, 1958)

Pressure, atm	Formation of H_2S, mg/liter after 18 hr	Pressure, atm	Formation of H_2S, mg/liter after 18 hr
1	22	800	53
200	21	1000	79
400	27	1400	8
600	39	1800	3

Finally, as ZoBell and Oppenheimer (1950) have discovered, one must distinguish between the effects of the hydrostatic pressure on growth and on the multiplication of the cells. Experiments have shown that a number of species, for example *Actinomyces balotrichis,* cease to multiply at 200 atm, whereas others, such as *Micrococcus euryhalis,* die at this pressure. Some species, like *Micrococcus aquivivius,* multiply readily even at 600 atm. Experiments by the same authors with *Serratia marinorubra* have shown that this organism, upon incubating four days in a nutrient medium at 23°C and from 1 to 200 atm, multiplied in the form of short rods; at 400 atm the rods were elongated, and at 600 atm multiplication ceased, although the still viable cells grew into separate long filaments (Fig. 6). When the pressure was lowered, the filaments divided into individual viable short rods.

In summarizing this information, it may be concluded that the elevated pressures in the deeper layers of the earth will limit the geological activity of the microorganisms only in certain special cases.

3. THE EFFECT OF THE SALT COMPOSITION OF WATER ON THE GROWTH OF MICROORGANISMS

The resistance of individual species of microorganisms to the concentration and composition of salts in water depends largely on

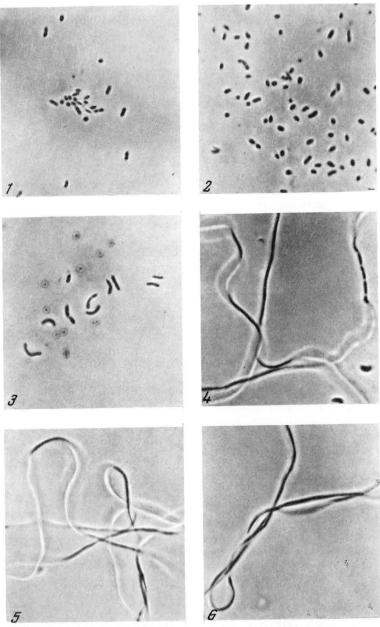

Fig. 6. *Serratia marinorubra* from cultures in nutrient media incubated for 96 hours at a temperature of 23°C and various pressures: 1—1 atm; 2—200 atm; 3—400 atm; 4-6—600 atm. Magnification × 600 (phase-contrast microscope) (ZoBell and Oppenheimer, 1950).

the conditions under which the given microorganisms live in nature. The most representative data are cited by ZoBell (1958) for sulfate-reducing bacteria (Table 14).

Table 14

Salt resistance of sulfate-reducing bacteria taken from various habitat localities
(after ZoBell, 1958)

Habitat	Salt resistance, % NaCl	Authors
Soils and deposits of fresh-water basins	0—1.5	ZoBell, 1958
Odessa harbors.	8—30	S. Z. Khait, 1924
Same	2—25	Baranick-Pikowsky, 1927
"	to 30	Saslawsky, 1928
"	5—30	L. I. Rubenchik, 1947
Oil wells	to 18	T. L. Ginzburg-Karagicheva, 1932
Sea salt extractions	to 30	Hof, 1935
Sulfur deposits	6—13	Iya and Srenivasaya, 1945b
Marine sediments	1.5—6	Kimata, Kadota et al., 1955
Ooze of marine canals.	3—10	van Delden, 1904
Mouths of rivers emptying into sea.	to 30	Baas Becking and Wood, 1955

Salt-resistant species as a rule do not grow if the sodium chloride concentration in the nutrient medium is lower than 1.5%. On this basis, van Delden (1904) established the existence of two species of sulfate-reducing bacteria: the saline *Vibrio aestuarii* and the fresh-water *Vibrio desulfuricans*. Baars (1930) showed that one form could be changed into the other by gradually changing the salt concentration in the nutrient medium. Nevertheless, as ZoBell (1958) has written, neither Rittenberg nor the other investigators working in his laboratory were able to confirm the results of Baars' experiments.

Later ZoBell (1958) determined the presence of sulfate-reducing bacteria in approximately 400 samples of various salinity stratal waters from oil deposits. Batches of 120 ml of nutrient medium containing various concentrations of salts were inoculated with one ml of the samples. Table 15 shows the number of samples in media of different salinities, out of the total number of 396 in which there was bacterial growth. In 209 samples, no growth was observed in any medium.

In spite of the existence of a number of microorganisms capable of growth at salt concentrations as high as 300 g/liter, the

Table 15

Growth of sulfate-reducing bacteria in media of
different salinities inoculated with samples of stratal
water from oil wells
(after ZoBell, 1958)

Medium			Number of samples in which there was growth in different media (marked by plus sign)
Distilled water	Sea water	Stratal water from wells	
+	+	+	38
+	+	0	8
+	0	0	3
0	+	0	27
0	0	+	26
0	+	+	71
+	0	+	14
Total number of samples			
63	144	149	

development of these same organisms is noticeably more intensive
at lower concentrations (50-60 g/liter). This has been mentioned by
B. L. Isachenko (1927) for Lake Tambukanskoye, L. I. Rubenchik
and D. G. Goykherman (1939) for the estuaries on the Black Sea
coast, and by V. A. Kuznetsova (1960) for microorganisms isolated
from oil stratal waters.

The growth of microorganisms may be retarded, however, not
only by a high total salt concentration in general, but also by the individual components of the salts in solution. In V. A. Kuznetsova's
opinion (1960), for example, the lack of sulfate reduction in the
ground waters of the Devonian deposits in the Zol'nyy Ravine and at
Mukhanovo and Zhiguley, which is also mentioned in papers by T. L.
Simakova and M. A. Lomova (1958) and by Z. A. Kolesnik (1955), is
due to the deleterious action of bivalent cations. The reason for the
inhibitory effect of bivalent cations on the development of sulfate-
reducing bacteria, however, is still unknown. The available data on
the adverse effect of cations of various salts upon the growth of
microorganisms have been summarized by Porter (1946), who lists
the following cations in ascending order of their inhibiting effect:
Na, K, NH_4, Mg, Ca, Ba, Mn, Fe^{++}, Zn, Fe^{+++}, Al, Pb, Cu, Hg, Ag.

4. THE EFFECT OF WATER CONTENT ON THE GROWTH OF MICROORGANISMS

The moisture in soil or rocks is one of the most important factors determining the growth of microorganisms. This problem has been studied in detail by D. M. Novogrudskiy (1946a, 1956), who states that the soil water, according to A. F. Lebedev, may exist in four states, which are schematically illustrated in Fig. 7.

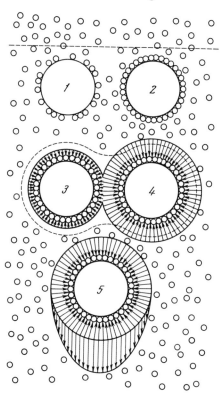

Fig. 7. Diagram showing the various states in which water may exist in the soil (after Lebedev). The circles symbolize molecules of water vapor: 1—soil particles of incompletely hygroscopic nature; 2— fully hygroscopic soil particles; 3, 4—soil particles with pellicular water; particle 4 is surrounded by a film of maximum thickness, so that the water moves from particle 4 to particle 3; this movement continues until the pellicles around both particles are equally thick; 5—soil particle with gravitational water.

Water in vapor form. This water moves within the air in the soil from areas of greater to lesser vapor tension. Lebedev has shown experimentally that in soils which hold more water than the maximum hygroscopic content, the air has a relative humidity of 100%. In this case, the soil microorganisms are always surrounded by air that is fully saturated with water vapor.

Hygroscopic water. This is water vapor adsorbed by soil particles. Hygroscopic water cannot move as a liquid but, as may be seen in Fig. 7, can move from some soil particles to others, containing more water vapor. The maximum amount of water vapor that the soil or rock is capable of absorbing from water-saturated air is called the maximum hygroscopicity. Hygroscopic water has a number of peculiarities. The larger the soil particle, the greater the thickness of the layer of hygroscopic water around the particle. In the case of a particle 0.25 mm in diameter, the thickness of the hygroscopic film will be 3×10^{-5} mm, and the number of layers of water molecules will be 137; with a particle size on the order of 0.001-0.0001 mm, the number and thickness of the layers of water molecules are ten times smaller. The peripheral layers of hygroscopic water molecules approach free water in their properties. Nevertheless hygroscopic water does not freeze even at very low temperatures and is distinguished by its sharply increased ability to dissolve salts.

Pellicular water. According to Lebedev's scheme, this water surrounds soil particles above the layer of hygroscopic water. It is held around the soil particles by the latter's sorption potential, which cannot become fully saturated through the sorption of water vapor. The greatest thickness of the layer of pellicular water corresponds to an amount of water equal to the maximum molecular moisture capacity of the soil. The latter, in turn, is determined as follows: moisture is added to the top of a column of soil until full saturation is reached; the water is then completely drained off, and the amount of moisture in the upper zone is determined. This magnitude characterizes the maximum quantity of moisture that can soak into the soil, or the maximum molecular moisture capacity. The maximum molecular moisture capacities for the different soil fractions are given in Table 16.

Pellicular water has the following peculiarities:

a) in the presence of pellicular water, the soil air is always saturated with water vapor;

b) pellicular water moves within the soil or rock as a fluid entirely through the action of molecular forces; it is not affected either by hydrostatic pressure or by the force of gravity; and such movement proceeds very slowly from layers with greater to those with less moisture content;

c) salts may dissolve in pellicular water and move by diffusion;

d) pellicular water freezes at $-1.5°$ C.

Gravitational water. This is the water in excess of the maximal molecular moisture capacity which has not been taken up by the soil particles. Its movement is due to gravitational force and it is subject to the laws of hydrostatic pressure. Its rate of movement is far greater than that of pellicular water. Lebedev includes capillary water in the category of gravitational water.

Novogrudskiy (1956) has stated that higher vegetation can utilize all forms of moisture except hygroscopic water. Pellicular water, however, because of its low mobility, is unable to satisfy

Table 16

Maximum molecular moisture capacity
of different soil fractions

Fraction	Diameter of particles, mm	Maximal molecular moisture capacity, %
Coarse sand	1.0—0.5	1.57
Medium sand	0.50—0.25	1.60
Fine sand	0.25—0.10	2.73
Very fine sand.	0.10—0.05	4.75
Ooze.	0.05—0.005	10.18
Clay.	0.005	44.85

the requirements of plants, so that they begin to wither when dependent upon this alone. Plants grow readily in soils with about 60% of the total moisture capacity.

As regards microorganisms, their relationship to the form and content of moisture is not yet sufficiently known. Various organisms have different water requirements. Walter (1931) divides micro-organisms from this standpoint into three groups classified by humidity:

1) xerophils, whose growth begins when the moisture content of the air is 85-90%; this group includes the saprophytic fungi;

2) mesophils, whose growth begins when the air moisture content is 90-95%; this group also includes saprophytic fungi;

3) hygrophils, which begin to develop when the relative humidity of the soil air exceeds 95%. These include the bacteria, normally not capable of development at smaller moisture contents.

The lower limits of moisture content have been studied in greater detail by Novogrudskiy (1946a and b) for a number of bacteria and saprophytic fungi. Thus when rocks contain maximal amounts of pellicular or hygroscopic water alone, all the pores in the rock will be filled with gas, whose relative humidity reaches 100%. Inasmuch as microorganisms correspond in size to the very smallest pores in the rock, they will exist under conditions of 100% humidity in the air or gas within the rocks. In other words, in most cases the conditions of natural moisture in the rock will allow the development of microorganisms.

5. THE RELATIONSHIP BETWEEN THE GROWTH OF MICROORGANISMS AND THE CONCENTRATION OF DISSOLVED ORGANIC MATTER

One of the fundamental factors stimulating bacterial growth is the presence of assimilable organic matter dissolved in the water.

A summary of the data in the literature on the influence of the concentration of organic substances upon bacterial growth may be found in Rahn (1934), who states that a deficiency of nutritive substances begins to appear when this concentration falls below the level of 0.1-0.01%. On the other hand, bacterial development may take place even at considerably smaller concentrations of organic matter. ZoBell and Grant (1942) and ZoBell, Grant and Haas (1943) observed marine bacteria growing readily at concentrations of organic substances lower than 0.1 mg/liter.*

The organic matter in ground waters may be derived either from surface contamination, when contaminating surface waters penetrate into the aquifer, or from the leaching of organic substances from adjacent sedimentary rocks. A third source of organic matter may be the oil with which the stratal waters come into contact.

The effect of surface contamination in increasing the number of saprophytic bacteria is discussed by Taylor (1958), who has summarized in a single table (Table 17) the data from a large number of public-health analyses of the waters from various sources in England. These data show that as the degree of contamination—or, in equivalent terms, the amount of organic matter—increases, there is a sharp rise in the numbers of saprophytic bacteria. The smallest numbers of bacteria were observed in the ground waters used for drinking.

Table 17

Average number of bacteria per ml in various
sources of water
(after Taylor, 1958)

Water source	Number of analyses	Average number of colonies per ml	
		Gelatin, 20°C, after 3 days	Gelatin, 37°C, after 24 hours
Unpolluted waters from wells . . .	344	36.5	3.2
Polluted waters from deep wells . .	118	3530	550
Small well heads.	133	3320	372
Creeks	109	1110	92
Rivers	319	8440	1340
Sewage.	25	11,000,000	270,000

---

*Editor's Note: Theoretically organisms need only an amount of molecules equal to one cell composition, for one division to take place.

The idea that the organic matter disseminated in rocks may serve as the source of energy not only for the development of oligocarbo- phils, but also for the sulfate-reducing bacteria, is discussed in a paper by V. N. Ryzhova and M. V. Ivanov (1961). These authors placed crushed sulfur-bearing limestone from the Rozdol sulfur deposit into flasks with ground glass stoppers, and poured sterile mineral medium in, up to the stoppers. A culture of sulfate-reducing bacteria was placed in the flasks simultaneously with the other ingredients. Growth of the desulfurizing bacteria was noted after two and four weeks, as black spots, indicating the foci of sulfate reduction and the formation of hydrogen sulfide. The authors state that in a number of experiments as much as 200 mg/liter of hydrogen sulfide was formed, and there were more than 25 foci of development of desulfurizing bacteria per flask (Table 18). The data in Table 18 show clearly that the organic matter occurring at natural concentrations in rocks is quite sufficient to support the development of desulfurizing bacteria. Similar data were obtained by O. Yu. Volkova and A. D. Tashinskaya (1961), who studied the genesis of the hydrogen sulfide in the Pyatigorsk mineral waters.

Table 18

Number of colonies of sulfate-reducing bacteria
grown by consuming the organic matter
disseminated in limestone and gypsum

Duration of experiment	Rock used	Conditions of experiment	
		Rock + sterile medium	Rock + culture + sterile medium
2 weeks	Limestone	16	14
	Gypsum	0	0
4 weeks	Limestone	25	19
	Gypsum	1.5	8

In addition to organic matter, the chief other substances that stimulate the growth of bacteria in the deeper layers of the earth's crust are hydrogen (in the simultaneous presence of oxygen) and inorganic substances whose oxidation can provide the energy needed for bacterial chemosynthesis.

CHAPTER V

The Distribution of Bacteria in Ground Waters and Sedimentary Rocks

Most studies of the bacterial population of internal waters have been made either for the purpose of a public-health analysis—in which case the number of *Escherichia coli* and the total number of saprophytic bacteria are determined—or else in connection with the study of oil deposits. In the latter case, samples of oil and stratal waters have been taken from depths down to 4225 m (Rybakova, 1957) and the individual physiological groups of bacteria or the total numbers of bacteria have been counted.

At the present time a number of facts are known which confirm the presence of bacteria in internal waters. Among geologists, however, there is a current opinion, expressed by P. F. Andreyev (1955), that oil occurrences and their stratal waters are sterile. In support of his position, the author uses the following arguments:

1) he casts doubt on all natural occurrences of bacteria in internal waters, and believes rather that the bacteria have entered along with the drilling fluids and have then multiplied in the disturbed oil strata;

2) he denies the existence of ancient viable forms of bacteria and considers it impossible for bacterial flora to infiltrate into a stratum from the surface.

Assuming, from V. A. Sulin's data (1948), an average vertical rate of flow of the surface water of 5 m per month, P. F. Andreyev reckons that 25 years would be required for surface waters to penetrate to a depth of 1500 m—and this is a period long enough to cause the bacteria to die in the absence of sufficient organic matter. Thus, in Andreyev's opinion, bacteria could not have contaminated such stratal waters.

By now, however, enough quantitative and qualitative analyses have accumulated to provide reliable basis for believing that the life processes of microflora do take place in internal waters, and Andreyev's views must be considered in error. Bacteriological analysis of the stratal waters from certain wells immediately after their drilling and activation has frequently revealed the presence of a rich and abundant microflora. It is not at all likely that a random microorganism introduced along with the mud slurry into a drill hold could have multiplied intensively to the large numbers found, and it is almost impossible for the mud slurry to penetrate laterally into the stratum because of the high stratal pressure.

On the other hand, the penetration of surface microflora into the depths through the infiltration of surface waters is fully possible. Analyses have shown that the dissolved organic matter in these waters never falls below 3-5 mg of carbon/liter, and the sedimentary rocks through which the waters pass contain up to 2 g of organic carbon per kg of rock. As experiments by M. V. Ivanov and V. N. Ryzhova (1961) have shown, the development of microflora under conditions in stratal waters is not limited by a lack of nutrient elements. Thus the seeding of internal waters by surface microflora is quite possible, and some species of microflora find the conditions here quite favorable to their development.

Finally, direct proof of the existence of bacteria in rocks and internal waters has been obtained by I. L. Andreyevskiy (1959) in the Ukhta oil fields, where the oil is extracted by mining methods. Here Andreyevskiy was able to take samples of oil, water and rock, under aseptic conditions, from the producing stratum immediately after the rock had been broken open—that is, under such conditions that microflora could not have been introduced along with the drilling tool, the mud slurry, etc. In numerous tests where the oil, water and oil-bearing sandstone samples were inoculated in van Delden and Giltay media, Andreyevskiy invariably observed the growth of desulfurizing and denitrifying bacteria. Similar results were obtained by M. V. Ivanov (1957b and c) in similar tests with stratal waters and rock samples from mines in the Shor-Su and Rozdol sulfur deposits. In none of these cases is there any occasion to suspect the introduction of bacteria by the drilling tools or the mud slurry, as P. F. Andreyev (1955) believes.

The bacterial population of underground waters may be characterized by direct count of the numbers of bacteria under the microscope, and the determination of the physiological groups or species making up the community. According to M. A. Peshkov (1948), modern staining methods using vital stains permit a fairly accurate distinction between live and dead bacteria in microscope analysis. Without citing all the literature on this question, let us consider the main aspects of the study of the bacterial population in rocks and internal waters.

1. FEATURES CHARACTERIZING THE DISTRIBUTION OF BACTERIA IN OIL DEPOSITS

The occurrence of oil and gas is usually associated with anticlinal folds, and the oil and gas reservoir rocks are most often sandstones, limestones or dolomites. As a rule, the reservoir rocks are overlaid by shales or other impermeable strata. At the lower surface the oil is usually in contact with stratal waters which also run along the surface of a water-impermeable bed.

The diagram in Fig. 8 shows that the contact between oil-bearing and water-bearing strata may be fairly complete or entirely absent. In the latter case the oil deposit is said to be closed; the isolation of the oil-saturated stratum from the stratal waters is usually due to the formation of a crust of secondary calcite deposited at the oil-water boundary (Ashirov, 1959b).

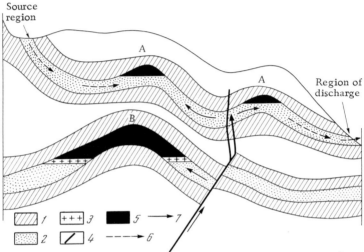

Fig. 8. Diagram of the structure of an open (A) and a closed (B) deposit of oil:

1—water-impermeable rocks; 2—water-permeable rocks; 3—deposits of secondary calcite; 4—fractures and faults; 5—oil; 6—paths of water's movement; 7—paths of oil migration.

Laboratory experiments by I. V. Sazonova (1961), as illustrated in Fig. 9, have shown that the precipitation of secondary calcite is caused by desulfurizing bacteria that form $CaCO_3$ as they reduce the SO_4 in $CaSO_4$, which is frequently present in the stratal waters of oil deposits.

Depending on the manner of its occurrence, the chemical composition of the oil may change within the formation (Vassoyevich and Amosov, 1953; Ginzburg-Karagicheva, 1953). The greatest changes probably take place after the deposit has begun to be exploited.

One index of the activity of microorganisms in a deposit may be their number, which may depend largely on the amount of water exchange in the deposit. A number of investigations (Z. I. Kuznetsova,

1957, 1959, 1961) have been devoted to this problem. Some results of bacterial population counts in the deposits of Dagestan are given in Table 19 and in Fig. 10. The region of source of the aquifer strata is located in the Chernyye [Black] Mountains, where these beds crop out at the surface. Farther on these beds pass through an oil deposit and then are again exposed at the surface in the Bragunov area, where they give rise to a number of isolated springs of water.

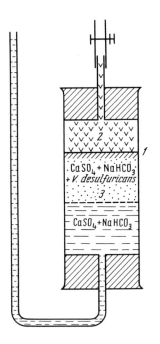

Figure 10 and Table 19 show that the water temperature in the region of "source" is 12-19°C, that dissolved oxygen is present in the water, and that the number of bacteria varies from 118 to 634 thousand per milliliter. In the area of the oil deposit the oxygen disappears, the number of bacteria decreases, and the desulfurizing bacteria make an appearance. Still farther on, in the region of discharge, the water temperature in some cases reaches 86°C, hydrogen sulfide is present, the thiobacteria increase in number, and the total number of bacteria in certain cases is almost as high as 1900 thousand per milliliter.

Investigations made by Z. I. Kuznetsova (1959) in the Terek-Dagestan province and in the Moscow region, the results of which are cited in Table 20, show that the number of bacteria ranges from 10 to 450 thousand/ml in the internal waters of both oil-bearing and non-oil-bearing regions. Staining by the Peshkov (1948) method with giemsa and light green has shown that practically all the bacteria are in the active state in water samples from wells with good water circulation and exchange.

Fig. 9. Diagram of the apparatus for experiments in the microbiological formation of secondary calcite: 1—secondary calcite; 2—oil; 3—sand with a culture of sulfate-reducing bacteria.

Within the oil deposits themselves, the numbers of bacteria frequently show a sharp increase after the oil is pumped out from the given stratum continuously for a number of years. For example, according to L. D. Shturm's data (1950a and b) (Table 21), during eight years of oil production of the Syzran' deposit, the number of bacteria in the stratal waters rose from 50 thousand at the beginning to several hundred thousand and even four million per milliliter.

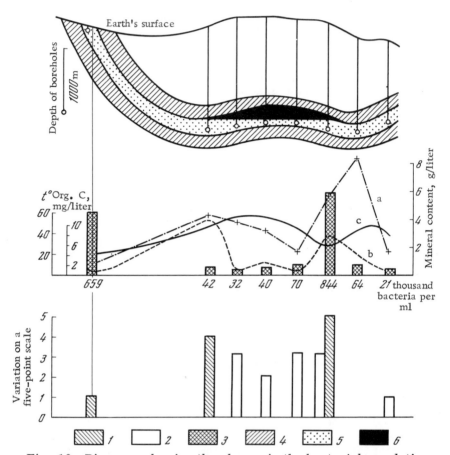

Fig. 10. Diagram showing the change in the bacterial population of the water along the dip of the aquifer stratus in the Chokrakian sediments of the Ternair and Makhachkala deposits;
a—mineral content (g/liter); b—organic carbon (mg/liter); c—temperature; 1—intensity of development of sulfate-reducing bacteria; 2—intensity of development of thiobacteria; 3—total quantity of bacteria per ml of stratal water (figures beneath columns); 4—water-impermeable rocks; 5—aquifer rocks; 6—oil.

As A. N. Meshkov (1958) has shown, considerable differences in the numbers of bacteria are observed in the oils of closed and open deposits. The data from Meshkov's analyses are given in Table 22. These data show that the total number of bacteria in the water and the oil depends on the rate of exchange of water, and increases when the flow of water in the deposit increases.

Table 19

Change in the microflora of stratal waters from the source
region to the region of discharge
(after Z. I. Kuznetsova, 1961)

Criteria	Source region	Region of oil deposits	Region of discharge
Dissolved O_2, mg/liter.	7—9	0	0
Temperature, °C	12—19	40—60	14—86
H_2S, mg/liter	0	68—70	2—35
No. of bacteria, thousands per ml	118—634	10—620	36—1900

Table 20

Numbers of bacteria in stratal waters
(after Z. I. Kuznetsova, 1957 and S. I. Kuznetsov, 1950b)

Stratigraphy	Locality of sampling	Total No. of bacteria, thousands per ml	Number of live cells, %	Total salt content of water, g/liter	Character of region
Tertiary deposits	Mirza Bek, Cheleken Peninsula	445	—	—	Petroliferous
	Glur, Cheleken Pen.	115	—	—	
	Bol'shoy Solonchak, Cheleken Pen.	133	—	—	
	Makhachkala, Terek-Dagestan oil province	229	99	68—70	
Permian	Buguruslay, Orenburg oblast'	151	—	—	Petroliferous
	Kalinovka, Kuybyshev oblast'	172	—	—	
Upper Carboniferous	Zagorsk, Moscow oblast'	48	96	—	Non-petroliferous
	Kovrov, Vladimir oblast'	10	97	—	
	Kolomna, Moscow oblast'	10	95	—	
Middle Carboniferous	Yelshanka, Saratov oblast'	8	—	—	Petroliferous
		25	—	—	
Carboniferous	Tula	50	69	—	Non-petroliferous
	Moscow	10	98	—	

Table 21

Change in the total number of bacteria in stratal waters with
the exploitation of the oil deposit
(after L. D. Shturm, 1950b)

Petroliferous region	Stratigraphic level	Number of bacteria, thousands per ml	
		At beginning of exploitation	After 8 years
Syzran	Carboniferous, coal-bearing formation	32	264
		24	173
		50	1900 629
Tuymaza	Carboniferous, coal-bearing formation	313	4355
	Devonian	606	1600

2. FEATURES CHARACTERIZING THE DISTRIBUTION OF BACTERIA IN SEDIMENTARY ROCKS

The study of the total numbers of bacteria in sedimentary rocks has followed two main tendencies. Some authors (Vologdin, 1947; Rippel, 1935; Schwartz and Mueller, 1958; Oppenheimer, 1958) have investigated sedimentary rocks for fossilized bacteria in ancient deposits, attempting to show the part played by bacteria in the cycles of various substances in the geologic past. Other authors (such as Ekzertsev and Kuznetsov, 1954) have attempted to determine the numbers and distribution of the bacteria in sedimentary rocks with the purpose of discovering the relationship between their distribution and the oil productivity of buried strata and to determine their present role in transforming the oil within the deposit.

a) Fossil Bacteria

In searching for fossil bacteria, thin sections of the rocks are usually prepared and the observable structures in them are studied under high magnification. The bacteria may be represented by cells encrusted with iron oxides, silica or other minerals. It is naturally difficult to identify the discernible structures reliably as

Table 22

Numbers of bacteria in various samples of oil, as determined
by direct counting
(after A. N. Meshkov, 1958)

Strati-graphic level	Deposit							
	Krasnoyarsk (blind)		Sultangulovskoye (open)		Yablonovskoye (blind)		Kalinovskoye (open)	
	Depth of oil, m	No. of bac-teria, thous./ml	Depth of oil, m	No. of bac-teria, thous./ml	Depth of oil, m	No. of bac-teria, thous./ml	Depth of oil, m	No. of bac-teria, thous./ml
Permian	354—380	172	Oil lacking	—	522—533	158	241—255	288
	362—366	366			532—561 567—582	217 88	238—248	334
Carbon-iferous	1601—1604	39	1615—1630	558	Oil lacking	—	Oil lacking	—
	1600—1611	64	1630—1640	263	Same	—	Same	—
	1589—1607	165	Oil lacking	—	"	—	"	—
	1604—1611	113		—	"	—	"	—
Devonian	2315—2320	72	2290—2296	271	"	—	"	—
	2256—2265	74	2265—2280	539	"	—	"	—
			2265—2280	441	"	—--	"	—

fossil forms of bacteria, but in numerous cases the identification
of these structures as fossilized bacteria cannot be doubted.

The oldest fossil bacteria have been found by A. G. Vologdin
(1947) in Precambrian deposits (Figs. 11 and 13). Thus microorganisms must have begun to take part in the cycle of materials
in the biosphere at least as early as the Precambrian Era. A
summary of the work done up to 1927 in studying fossil bacteria
is given in a book by Pia (1928). The most convincing work was
that of Ellis (1914), who found fossil bacteria in thin sections of
iron ores (Fig. 12). Vologdin (1947) came to recognize the role
played by iron bacteria in the formation of the Krivoy Rog Basin
ores, from his microscope investigations.

Studies of fossilized bacteria in salt domes have been made by
many authors. Rahn (1934) and Rippel (1935) by their microscope
studies established the presence of bacteria in thin sections of

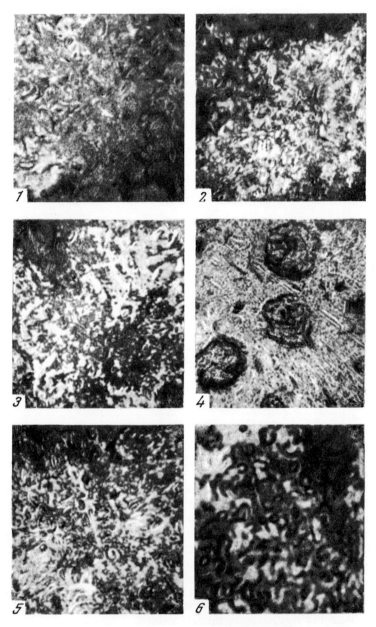

Fig. 11. Fossilized iron bacteria:
1—bauxite from Buksonskoye deposit in the Eastern Sayan Mts,
Cambrian, thin section × 1300; 2—bauxite from "Krasnaya

rock salt (Fig. 14). These have been studied in greater detail by Mueller and Schwartz (1955), who, after analyzing samples of modern salts from evaporite lakes and summarizing the material, concluded that some species of bacteria are capable of development even in concentrated salt solutions. In addition, by making aseptic collections of rock salt and sylvite samples from various salt domes, they established that these domes contained no live bacteria capable of growing in liquid nutrient media of various compositions. To find fossil bacteria, they dissolved samples of the salt and analyzed the remaining residue, stained by the Vinogradskiy (1924) method, directly under a phase-contrast microscope. Preserved in both the salts and the liquid inclusions, they discovered a number of bacteria and fungi. In five of eleven samples of rock salt, sylvite and carnallite, they observed empty sheaths of iron bacteria of the *Leptothrix* type (Fig. 15). Mueller and Schwartz thus attribute the black color of some specimens of carnallite and iron sulfides to the activity of desulfurizing bacteria during the precipitation of the salt.

Interesting work was also done by Oppenheimer (1958), who investigated samples of phosphorites from Gafza in Tunisia and from one of the islands of Oceania. The Tunisian specimens consisted of small, round, cemented phosphoritized fecal pellets of small organisms; here and there the broken tests of diatoms were found. Study of the feces of present-day microscopic organisms reveals the presence of a multitude of bacteria in them. Therefore Oppenheimer considers it justifiable to identify as bacterial organisms those structures whose morphology resembles that of bacteria and which are encountered in phosphorites (Fig. 16). Oppenheimer also suggests that in the future there will very likely be still more reliable basis for the identification of fossil bacteria since recent papers by Abelson (1956) have shown that amino acids can be found in the shells of fossil molluscs. In addition Abelson notes that some of the components of protoplasm may be preserved over the course of geologic time.

The most detailed and systematic analyses of rocks for the purpose of discovering the role of microorganisms in their

---

Shapochka" deposit in the Urals, thin section × 1300; 3—bauxite from Akmolinsk deposit, thin section × 1300; 4—bauxite from Altay deposit of pisolitic structure; the pisolitic grains are composed predominantly of iron bacterial formations; thin section × 120; 5—agalmatolite from the Ashudasta deposit in Kazakhstan, thin section × 1300; 6—kaolinite from the area of the "Samson" deposit in the Krasnoyarsk district, thin section × 1300 (after Vologdin, 1947).

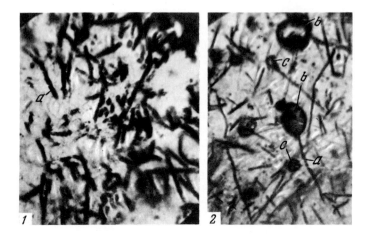

Fig. 12. Fossil bacteria in polished sections of iron ore:
a—hypha containing sporangia; b—ripe sporangia; c—young
sporangia; 1— × 800; 2— × 250
(after Ellis, 1914).

formation have been made by Vologdin (1947). These investigations, as the author says, began with a suggestion by the late Academician V. L. Komarov to search in fossilized materials for bacterial remains or indications of their activity. The results of A. G. Vologdin's microscope investigations may be summarized briefly as follows:

1. Ferruginous oolitic limestones of Permian age, collected in the Shchugor River area, in the Pechora River basin, contained fossilized remains of microorganisms in the form of filamentous sheaths filled with iron.

2. Permian red sandstones from the same area consisted of sand grains cemented by a ferruginous substance. The microstructure of the cement in these sandstones was made up of an accumulation of curved, densely packed filaments resembling bacterial rods.

3. In the Cambrian bauxites from the Bukson deposit, in the Eastern Sayan Mountains, some 40-50% of the volume consisted of occasionally nodular accumulations of filamentous bacteria-like formations which, from their structure and color, could only be the remains of iron bacteria.

4. In the Uralian bauxites of Devonian age, from the Krasnaya Shapochka deposit, microscope study revealed the presence of yellowish-brown accumulations of fossilized iron bacterial cells in the layering of the oolitic grains; these cells were especially abundant in the cementing mass.

5. A similar microscopic picture is presented by the Devonian bauxites from the Salair deposit, but here the spaces between the filamentous iron bacteria contain still smaller accumulations of tiny grains of aluminum oxide.

6. The Mesozoic bauxites with pisolitic structure from the Altay deposit contained colonies of iron bacteria, which occur mainly as loosely formed concretions in the pisolite grains. The pore spaces between the pisolites are filled with aluminum hydroxide, which Vologdin believes is the chief cement produced in the second phase of the formation of these bauxites.

In summarizing his microscopic study of the bauxites, Vologdin concludes that the principal structural element is the iron bacteria, which, to judge from the morphology of their remains, belong to various species. In other words, this bauxite facies was their ecologic niche, in which they grew in massive quantities, and the clotted accumulations of iron hydroxide were deposited wherever space was available. The iron bacteria were evidently fossilized very rapidly so that they were only slightly metamorphosed, this alteration being discernible only in a certain blurring of the primary outlines of their structures.

Later Vologdin studied thin sections of feldspathic rocks whose weathering has led to the formation of kaolinites. The author assumes that, as L. V. Pustovalov says, chemical kaolinization takes place in the deeper zone of the lithosphere, and that in the vadose zone this process occurs through the action of unknown organisms. The latter, as Vologdin supposes, are capable of utilizing the energy from the geochemical reaction involved in the breakdown of the feldspar molecule as the formation is broken up by physical factors. Examination of a number of feldspathic intrusive rocks from the zone of weathering has shown the feldspathic substance to be contaminated by a mass of bacteria-like microscopic bodies, which are more abundant in the more highly kaolinized rock.

He also analyzed thin sections of phosphorites, multicomponent mixtures containing a predominance of iron and calcium phosphates. In the Cambrian phosphorites from the Karatau region three components could be distinguished under the microscope: one was a group of yellow-brown ferruginous cells of iron bacteria; another was a group of small bodies of coccus-bacillus form, which were gray in reflected light (the phosphates were concentrated here); and the third was a dense, collomorphic mineral mass apparently made up of carbonates. Analysis of a number of limonites and brown ironstones has shown that their entire mass consists of dense accumulations of closely interlaced and of isolated cells which very closely resemble modern species of iron bacteria.

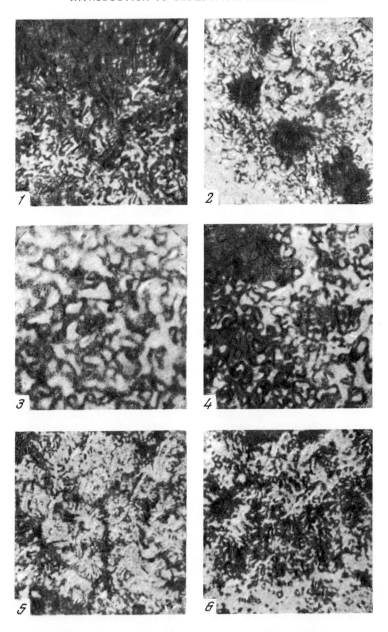

Fig. 13. Microstructures formed by iron bacteria:
1—phosphorite from the Karatau deposit in Kazakhstan, thin
section × 1300; 2—phosphorite from same deposit; dark =

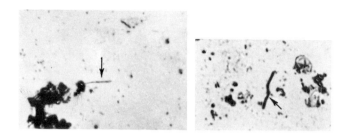

Fig. 14. Fossil bacteria (indicated by arrows) in
thin sections of rock salt
(after Rippel, 1935)

Vologdin believes that the composition of the ferruginous mass
filling the dead bacterial cells includes silica and alumina. This
opinion is supported by the fact that the bacterial structures in

Fig. 15. Sheaths of filamentous iron bacteria
from specimens of sylvite and carnallite
(after Mueller and Schwartz, 1955)

ferruginous microconcretions, light areas = phosphate mass;
thin section × 1300; 3—same, × 8000; 4—phosphorite from the
Salair deposit, Mesozoic, × 2600; 5—product of serpentiniza-
tion of pyroxenite from the area of the Teyskoye iron deposit:
light areas are gangue minerals, × 1300; 6—limonitized magnetite ore from the Abakanskoye iron-ore deposit in the
Krasnoyarsk district, thin section × 2600
(after Vologdin, 1947)

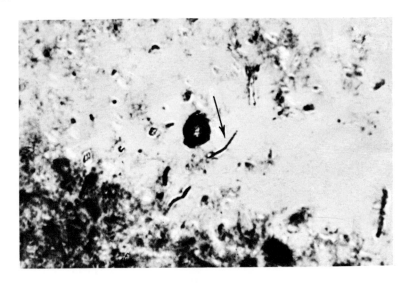

Fig. 16. Fossil bacteria (indicated by arrows) from
phosphorites (after Oppenheimer, 1958)

the limonites resist destruction even by strong hydrochloric acid.
Vologdin has observed distinct accumulations of fossilized cells
of iron bacteria in the Krivoy Rog ores, in the Proterozoic
ferruginous schists along the Angara River, and in the Lower
Paleozoic rocks of the Kara-tau Range, in the Early Cambrian
hematitic ores on the eastern slopes of the Yenisey Ridge, and
elsewhere. He believes that the formation of the limonites that
compose the "iron gossan" capping the deposits was in every case
due to biological processes in the vadose zone.

Critical evaluation of all this material leads one to the conclusion
that Vologdin has indeed observed structures very closely resembling bacteria. This is undoubtedly proof of intensive microbiological activity in the geologic past of this planet. His observations,
moreover, are consistent with those of Ellis (1914), Renault
(1895), Pia (1928) and other authors.

The occurrence of remains of microorganisms in various kinds
of caustobioliths is discussed in detail by V. O. Tauson (1947),
who states that silicified plant remains and so-called buds of calcareous or dolomitic nature have often been found in coal. Thin
sections of these formations frequently reveal fossilized plant
tissues in all their details. Often these tissues are partially
destroyed, the damage to them resembling that observed in the
tissues of modern plants. At the same time, the thin sections show

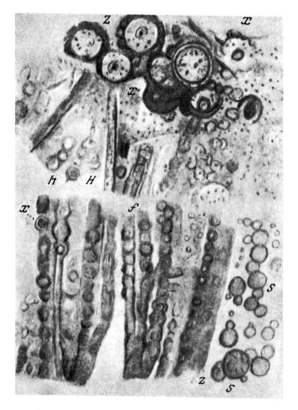

Fig. 17. ''Devonian'' fungus from brown
coal:
H and h are short chains of fungus cells;
Z—cells of algae partially destroyed by
fungus (x); S—yeastlike cell of fungus
spore
(after Tauson, 1947)

fossilized filaments or hyphae of parasitic and saprophytic fungi,
which spread through the damaged plant fossils in all directions.
There are also the sporangia of fungi which can be assigned to
particular families. Remains of fungi have also been found in
lignites and brown coals. The rocks in which the remains of
these organisms have been identified date from various geologic
periods.

Tauson (1947) mentions that numerous and well-preserved
fungus remains have been found in sandstone from Spitsbergen
Island and in calcareous shale from the Medvezh'ye Islands. These

rocks are Devonian. The sandstone contained fossil algae and two species of fungi. Remains of the same two fungus species were found in the shale as well; these had contributed to the destruction of wood, which was later fossilized. Tauson presents many examples of fossilized microbes found in various specimens from coal deposits of different geologic ages (Fig. 17). All this testifies that, beginning with the Devonian period, microorganisms have played a primary role in the destruction of plant remains and in the formation of fossil fuels.

For a final proof of the correctness of the views in this book, one may trace the role of bacteria in the present-day weathering of feldspathic rocks in the formation of the limonites in iron gossan and of iron pyrite deposits, in the creation of peat bogs, and in other activities.

b) The Total Numbers of the Bacterial Populations in Sedimentary Rocks

The total number of bacteria in rocks may be determined by S. N. Vinogradskiy's method (1924). This method of counting bacteria has been designed for soils, and consists of the following procedure: a drop of soil suspension is placed on a microscope slide, the slide is dried, and the material is stained with a vital stain such as erythrosine, Bengal pink, etc. In this process the bacterial protoplasm is colored red. The number of colored bacterial cells within some definite area of the preparation is counted and, correcting for the dilution of the soil, the total number of bacteria in one gram of soil is computed.

This method has given rise to a number of objections. One of its chief defects (ZoBell, 1946a) is the fact that vital stain reveals only the live and not the dead bacteria. This objection may be of little real significance, however, since after the bacteria have died, the enzymes within the cells should rapidly dissolve not only the protoplasm, but also the cell membrane. Experiments by M. F. Lazareva (1953), carried out with the aid of A. S. Razumova, in which the live and dead bacteria in natural waters were counted using the double staining technique with light green according to Peshkov's method (1948), have shown that the number of dead bacteria does not exceed 10% of the total number. Similar results were obtained by Strugger (1948), who used fluorescent microscopy to count soil bacteria.

Exaggerated results in bacterial counts can evidently be obtained with the microscope method if the enzyme complex with the cell was destroyed by the same mechanism which killed the bacteria. Under the conditions existing in internal waters and in rocks, however, such cases are probably extremely rare. Thus direct counts by the

microscope method should fairly accurately reveal the actual numbers of bacteria carrying on their life processes within the rocks.

The microscope method of counting of the bacterial populations
in soils (Naumova, 1933) and lake oozes (Kuznetsov, 1949a, 1952)
has shown a total of up to three billion bacterial cells per gram of
substrate studied. In fresh-water deposits the number of bacteria
is normally smaller in the deeper sediment layers (Kuznetsov,
1949a; Ekzertsev, 1948; Zavarzina, 1955), but does not fall below
100 million cells per gram dry weight. Using Peshkov's differential staining procedure, N. B. Zavarzina (1955) showed that in the
ooze deposits of Lake Biserovo, up to 40% of the cells counted
under the microscope were viable.

V. A. Ekzertsev (1951), V. L. Mekhtiyeva (1956, 1961), M. A.
Messineva (1961) and others have studied the distribution of the
total quantities of bacteria in sedimentary rocks. Before presenting
the results of their work, however, some of the possible sources of
error should be discussed. Since a mud slurry is the usual lubri-
cant in well drilling, there is some danger the drill core may be
contaminated by bacteria from the drilling mud. With this in mind,
Z. S. Smirnova (1957) has made a special study of the depth to
which the mud slurry penetrates into drill cores of different
lithologic compositions during the drilling process. For this
purpose, fluorescein or a culture of *Bacterium prodigiosum* was
introduced into the mud slurry directly in the borehole. The drill
core was washed with water immediately upon removal from the
borehole, and in a field laboratory separate concentric layers were
peeled off from its surface and analyzed chemically or bacteriologi-
cally. Table 23 gives the results of these analyses. These data show
that bacteria penetrate from the mud slurry deep into the drill core
only along fractures; penetration into an unfractured monolithic core
does not exceed 4-7 mm, even in sandstone. Consequently if the
sample is taken from the center of an unfractured core 89 mm in
diameter, one can rely on the validity of the data obtained.

A second possible source of error in analysis lies in the fact
that a sample for study under the microscope requires very great
dilution during preparation. Thus even a small degree of bacterial
contamination introduced may strongly influence the results of the
analysis. The Germanov method is described by Naumova (1933),
in which 1 g of pulverized rock is stirred in 100 ml of 1/4000 N
NaOH solution, and one drop of the resulting mixture, equal to 1/20
ml, is spread over an area of 4 cm^2. A count is then made, using an
ocular micrometer with a grid 4000 μ^2 in area, and the following
formula is used for calculation:

$$X = \frac{4 \cdot 10^8 \cdot 2000 \cdot a}{4000},$$

Table 23

Depth of penetration of *Bacterium prodigiosum* from a clay
solution into rock cores of various lithologic compositions
(after Z. S. Smirnova, 1957)

Lithology of sample	Depth from which sample was taken, m	Depth of penetration of bacteria into core, mm
Massive, dense dolomite	308	1
Silicified dolomitic, limestone, fracture fillings of pyrite and quartz	311—313	1—2
Highly porous calcareous dolomite	371—377	4—5
Very dense sandstone with calcareous cement	218—223	1.5—2.0
Solid, hard, dry sandstone	16.5	2—3
Friable sandstone	32	40
Blue, argillaceous marly sandstone	18.0	3
Friable, clayey sand	8.0	40
Viscous clay with sandstone flags	12.9	40
Sandy, friable clay	4	6.5
Dense, micaceous clay with an admixture of sand	36	5.0
Sandy clay, with layers of sand	208—213	40

where a is the average number of bacteria in an area of 4000 μ^2, and
X is the number of bacteria per gram of rock. In other words,
a single bacterium in the field of vision corresponds to 200
million bacteria in 1 g of rock. Thus to obtain reliable results
in counting bacteria, one must, besides following the procedure
described above, examine a large number of fields to give statisti-
cal results.

As an example, Table 24 presents the data obtained by V. A.
Ekzertsev (1951, 1956), who counted the bacteria in various
rock samples from the Buguruslan and Saratov regions. Ekzertsev associates the distribution of bacteria in the deeper rocks
with the occurrence of oil at the given level. In the samples
with clear indications of oil occurrence, the number of
bacteria ranges from 35 to 117 million per gram of rock; in the
overlying or underlying strata, as a rule, no bacteria were
observed.

M. A. Messineva, using microscope methods, has determined
the abundance of bacteria in sedimentary rocks from the Kolkhida
Lowland in Georgia and from the Tertiary deposits of Stavropol'.
She concluded (Messineva, 1961) that the number of bacterial cells
decreases sharply with increasing depth only in the first several

meters below the surface of the deposits. Farther down, the numbers of bacteria vary in relation to the facies and lithology of the rocks.

Table 24

Total numbers of bacteria in sedimentary rocks
(after V. A. Ekzertsev, 1951, 1956)

District from which core was taken	Stratigraphic level	Nature of rock	Depth of occurrence, m	No. of bacteria, million per gram of rock
Buguruslan	Permian: Kungurian stage	Oil-bearing limestone . . .	555—566	35
	Same	Dolomite, non-petroliferous, underlying	590—600	0
	"	Anhydrite.	670—680	94
	Permian: Kungurian stage	Dolomite, oil-saturated . .	583—593	105
	Same	Dolomite, non-petroliferous	658—662	0
	Carboniferous: Namurian stage	Dolomite, oil-saturated . .	724—735	117
	Same	Same.	745—752	70
	Middle Devonian	Sandstone, oil-saturated . .	1909—1912	47
Saratov	Carboniferous: coal measures	Oil-bearing sandstone . . .	871—874	23
	Same	Oil-bearing black clay. . .	1016—1021	12
	"	Underlying black clay . . .	1123—1131	0
	"	Sandstone.	1074—1080	35
	"	Underlying gray clay. . . .	1080—1086	0
	Carboniferous: Tournaisian stage	Oil-saturated dolomite. . .	1083—1089	70
	Middle Devonian	Oil-bearing sandstone . . .	2088—2093	70

Finally, studies of the numbers of bacteria in the deposits of the Khazarian stage in the ancient Caspian basin were made by V. L. Mekhtiyeva and S. B. Malkova (1958) and by V. L. Mekhtiyeva (1961); they established a relationship between the distribution of bacteria and the moisture content of the rocks, although their data are subject to some doubt. The maximum number of bacteria, according to their counts, was 3100 cells per gram of rock. In view of the large coefficient used in the final computation of the microscope count, however, it is not clear how Mekhtiyeva could have counted such small numbers of bacteria. Her figures are definitely outside the limits of accuracy of the method.

3. THE DISTRIBUTION OF THE INDIVIDUAL PHYSIOLOGICAL GROUPS OF BACTERIA IN GROUND WATERS AND ROCKS

The species composition of the microorganisms in the internal waters and the rocks of the upper layers of the earth's crust has been very inadequately studied; considerably more data are available on the composition and distribution of individual physiological groups of bacteria.

Usually analyses have been made of the water from wells drilled to obtain a water supply or to extract oil. Artesian water for drinking, as a rule, is obtained from depths not exceeding 100 m. Oil wells frequently reach far greater depths, and the stratal waters from such wells have been subjected to the most detailed microbiological study.

In artesian waters, investigations have been made primarily of the saprophytic microflora which in species composition is identical to the microflora in surface waters, and its numbers may serve as an index of the degree to which the aquifer is isolated by water-impermeable rocks from the surface soil waters. Table 25 shows that the quantity of saprophytic bacteria in artesian waters is quite small, reaching 300 cells per milliliter of water only in a few cases.

Table 25

Numbers of bacteria in artesian waters
(per milliliter)

Locality	No. of analyses	No. of saprophytes		Total number of bacteria	Ratio of total No. of bacteria to No. of saprophytes	Author
		Range	Average			
Mytishchinsk aqueduct	6	2—4	3	—	—	S. A. Ozerov, 1915
Magnitogorsk	1	1	—	8200	8200	A. S. Razumov, 1932
Waters in Cretaceous deposits of London aquifer basin	18	5—62	22	—	—	E. W. Taylor, 1958
Matsesta	5	0—75	25	15000	600	S. I. Kuznetsov, 1938b
Agura	2	0.5—2	1	9500	9500	S. I. Kuznetsov, 1938b

The first signs of bacteria in the deep internal waters of oil deposits were found in 1901 in the Baku oil fields by the engineer V. Sheyko, who attributed no significance to this, since the majority of scientists then considered oil to be an antiseptic substance. It was not until January, 1926, that Bastin (1926) published an article on sulfate-reducing bacteria in the stratal waters of oil deposits in the USA; later the same author described these bacteria in more detail (Bastin and Greer, 1930). In August, 1926, appeared an article by T. L. Ginzburg-Karagicheva (1932) describing her investigation of the stratal oil waters of the Apsheron Peninsula, in which she also found sulfate-reducing bacteria. These papers represent the first stage of an investigation designed to establish the presence, qualitative nature and composition of microflora in oil deposits.

Ginzburg-Karagicheva investigated the rocks and internal waters of the Baku, Groznyy and Naftalan oil fields and other deposits, where she found sulfate-reducing, denitrifying, ammonifying and other bacteria. Mekhtiyeva and Malkova (1958) analyzed rocks from wells in a number of oil fields in the Northern Caucasus foothills region for the presence of ammonifying, denitrifying, sulfate-reducing, nitrifying and nitrogen-decomposing bacteria, as well as those which ferment albumins, glucose and cellulose and decompose oil under anaerobic conditions. The presence of the above-listed bacterial groups was determined qualitatively, except for the saprophytes which grew on meat-peptone agar. The errors of their work consist in the lack of adequate quantitative analysis of the saprophytic bacteria; moreover the general purpose of their investigation is not fully clear. The authors have succeeded in showing that live active bacteria occur down to 800 m, and that their distribution has no relation to the lithology. But Mekhtiyeva's and Malkova's opinion that there is a direct connection between the numbers of bacteria and the natural moisture content of the rocks is not supported by their data. Thus the authors have had to make the reservation that the apparent discrepancies are due to differences in grain size and mineral composition.

Other investigators have studied the group composition of the microflora in underground waters in order to solve a number of specific geochemical problems. For instance, V. T. Malyshek and A. A. Maliyants (1935) and B. L. Isachenko (1946) discovered purple sulfur bacteria in the stratal waters of the Ordzhonikidze oil field at Baku at a depth of 2200 m, in the course of their attempt to learn the cause of the pinkish color of the ground waters in this deposit. It should be possible to trace the decreasing area of distribution of this group of bacteria as the oil is pumped out and the water level changed. Thus approximately six months after the oil began to be pumped out from this stratum, the stratal water no longer contained any purple bacteria. No one, at any other time or in any other place, has been able to find any noticeable growth of purple sulfur bacteria in the ground waters of oil deposits. Even the question of whether purple bacteria can develop in total darkness still remains unanswered.

Later, investigations of the role of sulfate-reducing bacteria in the formation of the hydrogen sulfide in stratal waters were made by L. D. Shturm (1950a and b) and supplemented by V. A. Kuznetsova (1957, 1960), V. A. Ekzertsev and S. I. Kuznetsov (1954) and others. These authors found that the occurrence of desulfurizing bacteria in the stratal waters of many oil deposits is associated with the presence of sulfates and oil in the water or rocks. In contradiction to this, however, such bacteria are lacking in the Devonian oil waters of the Urals-Volga oil province, according to Z. A. Kolesnik (1955), T. L. Simakova and M. A. Lomova (1958) and V. A. Kuznetsova (1960), despite the fact that the conditions often seem to favor their existence. Evidently, as V. A. Kuznetsova (1960) believes, the principal factor limiting the growth of sulfate-reducing bacteria in these waters is the excessive content of bivalent as compared to univalent cations.

In connection with the question of the anaerobic decomposition of oil and simultaneous formation of combustible gases in the deposits themselves, S. I. Kuznetsov (1950b) and V. A. Ekzertsev (1956, 1960) have investigated the distribution of bacteria, in some thirty oil deposits of the Urals-Volga oil province, that form methane from hydrogen and carbon dioxide or by decomposing the fatty acids and oil in the stratal waters. The distribution of the individual groups of bacteria in these waters is shown in Table 26. The data in this table indicate that the most widespread group of bacteria is that which destroys oil under anaerobic conditions and forms gaseous products.

Finally, Z. I. Kuznetsova (1959), S. A. Kolesnik (1955) and others have studied in detail the distribution of individual groups of bacteria in the Terek-Dagestan oil province. One feature of Kuznetsova's work is that she has attempted not only to discover the presence of microflora, but also to relate the distribution of the bacteria to the ecological environment and to the movement of the internal waters from the region of source to the region of discharge. Figure 10, shown earlier in this book, shows that as the water approaches the oil deposit, the content of dissolved organic substances increases, the oxidation-reduction potential decreases, sulfate-reducing bacteria appear, and their activity is intensified, so that reduction of sulfates takes place. Farther on, in the region of discharge, thiobacteria appear in spite of the lack of free oxygen.

The factors that determine the distribution and propagation of the thiobacteria have been studied in detail by G. A. Sokolova

Table 26

Frequency of occurence of methane-forming bacteria in
samples of oils and waters from oil wells in the Saratov,
Pugachev, Samar Luka and Trans-Volga Kuybyshev Oblasts
(numbers of occurrences)
(after V. A. Ekzertsev and S. I. Kuznetsov, 1954)

Deposit	Number of samples analyzed	Strati- graphic level	Methano- bacterium omelan- skii	Bacteria that decompose		
				Acetic acid	Hydro- carbons with gas formation	Oil, with formation of gas
Sokolovaya Gora.	5	Devon.	1	2	3	4
Pugachev	2	Carbon.	0	1	2	—
Syzran	6	"	3	4	4	2
Berezovka	4	"	2	1	1	2
Karlovo-Sytovka.	3	"	2	1	1	2
Gubino.	3	"	3	2	1	1
Zol'nyy ravine	2	"	1	1	1	2
Same	3	Devon.	2	3	2	3
Yablonovyy ravine. . . .	2	Carbon.	0	1	1	0
Same	3	Devon.	0	1	1	1
Borovka	2	Carbon.	1	2	0	1
Radayevka.	2	"	0	1	0	2
Kalinovka	2	Permian	2	1	2	2
Yablonovka	2	"	1	1	2	0
Chernovka.	2	"	1	0	0	0
Mukhanovo	3	"	3	3	1	2
Pokrovka.	4	Carbon.	1	2	0	3

(1961b), who has concluded, from a large amount of data, that the
thiobacteria, particularly *Thiobacillus thioparus*, occur only in
open deposits, where the stratal waters have some contact with the
surface waters containing oxygen. This problem will be discussed
in more detail later in this book, in Chapter VII.

As Ekzertsev and Kuznetsov (1954) have shown, the distribution
of the individual physiological groups of bacteria is closely related
to the oil content of the stratum. An example of this relationship
is seen in the data obtained by these authors by analyzing core
samples from one of the wells in the Syzran' deposit (Table 27).
However, such a relationship is not always observed. In closed
deposits, as a rule, microflora develop much less abundantly even
in the oil-producing strata. This applies both to the individual
groups and to the total numbers of microorganisms which Meshkov
(1958; see above, Table 22) has studied. An example is the Yablonovka deposit in the Kuybyshev oblast', where not one of the

bacterial groups listed in Table 27 was found in the core samples (Ekzertsev and Kuznetsov, 1954).

Table 27

Distribution of individual physiological groups of micro-organisms in the rocks of the Carboniferous B Coal Measures suite of the Syzran deposit
(after V. A. Ekzertsev and S. I. Kuznetsov, 1954)

Lithology of sample	Microorganisms					
	Desul-furizing	Methane-forming				
		Methano-bacterium omelanskii	Decomposing			Hydrogen-oxidizing
			Fatty acids	Oil	Glucose	
Sandy clay, overlying	−	−	−	−	−	+
Oil-bearing sand	+	+	−	−	−	+
Gray clay, underlying	−	−	−	−	−	−
Gray clay	−	−	−	−	−	−
Oil-bearing sand	+	+	+	+	+	+
Limestone, underlying	+	+	+	+	+	+

In summary, all this information on the distribution of the various physiological groups of bacteria in oils, oil-bearing rocks and stratal waters suggests the following conclusions:

1. "Dry" oils have considerably fewer bacteria than water-containing oils or stratal waters.

2. Bacteria that grow only in meat-peptone agar apparently are present largely as a result of contamination and, when found in large numbers, testify that the sample for analysis was improperly taken.

3. Sulfate-reducing bacteria as a rule occur wherever the water contains sulfides or free hydrogen sulfide.

4. The denitrifying and cellulose-decomposing bacteria cannot serve as evidence for the degree of denitrification or cellulose destruction, inasmuch as neither nitrates nor cellular tissue occurs in internal waters and rocks. Apparently these bacteria either make use of the small quantities of organic matter present in internal waters or else assimilate certain oil components anaerobically.

5. The presence of thiobacteria in oxygen-free waters evidently testifies to the high rate of water exchange and to the open structure of the given deposit.

6. Bacteria occur down to 4000 m of depth.

4. THE DISTRIBUTION OF MICROORGANISMS IN WEATHERED ROCKS AND THEIR ROLE IN THE PROCESS OF WEATHERING

In concluding this chapter on the distribution of microorganisms in rocks, some brief mention must be made of reports of bacteria and fungi in the weathered crusts of rocks and the role played by microorganisms in weathering processes. The numerous publications on this subject by soil microbiologists are of two kinds. The papers of one group attempt to explain the distribution in the weathering products of rocks of the various groups of bacteria, mainly saprophytic, which grow in meat-peptone media (Krasil'nikov, 1949a; Tauson, 1948; Yaroslavtsev, 1952; Novogrudskiy, 1946a and b). The others report experimental studies of the effect of various microorganisms in altering various minerals or rocks introduced into nutrient media (Ravich-Shcherbo, 1928; Glazovskaya, 1950).

The papers of the first group may be represented by N. A. Krasil'nikov's studies (1949a and b, 1956). This author has noted that the surfaces of basalt and tuff rocks in Armenia are covered by an altered weathering crust some 5 mm thick. In studying the layer-by-layer distribution in these rocks of bacteria that grow in meat-peptone agar, Chapek medium and must agar, Krasil'nikov found that microorganisms are present on the surface in hundreds of thousands per gram of rock, whereas their numbers decrease as one penetrates deeper into the rock. Below the weathered crust, bacteria are for all practical purposes absent. On this basis Krasil'nikov concludes that the microorganisms found have contributed to the weathering of the rocks investigated. This conclusion, however, seems very debatable. It is quite unclear how saprophytic microorganisms that grow only in media with high contents of organic matter could have taken part in destroying igneous rocks, which contain no organic substances. It is far more likely that Krasil'nikov's bacteria entered from the air into the already weathered, porous rock, and subsequently showed some growth when placed in a nutrient medium.

There can be no question that certain groups of bacteria do contribute to the weathering of both sedimentary and igneous rocks, but it is equally clear that this question cannot be answered on the basis of single tests, especially in such media as meat-peptone agar and must agar. As in the study of other problems in geological and general ecological microbiology, it is not enough to find a possible cause for a particular process; one must still discover the appropriate substrate in nature which has been altered by the microorganisms, as well as a realistic medium in which the microorganisms are active. In view of these observations, the present writers believe, for example, that the role of thiobacteria in weathering sulfur (see Chapter VII) and sulfide (see Chapter VIII) deposits may be considered proved, inasmuch as not only the microorganisms themselves, but also the products of their activities—sulfuric acid and secondary sulfate minerals—have been found in nature.

Although the role of microorganisms in weathering may, of course, be demonstrated under laboratory conditions, it is impossible to agree with the methodology or the conclusions of Yu. A. Ravich-Shcherbo (1928), who studied the effect of pure cultures of lactic acid and butyric acid bacteria in dissolving finely pulverized calcite, aragonite, dolomite, magnesite and siderite in media with 100 cm^3 of malt solution, 3 g maltose and 1 g Witte peptone. Everything in this work, from the selection of microorganisms studied to the composition of the medium, is so highly arbitrary and so far from natural conditions that the results lead only to confusion. It is all the more surprising and regrettable that this paper was dedicated to Academician V. L. Omelyanskiy, the first to pose correctly the question of the role of microorganisms in weathering rocks (Omelyanskiy, 1927).

Somewhat unexpected results were obtained by G. M. Glazovskaya (1950). She, to begin with, avoided complex nutrient media with large amounts of organic substances; secondly, she worked not with pure cultures, but with a mixture of species taken from the weathered crust; in the third place, she formulated the objectives of her investigation clearly and precisely; and, finally, she judged the development of microorganisms and their activity not only from the external appearance of the experimental dishes, but also by chemical criteria. From her data it appears that the leaching of potassium, calcium and iron from rocks by microflora is sharply intensified when 0.2-0.4% of a readily assimilable organic substance—glucose—is added to the mineral medium. In the tests without the addition of organic matter, although growth of microorganisms was observed, the elements were leached from granite, biotite, orthoclase and muscovite at very slow rates.

In concluding this section, it must be noted that the role of microorganisms in rock weathering has still been very inadequately studied and—what is worse—that the methods of the majority of existing studies will not withstand criticism.

CHAPTER VI

The Role of Microorganisms in the Formation and Destruction of Fossil Fuel Deposits

1. THE PRODUCTION OF ORGANIC MATTER BY MICROORGANISMS

One of the principal aspects of the activity of live organisms—particularly microorganisms—is the formation and destruction of organic matter. As Ye. Rabinovich has stated (1951), about one billion metric tons of organic compounds are oxidized to carbon dioxide and water on the earth annually. At such a rapid rate of decomposition, and without the formation of new supplies, all the organic matter on this planet would be consumed in 10 to 20 years. In the oxidizing process, part of the latent chemical energy in the organic matter is consumed in supporting life; the greater part, however, is lost as heat. A small portion of this energy fails to be decomposed and is preserved as coal, peat or oil for millions of years under a protective mantle of sedimentary rocks.

The constant renewal of life is possible only if the energy lost as heat is somehow replaced from some external source, such as sunlight, that is constantly supplied to the earth. Light energy can be transformed into chemical, electrical, mechanical or heat energy, but much of the heat energy is dissipated in conversion to other forms, and this dissipated heat energy cannot be converted back into any other kind of energy.

For the transformation of light energy into chemical energy, some mechanism is required that will prevent the light from being converted into heat: this agent is chlorophyll, which makes photosynthesis possible. The green plants are the only inhabitants of the earth which enable animals, fungi and the majority of bacteria to exist, as they are the only organisms which accumulate chemical energy from sunlight and thus play a positive role in the balance of organic substances in nature.

Many authors have tried to calculate the total organic production due to photosynthesis on the earth. The resulting data, as compiled by Rabinovich (1951), are cited in Table 28. Rabinovich's

Table 28

Fixation of carbon by terrestrial and marine vegetation
(after Ye. Rabinovich, 1951; corrected by G. G. Vinberg, 1960)

Habitat of vegetation	Area, million km^2	Average yearly fixation of carbon, metric tons per hectare	Total average yearly fixation of carbon, metric tons	
Dry land.	149	1. 3	$19 \cdot 10^9$	after Rabinovich, 1951
Ocean		3. 57	$155 \cdot 10^9$	
Ocean	361	1—2	35—$70 \cdot 10^9$	after Vinberg, 1960

computations for the world's ocean are taken from papers by Riley (1938, 1939, 1941), but Steeman Nielsen's work (1952, 1955, 1958) has shown that Riley's figures for the total magnitude of photosynthesis are too high. A detailed critical review of this work has been made by G. G. Vinberg (1960), who, from a comparison of all the available information, cites the most likely rate of photosynthetic fixation of carbon in the ocean as 35-70 billion metric tons per year. This is a measure of the geological activity of chlorophyll-containing microorganisms in the formation of organic matter.

In principle, the organic matter in bodies of water may be formed not only through photosynthesis by green plants, but also by bacterial chemosynthesis. A. G. Rodina (1951) believes that we must depart from the former tradition of considering the green plants as the only source of the primary production of organic matter, and take the chemosynthetic activity of bacteria into account as well. From the energy standpoint, however, as mentioned above, there is an important difference between photosynthesis and chemosynthesis. The source of energy for bacterial chemosynthesis in water may be from oxidation of methane, hydrogen, hydrogen sulfide, ammonia or ferrous oxide (Kuznetsov, 1955c). In natural bodies of water these substances normally arise either from the mineralization of organic matter or as a result of reactions involving organic substances, as, for example, the formation of hydrogen sulfide in the reduction of sulfates or the formation of ferrous iron salts, utilizing energy from the anaerobic decomposition of organic matter.

Thus bacterial chemosynthesis ultimately uses the energy that green plants obtain from the sun and concentrate in the organic matter of their tissues. In other words, bacterial chemosynthesis, as G. G. Vinberg (1960) has stated, is merely a stage in the utilization of primary energy, and is thus identical to the consumption of energy by heterotrophic organisms. Therefore chemosynthesis is a secondary process based on energy derived from organic matter created by photosynthesis; and photosynthesis is, for all practical purposes, the only source of the primary production in bodies of water. Similar views are held by S. I. Kuznetsov (1952, 1955b), Yu. I. Sorokin (1958a, 1959) and other scientists.

In view of these considerations, it is quite impossible to understand the assertions by A. Ye. Kriss (1958) and Ya. K. Gololobov (1955) that bacteria are the predominant agent in the synthesis of organic matter in the Black Sea and that the annual production by the bacterial biomass greatly exceeds the production by phytoplankton. This would be possible only if the Black Sea, in addition to light, also has some other source of energy that might be directly utilized by the bacteria in their chemosynthesis of organic matter. Kriss, envisaging no other possible source of energy, makes the suggestion—which in his later papers becomes an assertion—that the energy for the development of the purple bacteria is derived from radioactive decay (Kriss, 1953; Kriss and Rukina, 1953). Nevertheless, even if one admits that purple sulfur bacteria can use energy in this form, simple calculations (Kuznetsov, 1956) show that the natural radioactivity of the Black Sea water is not nearly enough to provide the energy for the production by the bacterial biomass mentioned by Kriss. The fundamental error of Kriss's reasoning results from the fact that he and his coworkers (Kriss and Markianovich, 1954; Kriss and Lebedeva, 1953; Kriss, 1954) obtained highly exaggerated values for the production by the bacterial biomass in the Black Sea because they used a faulty procedure in computing the bacterial production. For this reason they have had to seek some other special source of energy for chemosynthesis.

Later on, without questioning Kriss's deductions, geologists began to interpret the data in their discussions of the genesis of oil. For instance, N. B. Vassoyevich (1955) in one of his papers tabulates the balance of organic matter in the Black Sea, on the basis of data from O. A. Radchenko supplemented by N. B. Vassoyevich (1955) himself. The data in his table indicate that the annual phytoplankton production—that is, the magnitude of the primary yearly production of organic matter—is 274 million metric tons, whereas the secondary production of organic matter, formed through the activity of bacteria alone, amounts to 1800 million metric tons according to his minimal figures. In computing the organic matter balance in the Black Sea, both these quantities are added together. The absurdity of these computations is obvious. In the first place, the secondary production—that is, the production by organisms growing at the expense of primary production—could not be more than 30% of the amount of organic matter formed by photosynthesis.

Secondly, in the material balance of a body of water one cannot add together the primary and secondary production of organic matter, since the secondary production is derived from primary production. In other words, the same quantity has been used twice. As a result of these errors in calculating the balance, Vassoyevich concludes that plankton production over the course of 1000 years in the Black Sea has created 6.5 metric tons of organic matter per square meter of the bottom, which is quite sufficient to form oil in the Black Sea, whose basin resembles those in which oil-forming sediments were deposited in the geologic past.

The difference between the "gross primary production" of organic matter in a body of water and the "net production" must also be clearly understood. The latter quantity represents the amount of organic matter left in a body of water after respiration of the phytoplankton and decomposition by bacteria. If 6.5 metric tons of organic matter per m^2 were being formed annually in the Black Sea (and this figure is unlikely in itself), this still does not mean that all this organic matter would be deposited on the bottom to become, eventually, the organic matter in oil-forming rocks. In the eutrophic Black Sea, according to Vinberg's data (1948), the net production of organic matter is no more than 13% of the gross primary production. Moreover this is the maximum quantity that can be found in fresh-water bodies. In dystrophic lakes the rate of destruction frequently exceeds the primary production of organic matter, resulting in a negative balance. In the sea, the net production of organic matter is probably no more than a fraction of a percent of the gross primary production.

2. THE ROLE OF MICROORGANISMS IN THE FIRST STAGES OF THE DECOMPOSITION OF ORGANIC MATTER DURING SEDIMENTATION

Kuznetsov (1949a, 1952) has studied the role of microorganisms as they destroy the individual components of the organic matter in Lake Beloye, in the Moscow Oblast'. The dead plankton, sinking through the 12 m of water to the bottom of Lake Beloye, undergoes aerobic decay. Suspended particles from various depths in the water, after being collected through a membrane filter, may be characterized by appropriate staining and microscopic analysis.

Figure 18 shows that in the surface layers of water, during the "bloom" in the spring and summer seasons, most of the suspended particles consist of planktonic organisms. Simultaneous analysis of suspended particles from a depth of 7 m has shown that in summer, as the plankton particles settle to this depth, some 90% of their mass is decomposed. Still less plankton reaches a depth of 12 m.

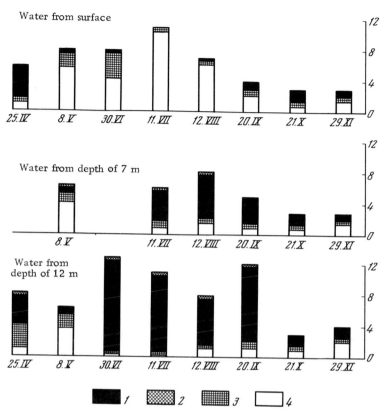

Fig. 18. Composition of material suspended in water of
Lake Beloye in 1940:
1—iron hydrates; 2—iron bacteria; 3—formless organic
detritus; 4—plankton and bacteria.

The amount of formless organic detritus increases as a result of
the decay of the plankton.

The rate of decay of the plankton organic matter is indicated by
comparing the chemical composition of the plankton and of the
surface layer of the sediment. Data from such comparative
analyses, made by T. A. Speranskaya (1935), are given in Table 29.
The percentage of organic matter decay is computed theoretically
from the assumption that the mineral components of the plankton
remain unaltered and the ash content of the ooze deposits is determined as a whole. The calculations are given in detail by Kuznetsov
(1949b, 1952). The actual decomposition of the plankton apparently
begins with autolysis of the dead cells, accompanied by release of
the readily assimilable substances into the surrounding medium

Table 29

Composition of the organic matter in the plankton and the
surface layer of the ooze in Lake Beloye at Kosino (% of
dry weight)
(after T. A. Speranskaya, 1935)

Component	Plankton	Surface layer of ooze	Amount of disintegrated organic matter in plankton, % of original
Ash	6.4	46.4	
Wax and bitumens.	14.15	6.5	93.6
Hemicellulose.	29.7	7.1	96.7
Cellular tissue.	10.2	6.1	91.7
Lignin	31.4	30.1	86.8
Total nitrogen.	8.1	2.5	95.7

(Gayevskaya, 1948); these assimilable substances are mineralized
by the bacterial population. The first to be mineralized are the
proteins, carbohydrates and, probably, hydrocarbons. The result
is the formation of an aqueous humus which, according to Keys,
Christensen and Krogh (1935), accounts for 85-90% of the dissolved
organic matter in marine water. P. V. Novobrantsev (1937)
indicates that the same proportion of the organic matter as
aqueous humus is in fresh waters as well.

The organic substances formed in a body of water by photosynthesis, and those that enter it from outside as terrestrial peaty
detritus, ultimately settle to the bottom to form ooze deposits
after undergoing decay in the water, as described above. Here
the final decomposition takes place, its intensity depending on the
content of "readily assimilable nitrogen"—that is, of nitrogen that
goes into solution by hydrolysis with 5% sulfuric acid.

The composition of the organic matter in the sediments of a
number of fresh-water lakes has been analyzed in detail by S. I.
Kuznetsov, T. A. Speranskaya and V. D. Konshin (1939). The
results of analyses of the oozes in Lake Chernoye at Kosino are
given in Table 30, which shows that hemicellulose, cellular tissue
and substances separated out in alcohol-benzene extract are most
rapidly decayed in the uppermost or surface layer. Below a depth
of 1 m, the composition of the organic matter remains extremely
stable. This is consistent with the microbial population content
(Karzinkin and Kuznetsov, 1931; Kuznetsov, 1938a, 1950a; Khartulari, 1939; Ekzertsev, 1948; and others). The number of microorganisms capable of destroying the organic matter in sediment
drops to zero at 1 m of depth, even though chemical analysis
indicates the presence of cellular tissue, hemicellulose, hydrocarbons and other such components.

Table 30

Composition of the organic matter in the oozes of Lake
Chernoye at Kosino

Depth from surface of ooze, m	Ash content, % of dry weight	Components, % of organic matter			
		Alcohol-benzene extract	Hemicel-lulose	Cellular tissue	Humic complex
0—0.15	49.3	7.4	14.5	7.7	62.0
1	49.1	5.8	8.9	5.6	62.0
2	47.3	5.4	7.5	4.4	66.8
3	48.6	4.6	7.0	4.4	68.7
5	46.6	4.9	6.3	6.6	70.6

Hence the available chemical and microbiological data testify
that, although microorganisms do take part in transforming the
organic matter of sediment deposits into fossil fuels, this occurs
only in the initial stages of decomposition.

3. THE ROLE OF MICROORGANISMS IN THE GENESIS OF PEAT, BROWN COALS AND BITUMINOUS COALS

Peat is the only caustobiolith whose formation on a wide scale
can be observed at the present time. Layer-by-layer study of
vertical sections through peat bogs has revealed three principal
layers: 1) a surface layer in which oxidizing conditions predominate; 2) an intermediate layer with an alternation of oxidizing and
reducing conditions depending on the climate and weather; and
3) a lowest layer dominated by a reducing environment. The composition of the peat-forming vegetation and the oxidation-reduction
conditions determine the distribution of the microflora and the
decay of the organic matter. Microbiological analyses of peats
have been undertaken by D. A. Begak and N. M. Belikova (1934),
N. M. Kurbatova-Belikova (1951, 1954), V. K. Neofitova (1953), and
others.
Study of the vertical distribution of the total bacterial population
of peat bogs (Kurbatova-Belikova, 1954) has revealed 700 million
bacteria per gram of dry peat in the surface layer of the Beren-
deyevo swamp, whereas at a depth of 25-50 cm the number
decreased to 25 million per gram and remained at this value
down to 6 m of depth. The numbers of bacteria in the Maloye
Bolch'ye upland peat bog are shown in Table 31.
The peat-forming process itself has been studied in laboratory
experiments. Belikova (1931) attempted to reproduce the

Table 31

Vertical distribution of microorganisms in the Maloye
Bolch'ye peat bog, in thousands per gram of dry peat
(after N. M. Kurbatova-Belikova, 1954)

Depth, cm	Moisture, %	Type of peat	Degree of decomposition, %	Number of microorganisms		
				Sapro-phytes	Total No. of bacteria	Live molds
					Microscope analysis	
25	93.5	Sphagnum	5	3,400	45,000	0
35	95.7	"	15	11,000	154,000	1,000
50	93.5	"	30	1,000	80,000	500
100	91.1	Cotton-grass	40	13,000	118,000	0
175	88.8	Scheuchzeria	35	3,400	38,000	0

decomposition of sphagnum mosses to which bacterial microflora isolated from a peat bog had been added. Even with the
addition of mineral nutrient substances, the decrease in the dry
weight of the sphagnum in the experiment did not exceed 8%. On
the other hand, mosses were rapidly decomposed by a culture of
the fungus *Merulius lacrimans*, even in the absence of added
nutrient substances: after one to three months the loss of dry
weight by the mosses was 60%, the plant remains lost their
structure, and colored substances appeared.

These results prompted V. K. Neofitova (1953) to make a
detailed study of the fungus flora in peat deposits. From the
surface layer of the Gladkoye Boloto peat bog, in the Tosnenskiy
Rayon of the Leningrad Oblast', she isolated 74 species of fungi
belonging to 24 genera; of these, 54 species were hyphomycetes
and 16 were plant molds. In summer, because of the sun's warming
of the upper 50 cm of peat, there were 3 million fungus spores per
gram of peat, whereas below 60 cm there were no live spores of
fungi. In winter the number of spores dropped to 170 thousand per
gram of peat. Neofitova's laboratory experiments with the microscope showed that mosses decayed for two months were highly
decomposed and that the hyphae of mold fungi had entered the
cells and destroyed the sphagnum tissues. The author believes that
the chief organisms causing peat formation are the mold fungi, and
that later the bacteria further decompose the dead plant tissues.

Good aeration, the presence of organic substances available to
organisms and the high temperatures prevailing in the upper layers
of a peat bog promote the activity of the microorganisms in the

upper layer of the peat, so that the actual transformation of the plant material into peat occurs rapidly and is completed in the course of a few vegetation periods. Kurbatova-Belikova (1954) considers that during the short time in which a given layer of peat is close to the surface of the peat bog, the main features of the layer are created and thus reflect the conditions under which it was formed.

The chief chemical peculiarity of peat, brown coals and bituminous coals is their high content of lignin and humic acids. These caustobioliths, according to Tauson (1947), are formed as follows: the initial material is principally plant remains; in the case of peat, these are present-day mosses, marsh and woody vegetation. The initial materials of brown coals are mostly fossil swamp cypress, Mexican cypress or very similar trees. As paleontological studies have shown, the original material of brown coal was not so much swamp vegetation as large trees growing in dry forests. Study of the conditions under which brown coals occur leads to the conclusion that the overwhelming majority of these humic rocks were formed on the sites of dry forests, and in only a few cases on the sites of wooded swamps. Brown coals were formed under conditions similar to those characterizing the formation of modern forest peats. Numerous investigations of the formation and occurrence of brown-coal deposits indicate no obstacles to the activity of microbes in decomposing and humifying plant remains in the Tertiary period.

Bituminous coals show a much greater variety in chemical composition (Stadnikov, 1935). They were formed throughout the Paleozoic and much of the Mesozoic, but, as Fig. 19 shows, most bituminous coal deposits date from the Carboniferous and Permian periods—the time of the greatest flourishing of the fernlike plants. Paleontological investigations show that the fossil horsetails (*Equisetum*) had long underground rootstocks resembling those of modern swamp vegetation. Thus the Paleozoic forests that gave rise to the bituminous coals apparently grew in swamps. This is supported by evidence of adaptations to swamp life by the Lepidodendra and Sigillariae: these plants, the original material of bituminous coal, had trunks expanded in the lower portions and roots spreading out horizontally.

Tauson (1947) believes that the Paleozoic bituminous coals were formed under approximately the same conditions as the brown coals of the Tertiary or the forest peats in the modern swamps of Virginia. In his opinion, all these caustobioliths were formed in two phases. "The first phase was a period of comparatively rapid decomposition of the unstable substances in the plant remains and of accumulation of stable compounds and products such as lignin, cutin, suberin and sporopollenins. The second phase was a period

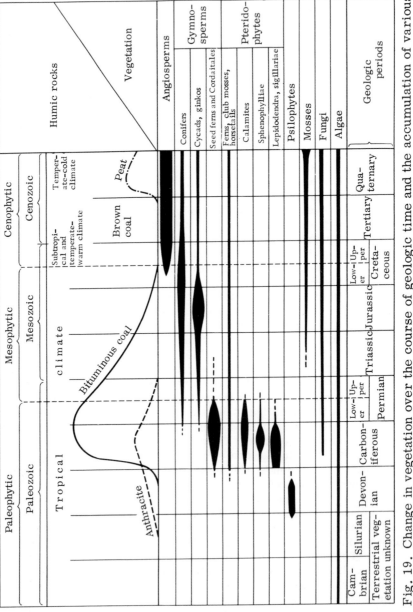

Fig. 19. Change in vegetation over the course of geologic time and the accumulation of various indurated caustobioliths (after Tauson, 1947).

of slow transformation of these substances into still more highly stable products, such as the conversion of humic acids readily soluble in alkali into the humic substances of bituminous coals, which are completely insoluble in all solvents" (Tauson, 1947, p. 126). The processes of the first phase are biological and take place under aerobic conditions, whereas those of the second phase are anaerobic; the second phase is biogenic in the case of peat, and abiogenic in the case of bituminous coals.

4. THE ROLE OF MICROORGANISMS IN THE FORMATION AND TRANSFORMATION OF OIL AND GAS

a) The Genesis of Oil

The problem of the origin of oil has been studied by numerous researchers, both theoretically and through field and laboratory investigations. It has been the subject of many scientific conferences. A summary of the information on this question may be found in the symposium volume, "Proiskhozhdeniye Nefti" ["The Origin of Oil"] by Bakirov et al., 1955, and in books by N. B. Vassoyevich (1955), V. B. Porfir'yev (1960) and others.

Proceeding from the assumption that oil is of biogenic origin, chemical and microbiological studies have been made of the changes in the form of the organic matter in modern fresh-water sediments during their burial (Messineva and Pankratova, 1941; Messineva and Gorbunova, 1946; Kuznetsov, Speranskaya and Konshin, 1939; Kkartulari, 1939; and others). Nevertheless, in spite of the multitude of sediment samples studied from various lakes, taken from depths down to 10 m below the surface of the deposits, it has been impossible to discern any regular increase in the content of oillike products with increasing depth, or even of substances that could be separated by alcohol-benzene extract. It has also proved impossible to find any specific microflora capable of transforming phytoplankton remains into substances closely resembling hydrocarbons. A microzonal investigation of sediments by B. V. Perfil'yev (1927, 1952) has revealed an annual increase of about 1 mm in the ooze deposits in lakes. With the same methods, A. D. Pel'sh (1939), S. I. Kuznetsov (1952) and V. A. Ekzertsev (1948) have discovered that all the processes in the decay of the organic matter and in the exchange between the sediment water and the lake water take place entirely in the uppermost, surficial layers within a thickness of no more than 0.5-1 m.

A team of scientists headed by V. V. Veber (1955) has made a study of the role of present-day deposits in the genesis of oil in marine bays and lagoons. This work was done in the Akhtanizov

and other esturaries of the Black Sea and in the mouth of the Kura
River on the Caspian Sea. T. S. Remezova (1950) has studied the
microbial population that contributes to the decomposition of plant
remains, and has shown that the process occurs under anaerobic
conditions. The existence of sulfate-reducing bacteria, hydrogen
sulfide and low oxidation-reduction potentials in this environment has
been established. M. A. Messineva (1950) has thrown some light on
free fermentation agents in decomposing dead vegetation. Analyses
have revealed a change in the elemental composition of the organic
matter, but here, too, no regular increase in the hydrocarbon
content was found.

The hypothesis of the biogenic formation of oil has been, perhaps,
most thoroughly elaborated by ZoBell (1943, 1958) and by Davis
and Updegraff (1954). After studying a great number of marine
sediments, ZoBell found that they contained many bacteria capable
of accelerating various biochemical reactions. He believes that live
bacteria actually inhabit the producing strata of oil deposits and have
not been introduced from outside by drilling, and that they are in
dynamic equilibrium with their surrounding medium.

Table 32

Composition by elements of the organic matter of oil
and of the initial organic matter from which oil may
have originated (%)

Element	Organic matter		
	Marine organisms	Marine humus	Oil
Carbon	45—32	52—58	82—87
Hydrogen	5—9	6—10	11—14
Oxygen	25—30	12—20	0.1—5
Nitrogen	9—15	0.8—3	0.1—1.5

If oil has indeed been formed from organic matter, there can be
no doubt that bacteria have taken part in this process, since the
organic remains of both plant and animal origin are readily altered
by microorganisms. By comparing the amounts of plankton, humus
and oil present (Table 32), ZoBell concluded that in present-day
marine sediments, the organic matter is gradually transformed into
marine humus, whose chemical composition is closer to that of oil
than is the original organic matter. The data in Table 32, moreover,
show that in the transition from organisms to oil the contents of

carbon and hydrogen increase, and those of oxygen and nitrogen decrease.

In their anaerobic destruction of plant remains and the organic matter in humus, bacteria form methane, and also simultaneously create a small quantity of liquid hydrocarbons, which are a component part of the bacterial cell, as Jankowski and ZoBell (1944) discovered in cultivating *Vibrio desulfuricans* in caprylic acid. These hydrocarbons are more stable than the plasma of the bacterial cells; therefore ZoBell believes that, although they are formed in small quantities, they can be accumulated in sedimentary rocks. Thus the hydrocarbons in oil-forming rocks originate from the remains of vegetation that has undergone bacterial decomposition and from the hydrocarbons liberated as a result of the death of the bacterial cells.

Unsaturated hydrocarbons may become saturated by bacteria which activate molecular hydrogen. The amino acids liberated after the death of bacteria and after hydrolysis of their protein compounds may be deaminated to fatty acids. Methane may be formed in the reduction of carbon dioxide by hydrogen, according to the reaction: $CO_2 + 4H_2 = CH_4 + 2H_2O$. All these substances are found in the producing strata of oil deposits. Ultimately the marine bacteria, after destroying plant remains in which hydrocarbons are dispersed, or after dissolving the carbonate rocks in which oil is disseminated or, finally, after saturating the dispersed oil with carbon dioxide and methane, also probably increase its mobility and thus enable it to accumulate in reservoir rocks and oil traps.*

The individual aspects of ZoBell's schematization of the biogenic formation of oil are well founded scientifically, but all his suppositions as a whole still remain only hypotheses. Up to the present, no noticeable accumulations of oil have ever been found anywhere in the ooze deposits of bodies of water, although the sediments of fresh-water lakes would seem to present all the most favorable conditions for this process, as described by ZoBell.** Moreover, the total organic matter in the sediments is as much as 50% of the dry weight, and no discernible increase in the amount of hydrocarbons has been observed with increasing depth of the deposits (Kuznetsov, Speranskaya and Konshin, 1939; Kuznetsov and Khartulari, 1941). At present there is still no sufficiently well founded

---

* Editor's Note: See Baker, E. G., An hypothesis concerning the accumulation of sediment hydrocarbons to form crude oil: Geochim. Cosmochim. Acta, 19:309-317, 1960.

** Editor's Note: See Smith, P. V., Studies on the origin of petroleum: occurrence of hydrocarbons in recent sediments: Bull. Am. Ass. Pet. Geol., 38:377-404, 1954.

basis in fact for the hypothesis of the biogenic origin of oil. Eight current hypotheses have been critically analyzed by Messineva (1947, 1955), and from the microbiological standpoint not one of them is convincing enough to be finally adopted.

b) The Role of Microorganisms in the Anaerobic Destruction of Oil

The role of microorganisms in the present destruction or transformation of oil and combustible gas deposits deserves more attention (Kuznetsov, 1957a). The universal presence of hydrocarbon gases in oil deposits has naturally led to the idea that methane and other gases may be formed in the anaerobic decomposition of oil. Many analyses have been made of the gas escaping to the surface together with oil, as well as of the gases dissolved under formational pressure in the oil and internal waters of the deposits. These analyses, systematically summarized by V. V. Belousov (1937), K. B. Ashirov and S. T. Maksimov (1958), G. A. Mogilev-skiy (1953) and others, have shown that the marginal waters of oil deposits contain large quantities of methane and its homologues. The farther the samples of water were taken from the margin of the oil deposit, the smaller were their contents of dissolved gases.

All this has suggested that the anaerobic destruction of oil is taking place at the present time. On the other hand, the actual agent that decomposes oil anaerobically and forms gaseous products is still unknown.

The formation of methane by the anaerobic decomposition of organic matter has been most thoroughly studied by Barker (1956), whose researches show that fatty acids may be destroyed, and methane formed as a result. An acetic acid molecule is detached from the fatty acid simultaneously with the attachment of carbon dioxide and water molecules. This results in the formation of a fatty acid of a lower series, while the acetic acid breaks down to form methane and water. Consequently, if methane is to be formed, oil must contain fatty acids in addition to hydrocarbons. The analyses cited by A. Ya. Dobryanskiy (1948), however, show that only minimum quantities of fatty acids are present in oils.

B. V. Porfir'yev and I. V. Grinberg (1957) in considering the transformation of organic matter in a fossil state attribute great importance to the possibility that it may react with water under high pressure and temperature. They believe that under these conditions the active centers of the organic matter—the $C = C$, $C = O$ and other groups—may combine with water. This reaction would begin with the formation of hydrates, which are then destroyed at high temperatures. The process may involve the following steps:

1. Reaction of the "active group" with water, according to Porfir'yev, and the formation of fatty acid:

$$
\begin{matrix}
\text{H H} \\
\diagdown\diagup \\
\text{R}-\text{C} \\
| \qquad \diagdown \text{C}=\text{O}+\text{HOH} \\
\text{R}-\text{C} \diagup \\
\diagup\diagdown \\
\text{H H}
\end{matrix}
\qquad\longrightarrow\qquad
\begin{matrix}
\text{H H} \\
\diagdown\diagup \\
\text{R}-\text{C}-\text{H} \\
| \\
\text{R}-\text{C}-\text{C}-\text{OH} \\
\diagup\diagdown \quad \| \\
\text{H H } \; \text{O}
\end{matrix}
$$

Although this reaction can take place chemically only at high temperatures and pressures, this does not eliminate the likelihood of its occurring biologically at a temperature of $18\text{-}20^\circ\text{C}$.

2. Decomposition of the fatty acid, according to Barker, with the formation of methane and a fatty acid of lower series and, ultimately, breakdown of the acetic acid to liberate methane:

$$2\text{R}-\text{CH}_2-\text{CH}_2-\text{COOH}+2\text{H}_2\text{O}+\text{CO}_2 \rightarrow 2\text{R}-\text{COOH}+\underline{2\text{CH}_3\text{COOH}}+\text{CH}_4$$
$$\downarrow$$
$$2\text{CH}_4+2\text{CO}_2$$

Another way in which gaseous products can be formed in the anaerobic decomposition of oil has been suggested by I. L. Andreyevskiy (1959), who believes that the decomposition of the molecules of the separate components of oil may take place through nitrogen bridges, and that this may be the reason for the comparatively large amount of nitrogen in petroleum gases.

From the standpoint of these hypotheses, Ekzertsev and Kuznetsov (1954) have studied the distribution of methane-forming bacteria in the stratal oil waters of a number of Middle Volga oil and gas deposits. Figure 20 shows that almost everywhere the stratal waters contain bacteria that form methane from hydrogen and carbon dioxide, as well as bacteria that break down fatty acids to form methane. In many cases these researchers also found organisms that formed gas in Barker medium in which the only source of carbon was the oil from the Kalinovka deposit. Figure 21 shows that methane-forming bacteria are almost completely absent from the closed deposits of the Yablonovka ravine, but are widely represented in many open deposits.

The widespread occurrence of sulfate-reducing bacteria is consistent with the high contents of hydrogen sulfide and sulfides in the internal waters of Permian and Carboniferous deposits (Ashirov, 1959a). This also suggests that oil deposits should contain microorganisms which decompose oil and form gaseous products. Ginzburg-Karagicheva (1953) and V. A. Ekzertsev (1956, 1958, 1960) have studied this problem.

If oil, a core sample and a solution of ammonium phosphate as a source of phosphorus and nitrogen are placed in a small test tube

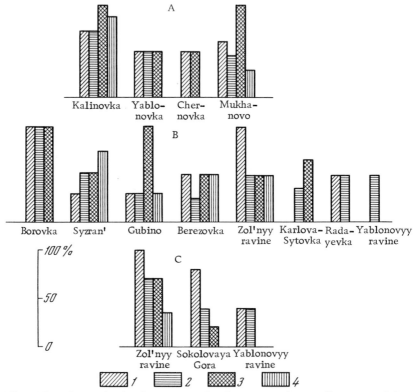

Fig. 20. The principal groups of microorganisms discovered in the oil deposits of the Ural-Volga oil province (% samples containing microorganisms).
Systems: A—Permian, B—Carboniferous, C—Devonian.
1—bacteria that decompose oil with the formation of gas; 2—bacteria that decompose fatty acids up to the formation of gaseous products; 3—bacteria that form methane from hydrogen and carbon dioxide; 4—sulfate-reducing bacteria.

(Fig. 22), and this tube is then lowered into a larger test tube filled with a solution of $NH_4H_2PO_4 + MgSO_4$, a bubble of gas will form in two to four weeks above the oil and core sample. The amount of this gas increases with time and may reach several cubic centimeters. From the test tubes in which gas was formed, V. A. Ekzertsev isolated about 20 organisms that formed gas in test tubes inverted in a mineral medium to which sterile oil had been added as the only source of organic matter. Among the microorganisms described by Ekzertsev were species closely resembling *Methanococcus mazei* and *Sarcina methanica*.

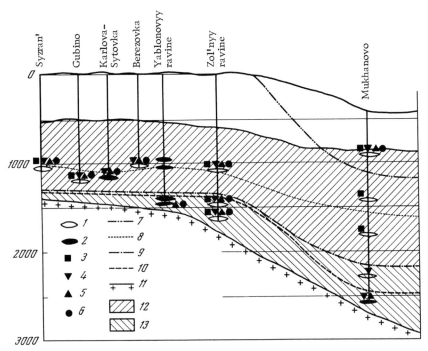

Fig. 21. The distribution of certain groups of bacteria in the ground waters of a number of oil deposits in the Middle Volga region:

1—oil deposits of the open type; 2—oil deposits of the closed type; 3—sulfate-reducing bacteria; 4—*Methanobacterium omelanskii;* 5—bacteria that decompose fatty acids with the formation of methane; 6—bacteria that decompose oil down to the formation of gaseous products; 7—bottom of Permian deposits; 8—B_2 level of carboniferous; 9—bottom of Carboniferous Tournaisian stage; 10—bottom of Carboniferous Famennian stage; 11—boundary at top of crystalline basement complex; 12—zone of hydrogen sulfide rocks; 13—zone of ferruginous rocks lacking hydrogen sulfide.

Table 33 shows the results of analyses of the gases formed in the decomposition of various samples of oil. In both V. A. Ekzertsev's (1956) and Ye. N. Bokova's (1953) experiments, the gas that was formed contained from 21 to 40% methane and from 60 to 75% nitrogen. The gases formed in the decomposition of various oil types by pure bacterial cultures were found to have approximately the same composition (Table 34).

It is interesting that the gases dissolved in the stratal waters of a number of deposits have compositions very similar to the

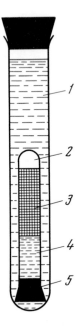

Fig. 22. Diagram showing the arrangement of an experiment in the anaerobic decomposition of oil (after Ekzertsev and Kuznetsov, 1954): 1—solution of $NH_4H_2PO_4$ + $MgSO_4$; 2—gas; 3—oil mixed with core sample; 4—mineral solution; 5—rubber stopper.

gases obtained in Ekzertsev's experiments, especially if the stratal water samples were taken with a depth sampler, thus guaranteeing the retention in the sample of the gases present in solution under the stratal conditions. The results of analyses for the contents of gases in stratal waters (Table 35) show that in numerous cases nitrogen is as much as 54% of the total volume of all the dissolved gases.

Thus the question arises: what is the origin of the nitrogen in the natural gases of oil deposits? Is it derived from the air, or from the decomposition of nitrogen-containing substances in the oil? V. V. Belousov (1937) and A. A. Kozlov (1950) state that the atmospheric origin of the nitrogen in petroleum gases is readily

Table 33

Chemical composition of the gases formed in
the bacterial decomposition of oil
(after data from V. A. Ekzertsev, 1958, and
Ye. I. Bokova, 1953)

Locality of oil sample and conditions of experiment	Composition of gas, volume %			
	CH_4	H_2	CO_2	N_2
Ekzertsev's experiments				
Sokolovaya Gora; oil + core sample	35	0.0	3.0	62
Same	32.5	0.0	2.8	64.7
Novo-Stepanovka; oil + core sample	33.4	0.0	2.3	64.3
Archeda; oil + petroliferous sandstone	40.0	0.0	3.4	56.6
Same	35.0	0.0	3.2	61.8
Verkhovskaya structure; oil + gas-bearing limestone	33.4	0.0	2.3	64.3
Same	27.8	0.0	2.9	69.3
Bokova's experiments				
Southern Sakhalin; oil + residues from sewage liquid	20.9	0.6	4.6	73.9

Table 34

Composition of gas formed in the decomposition
of various oil samples by pure cultures of
bacteria
Duration of experiment two years
(after V. A. Ekzertsev, 1960)

Culture	Locality of oil	Composition of gas, volume %			
		CH_4	H_2	CO_2	N_2
1	Pilyugino	35.4	0.0	2.1	62.5
3	"	34.3	0.0	4.3	61.4
7	Novo-Stepanovka.	27.0	0.0	4.9	68.1
8	"	20.0	0.0	2.9	77.1
10	Yelshanka	25.1	0.0	2.3	72.6
12	"	15.3	4.4	2.2	78.1
15	"	20.0	5.0	5.0	70.0
18	Sokolovaya Gora	20.6	0.0	2.9	76.5
20	"	23.5	0.0	1.9	74.6

proved by the presence of a definite amount of argon. Argon should be lacking in gases formed by anaerobic decomposition of the organic matter in oil, inasmuch as the plants which ultimately gave rise to the oil did not assimilate argon during their lifetimes. About 79% of air is nitrogen, and 0.9325% is argon. Hence the ratio of argon to nitrogen in the air amounts to

$$\frac{Ar \cdot 100}{N_2} = 1.18\%.$$

Let us assume the Ar/N_2 ratio in the gas to be tested is the same as in air, and let this be designated as a:

$$\frac{\dfrac{Ar}{N_2}\ (\text{gas to be tested})}{\dfrac{Ar}{N_2}\ (\text{air})} = \frac{\dfrac{Ar\ (\text{gas}) \cdot 100}{N_2\ (\text{air})}}{\dfrac{Ar\ (\text{air}) \cdot 100}{N_2\ (\text{air})}} = \frac{\dfrac{Ar\ (\text{gas}) \cdot 100}{N_2\ (\text{gas})}}{1.18} = a.$$

In the case of air, $a = 1$. If nitrogen of biochemical origin is present in the gases, then a will be less than 1.

Table 35

Analysis of gases dissolved in stratal waters taken with a depth sampler
(after K. B. Ashirov and S. P. Maksimov, 1958)

Deposit	Stratigraphic level	Number of wells	Composition of gas, volume %			
			Total hydro-carbons	CO_2	N_2	H_2
Zol'nyy ravine	Devonian	65	69	6.1	25.9	0
		42	56.9	4.3	39.4	0
Pokrovka	Carboniferous, coal measures	21	·46.6	0	53.4	0
Novo-Stepanovka	Permian, Kalinovka formation	501	48.4	0	51.6	0
Mukhanovo	Permian, Kungurian stage	102	33.09	21.81	42.38	2.72

Table 36 shows Belousov's determinations (1937) of the argon: nitrogen ratio in various natural gases. These data indicate that a is less than unity for the gases of the Urals–Emba region and the Mel'nikovskoye (Saratov Oblast') and Ishimbayevo (Tatar ASSR) deposits. Hence the oil must be breaking down rapidly to gaseous products in these deposits. The situation is otherwise in the Bay-chunas deposits and in the Ukhta region.

Table 36

Chemical composition of some natural gases
(after V. V. Belousov, 1937)

District and deposit	% of Volume			a
	CO_2	CH_4 + heavy hydrocarbons	N_2	
Urals-Emba district, Makat	0.4	94.9	4.7	0.15
" " Sagiz.		91.2	8.2	0.3
Average of 18 analyses:				0.5
Ukhta district	2.2	94.5	0.7	1.8
Baychunas (natural outcrop)	0.5	97.8	1.80	1.4
	0.2	93.7	5.0	0.7
Average of 32 analyses:				1.1
Saratov oblast', Mel'nikovskoye	0.9	81.1	18.0	0.39
	0.2	50.9	48.8	0.72
	3.9	42.9	53.2	0.70
Tatar ASSR, Ishimbayevo		79.1	20.0	0.10
		85.0	14.5	0.14

Thus microbiological investigations have shown that biogenic decomposition of certain oils, accompanied by the formation of combustible gases, can take place. Data obtained by geologists and hydrogeologists have shown how the decomposition of the oil directly in the deposits may be established. On the other hand, N. A. Kalinin et al. (1955) have cast doubt on the above conclusions.

V. O. Tauson and V. I. Aleshina (1952) have suggested that oil may be decomposed anaerobically by the oxygen of sulfates through the agency of sulfate-reducing bacteria. Tauson observed the formation of hydrogen sulfide in a mineral medium in which oil was the only source of organic matter. On the basis of his energy computations, he determined that the volatile hydrocarbons would be oxidized to carbon dioxide and water, whereas the heavier ones would become polymethylenes. In other words, paraffin-base petroleum will be transformed into naphthene oils, since the naphthenic hydrocarbons are stable under anaerobic conditions and are not assimilated by desulfurizing bacteria.

T. L. Simakova and her several colleagues (1958) have worked on this subject. In contrast to earlier papers, these studies included chemical analysis of the oils. The experiments showed that under anaerobic conditions, paraffin-base oil is decomposed by "green bacteria" which the authors identify as *Pseudomonas fluorescens denitrificans* and *Vibrio desulfuricans*. In this process the destruction of the solid paraffins leads to the formation of water-soluble organic substances, so that the percentage of naphthenic hydro-carbons in the residual oil increases. It is true, however, that the manner in which these authors carried out their experiments leaves some room for doubt that anaerobic conditions were actually created. Simakova states that the air above the nutrient medium with the oil was removed by a stream of nitrogen. Commercially available nitrogen, however, contains up to 2% oxygen, and this small amount of oxygen is exceedingly difficult to remove from the nitrogen. Moreover the authors introduced more than 100 g of oil into the experiment, and obtained a 5% decrease in the paraffins. If this process took place anaerobically through the oxidation of the paraffin by the oxygen from the sulfates, a considerable quantity of hydrogen sulfide should have been produced. This was apparently not observed, since the authors make no mention of any intensive production of hydrogen sulfide. Thus the suspicion inevitably arises: was the oil actually oxidized under anaerobic conditions?

Ashirov (1961) has some very interesting data on the changes in the properties of oil directly in the deposit during the course of long exploitation, when sulfate waters may have been introduced. In the Kalinovka deposit the change in the oil, amounting to an increase in its heavy tar-containing fraction, occurred in the open part of the deposit. In the closed portion the oil showed no changes. This indicates that when the rate of exchange of the stratal waters is accelerated, the oil microflora activity intensifies, thus altering the oil within the producing strata of the deposit itself.

c) Aerobic Processes in the Oxidation of Oil and Combustible Gases

Studies of the oxidation-reduction environment in oil deposits of a number of regions by Z. I. Kuznetsova (Al'tovskiy, Kuznetsova and Shvets, 1958) and V. A. Kuznetsova (1960) have shown that, as a rule, the oxidation-reduction potential in oil deposits does not exceed $rH_2 = 12-14$, and most frequently $rH_2 = 7-8$. Thus oil occurs in nature in a strongly reducing environment.

When the reservoir rocks and the overburden are highly fractured, the oil, which is under high formational pressure, may rise to the earth's surface. Here, with the drop in pressure and temperature, depending on the nature of the oil, paraffins, ozocerite or bitumens of the petroleum asphalt type may be given off. Upon reaching the earth's surface, the individual components of the oil may evaporate or be oxidized by microorganisms.

The Role of Microorganisms in the Formation of Ozocerite Deposits

According to current theories (Khramov, 1952; Porfir'yev, 1949), ozocerite may become separated from oil as a result of a decrease in the former's solubility as the oil's temperature drops when it enters into the upper layers of the earth's crust, or by the removal of the lighter fractions and cyclic hydrocarbons, which stabilized the ozocerite and prevented its separation, from the oil.

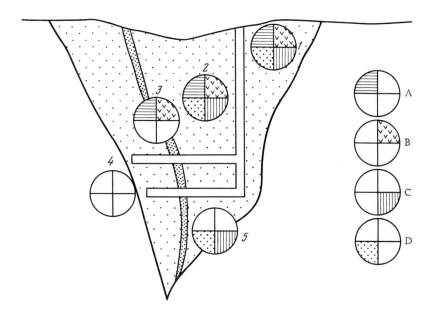

Fig. 23. The distribution of microorganisms that oxidize hydrocarbons in the rocks of the Borislavskoye ozocerite mine (schematic diagram)
Bacteria that oxidize: A—benzine, B—ligroin, C—kerosene; D—solar oil (petroleum).
1—samples of ground water; 2—ozocerite-bearing rocks; 3—liquid ozocerite; 4—rocks without ozocerite; 5—oil (after Shturm and Rozanova).

Microorganisms may play a considerable role in oxidizing cyclic hydrocarbons. With this in mind, L. D. Shturm and G. I. Rozanova studied the microflora that oxidize the hydrocarbons in the oils, ozocerites and host rocks of the Borislavskoye mine. Their data suggest that the oil, rising from below, enters an environment of lower pressure, where solubility decreases, ozocerite is separated, and light oil results. The few bacteria present in these oils include none that oxidize cyclic hydrocarbons, and there is a predominance of species that oxidize the heavy fraction. There are no bacteria capable of oxidizing hydrocarbons in the rocks outside the area of ozocerite occurrence. The ozocerite itself undergoes partial biological oxidation in the oxidizing environment. The formation of ozocerites is evidently determined principally by physical factors. A similar picture is observed in the case of the oils in which the heavy fraction consists of tars and petroleum asphalts.

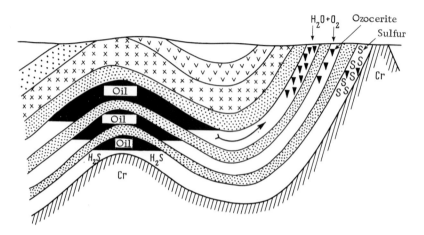

Fig. 24. Diagram of the geologic structure of the Shor–Su deposit of oil, sulfur and ozocerite.

Such a paragenesis of oil and ozocerites has been thoroughly traced by geologists in the Shor–Su deposit (Uklonskiy, 1940). The accompanying illustration (Fig. 24) shows that the oil and ozocerites occur at the same stratigraphic level. The fourth petroliferous anticline remained closed and contains oil, whereas the second anticline was exposed by erosion, the oil-bearing strata cropped out at the surface, and the beds at the present time contain ozocerite.

Oxidation of oil emerging naturally at the earth's surface has been observed by Tauson (1928a) at Supsa. A number of researchers have identified a great many different species of microorganisms that oxidize individual components of oil (ZoBell, 1946c; Davis, 1956; Osnitskaya, 1942, 1948; Bokova, 1947; Davis and Updegraff, 1954; Tauson, 1925, 1928a, b and c), and E. Beer-stecher (1954) has made a summary of all these papers. Tauson estimates the rate of oxidation of the oil in storage tanks at 25 metric tons per hectare each year. Large amounts of oil are oxidized in the soil and in bodies of water (Voroshilova and Dianova, 1950, 1952).

The Oxidation of Combustible Gases

There is some accumulation of combustible gases in almost every oil deposit. Since the formational pressure in the deposit may be several hundred atmospheres, most of this gas is dissolved in the oil and the stratal waters. As the deposit is exploited, the formational pressure drops, the solubility of the gases in oil decreases, and the first to be separated out into the gaseous phase are the less soluble gases: nitrogen, methane and propane. Table 37 shows that as the formational pressure reduces to atmospheric pressure, one metric ton of oil may give off up to 288 m^3 of gas, as found in the Mukhanovskoye oils from the fourth stratum of the Devonian deposits. Some data on the composition of the gases dissolved in oils under natural pressures existing in the oil stratum are given in Table 37.

Table 37

Properties of the gases dissolved in the oil of some deposits
of the Kuybyshev Volga region
(after K. B. Ashirov and S. P. Maksimov, 1958)

Deposit	Stratum	Oil density	Initial stratal pressure, atm	Gas factor*	Composition of gases, volume %					
					Nitrogen	Methane	Ethane	Propane	Butane	Pentane
Karlovo-Sytovka	B1 + B2	0.852	116	15	23.8	29.0	16.0	15.0	9.4	4.2
Zol'nyy	B2	0.839	117	100	4.0	43.0	19.0	17.9	8.6	3.6
	D1	0.807	180	111	5.8	31.7	23.4	22.6	11.1	5.3
Semyye vody	B2	0.896	132.5	19.4	21.6	29.6	13.0	16.9	8.6	3.4
Mukhanovo	B1	0.850	236	37	8.3	28.5	21.2	24.0	8.6	5.5
	D-IV	0.807	325	288	4.5	52.8	19.3	12.5	6.5	3.9

*The gas factor is the number of cubic meters of gas separated in the extraction of one metric ton of oil.

The petroleum gases that occur under high pressure will pass along fractures and tectonic faults and diffuse through the overlying sedimentary rocks, thus to penetrate into a region of lower pressures and finally reach the earth's surface, as illustrated by the diagram of an oil deposit in Fig. 25. Here, in the beds close to the surface, biological oxidation of the hydrocarbon gases takes place.

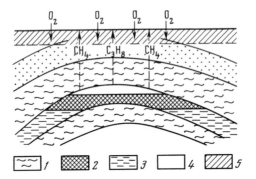

Fig. 25. Diagram illustrating the diffusion of gas from an oil deposit to the earth's surface: 1—water-impermeable rocks; 2—oil-bearing rocks; 3—water-bearing rocks; 4—gas-bearing rocks; 5—zone of oxidation of the diffusing gases from the hydrocarbon-oxidizing microflora (after data from G. A. Mogilevskiy).

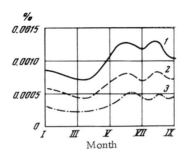

Fig. 26. Quantity of hydrocarbon gases in the subsoil air over a gas deposit in different seasons of the year (in %): 1—total amount of gas; 2—methane; 3—heavy fractions.

Table 38

Species of bacteria that oxidize gaseous aliphatic hydrocarbons*

Species	Hydrocarbon on which the initial isolation of the culture was made	Hydrocarbons					Author
		CH_4	C_2H_6	C_3H_8	C_6H_{14}	Gasoline	
Bacterium methanicum	CH_4	+	0	—	—	—	Münz (1915)
Mycobacterium methanicum	CH_4	+	—	+	—	—	N. B. Nechayeva (1949)
Mycobacterium flavum v. *methanica*	CH_4	+	—	+	+	—	N. B. Nechayeva (1949)
Mycobacterium perrugosum v.*ethanica*	C_2H_6	0	+	+	+	—	Ye.N. Bokova (1954)
Mycobacterium paraffinicum	C_2H_6	0	+	+	—	+	Davis et al. (1956)
Mycobacterium rubrum v. *propanica*	C_3H_8	0	0	+	—	—	Ye.N. Bokova (1954)
Nocardia sp.	C_2H_6	0	+	—	—	—	Davis et al. (1956)
Pseudomonas propanica	C_3H_8	0	0	+	—	+	M. Dostalek (1954)

*Plus sign indicates bacterial development; 0 indicates no bacterial development; minus sign means no experiment was conducted.

As the researches of Münz (1915), N. B. Nechayeva (1949), Ye. N. Bokova (1954), Ye. N. Bokova et al. (1947), Davis (1956b), M. Dostalek (1954), S. I. Kuznetsov and Z. P. Telegina (1957) and other authors have shown, a number of microorganisms take part in the oxidation of methane, ethane and propane. In so doing, as the data in Table 38 indicate, many of these microbes oxidize hydrocarbons selectively.

The concentration of hydrocarbon gases in the subsoil air does not usually exceed 0.001%, even above oil deposits (Kotov, 1953), and is smallest during the winter months, as Fig. 26 shows. Over oil deposits, the quantity of hydrocarbon gases usually

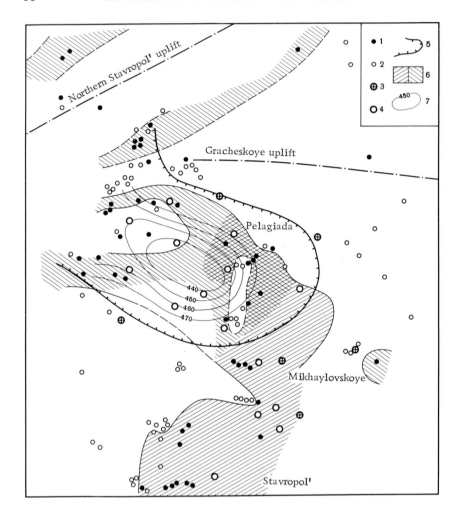

Fig. 27. Sketch-map comparing the areal distribution of hydrocarbon-oxidizing bacteria with data on subsequent drilling in the Pelagiada gas deposit in the Stavropol' district: 1—springs with hydrocarbon microflora; 2—springs without hydrocarbon microflora; 3—boreholes touching water in the Karaganskian and Khadumskian deposits; 4—boreholes touching gas; 5—water/gas contours in Khadumskian deposits; 6—zones of distribution of hydrocarbon microflora in ground waters, according to survey data of 1946 and 1947; 7—structure contour lines along top of the Khadumskian strata (after A. G. Mogilevskiy, 1957).

Table 39

Utilization of minimum concentrations of methane and propane by hydrocarbon-oxidizing bacteria

Conditions of experiment	Content of hydrocarbons, %		Duration of experiment, hours	Content of bacteria in 1 g of soil or 1 ml of culture, millions	
	Methane	Propane		At beginning of tests	At end of tests
Extraction of natural subsoil air from oil district through pipe with soil to which *B. methanicum* culture was added	0.0099 0.0443	— 	72 30	0.1 0.1	10 10
Extraction of air by addition of propane through culture of propane-oxidizing bacteria	— 	0.000 0.0007 0.04	72 72 72	6. 8 8	7.0 17.2 191.5

increases unevenly in the deeper beds, its amount depending on the rate of its diffusion through the sedimentary rocks and the rate of oxidation by microorganisms.

Laboratory experiments have shown (Kuznetsov, Kuznetsova and Smirnova, 1947), that methane-oxidizing and propane-oxidizing bacteria can develop if air with minimum contents of gaseous hydrocarbons is drawn through the nutrient medium or the soil. Table 39 gives the results of these experiments.

V. A. Sokolov (1948) gives some idea of the amount of gases lost from a deposit by diffusion. After examining a large number of analyses of the gases in subsoil air over oil deposits, and from appropriate calculations, he concludes that every accumulation of gas that is under isostratal pressure loses, per km^2, an amount of gas on the order of 100 thousand metric tons each million years. In other words, in an area of 1 km^2 over an oil deposit the bacteria annually oxidize about 100 kg, or 150 m^3, of hydrocarbon gases, computed as methane.

Numerous analyses by G. A. Mogilevskiy (1957) of the distribution of bacteria that oxidize hydrocarbons in the strata beneath the soil have shown that, as in Fig. 27 for the area of the Stavropol' uplift, the distribution of the bacteria very closely follows the contours of the gas deposit. Thus if the values cited by Sokolov are recomputed for the oil deposits formed during the Tertiary period, the oxidizing activity of the microorganisms should amount to some millions of metric tons of gas per km^2 of the oil deposit.

CHAPTER VII

The Role of Microorganisms in the Formation and Destruction of Sulfur Deposits

The first ideas that microorganisms may have participated in the formation of sulfur deposits were expressed by V. I. Vernadskiy as early as 1912; actual data, however, have begun to be gathered only in recent years. One of the pioneering microbiological investigations in this field was reported by L. D. Shturm and T. L. Simakova (1928), who studied the distribution of thiobacteria and sulfate-reducing bacteria in the sulfur-bearing rocks of certain deposits in the USSR. Later, in 1945 appeared the studies of Indian investigators, who observed the formation of sulfur deposits on the shores of the Gulf of Bengal (Iya and Srenivasaya, 1944, 1945a and b). Finally, Bonython and King (1956) and Bonython (1956) investigated the sulfur deposits in Australia, and Butlin and Postgate (1954) in the lakes of Cyrenaica.

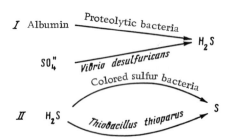

Fig. 28. Diagram of the microbiological processes leading to the formation of sulfur deposits (after Isachenko, 1958).

A more general view of the possible participation of microorganisms in creating sulfur deposits is provided by B. L. Isachenko (1958). His hypothesis of the formation of sulfur deposits, schematized in Fig. 28, is the following: the first event to take place is the biogenic formation of large quantities of hydrogen sulfide; second, the hydrogen sulfide is oxidized to molecular sulfur by thiobacteria or by sulfur purple bacteria.

1. SOME DATA ON THE PHYSIOLOGY OF THE ORGANISMS THAT TAKE PART IN THE FORMATION AND DESTRUCTION OF SULFUR DEPOSITS

The principal organisms that participate in forming and destroying sulfur deposits are *Vibrio desulfuricans, Thiobacillus thioparus* and *Thiobacillus thiooxidans.* The general physiology of these organisms has been quite thoroughly studied (Postgate, 1959; Vishniac and Santer, 1957; Lis, 1958), but certain aspects of their ecology still remain unclear. Some characteristic features of the physiology of these organisms are described below.

Vibrio desulfuricans. The optimal environment for the development of sulfate-reducing bacteria, including *V. desulfuricans,* is created by the presence of assimilable organic matter or molecular hydrogen, anaerobic conditions and an almost neutral pH. As a rule, *V. desulfuricans* is active in natural environments where the oxidation-reduction potential is below $rH_2 = 10$. These requirements are found in the majority of the stratal waters of oil deposits, where rH_2 fluctuates between 6 and 8; evidently close to the optimal for the growth of *V. desulfuricans.* The second necessary condition for the development of this microorganism is the presence of a reducing agent or a source of energy for the reduction of sulfate to hydrogen sulfide.

The first study of organic substances that might serve as a substrate for the development of sulfate-reducing bacteria was made by V. O. Tauson and V. I. Aleshina (1932), whose experiments with an enrichment culture of *V. desulfuricans* showed that bacteria developed and hydrogen sulfide formed when a large variety of organic substances, including even crude oil, were introduced into the nutrient medium.

Recently, however, the growth requirements have been reexamined. Methods have been worked out (Sorokin, 1952) by which pure cultures of *V. desulfuricans* can be obtained fairly simply. Data from various authors on the assimilation of different organic substances by such cultures, summarized by Postgate (1959), show that this organism is extremely selective in regard to its source of organic matter and assimilates only lactic and formic acids and certain sugars. It does not assimilate fatty acids, including acetic acid, to say nothing of hydrocarbons. Because the organisms are so widely found in nature, these data suggest an experimental study to determine whether hydrogen sulfide can be formed by the biological reduction of sulfates in enrichment cultures of *V. desulfuricans* when natural substrates such as lake ooze or crude oil are the source of organic matter. Data from N. N. Lyalikova (1955) and V. A. Kuznetsova et al. (1957) on this problem are given in Table 40. These show that a number of natural substrates, including fresh-water lake oozes and crude oil, do provide the necessary organic matter for the reduction of sulfates in experiments with enrichment cultures of *V. desulfuricans*.

Table 40

Formation of hydrogen sulfide by enrichment cultures of *Vibrio desulfuricans* on natural substrates (after N. N. Lyalikova, 1955).

Source of organic matter	Duration of experiment, days	Amount of H_2S at end of incubation period, mg/liter		
		Medium without sulfates (a)	Medium with $MgSO_4$ added (b)	Added material (b—a)
Ooze from Lake Beloye, Moscow Oblast'. . . .	32	375	570	195
Ooze from L. Biserovo .	26	66	82	16
" " L. Il'men. .	120	95.7	170	74.3
" " L. Dolgoye .	30	0	0	0
" " L. Maloye Medvezh'ye.	62	37	105	68
Oil from Kalinovka . .	94	31	260	229
" " "	210	20	385.5	365.5

Recent investigations, summarized by Yu. I. Sorokin (1956), have shown that sulfate-reducing bacteria may use molecular hydrogen as the source of energy for their growth, according to the reaction: $CaSO_4 + 4H_2 = CaS + 4H_2O$. In this process the sulfates are reduced to sulfides, and the energy thus liberated is used to promote the assimilation of free carbon dioxide and the growth of *V. desulfuricans*.

Thiobacillus thioparus. The colorless and purple sulfur bacteria have been considered of great importance in the formation of molecular sulfur. This was the view of Butlin and Postgate (1954), who studied the lakes of Cyrenaica. M. V. Ivanov (1957a and c) has shown that the chief role in the oxidation of hydrogen sulfide to molecular sulfur is played by *Thiobacillus thioparus*. G. A. Sokolova (1961b) isolated pure cultures of this organism and studied a number of its physiological properties. One of the main factors affecting the life processes of *Th. thioparus* is the oxidation-reduction conditions in the surrounding medium. The results of experiments to determine the oxidation-reduction limits within which this organism oxidizes hyposulfite to molecular sulfur (Kuznetsov and Sokolova, 1960) are cited in Fig. 29. This graph shows that the most intensive bacterial growth and oxidation of hyposulfite took place when the oxidation-reduction potential was from rH_2 10 to 16.*

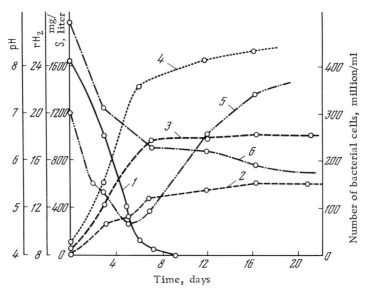

Fig. 29. Dynamics of the oxidation of hyposulfite, changes in the oxidation-reduction potential and the pH of the medium, and the accumulation of sulfur in molecular and sulfate form in a culture of *Thiobacillus thioparus* (after Kuznetsov and Sokolova, 1960):
$1 - S/S_2O_3^{++}$; $2 -$elemental S; $3 - S/SO_4^{++}$; $4 -$number of bacteria; $5 - rH_2$; $6 - pH$.

Further study of various sulfur compounds oxidized by *Th. thioparus* has shown that this organism can derive its required

* Editor's Note: This may also indicate the relative rate of oxygen consumption during oxidation.

energy from the oxidation of sulfides to molecular sulfur, calcium sulfide being especially readily oxidized at low rH_2 values. Sodium sulfide begins to be oxidized bacterially only when a certain amount of it has already been oxidized by the oxygen in the air in a purely chemical reaction.

   Thiobacillus thiooxidans.   Certain peculiarities of the physiology of *Thiobacillus thiooxidans* are of interest, inasmuch as this organism plays an important role in the oxidation of sulfur to sulfuric acid. It was known as early as the work of Waksman and Joffe (1921, 1922) that the optimal pH for the development of this species was 2. This organism is autotrophic, and hence does not require organic matter for its growth.

   Natural sulfur deposits are frequently saturated with sulfide-bearing stratal waters, creating anaerobic conditions which preserve the sulfur from further oxidation. Therefore it is of interest to determine the oxidation-reduction potential at which sulfur is oxidized, and the crystal forms of sulfur most readily oxidized.

   Data from G. I. Karavayko (1961), cited in Fig. 30, show that when *Th. thiooxidans* grows in a nutrient medium in oxidizing conditions with molecular sulfur, the amount of free sulfuric acid increases sharply, the pH of the solution drops from 4.9 to 2.2, and the rH_2 rises from 22.4 to 25.3. Experiments have shown that the intensity of the biogenic oxidation of sulfur depends chiefly not on the form of the crystals but on their size. The freshly precipitated sulfur formed at the water line of hydrogen sulfide springs is the most readily oxidized.

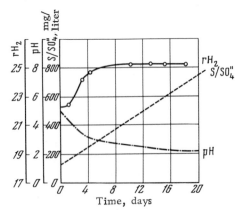

Fig. 30. Change in the oxidation-reduction potential, the pH and the content of sulfates in a culture of *Thiobacillus thiooxidans* (after Karavayko, 1961).

A review of the results of laboratory investigations concerning the sulfur cycle suggests the following conclusions:

1. Sulfate-reducing bacteria, occurring together with other organisms, can develop and reduce sulfates by deriving their hydrogen from a great variety of organic substances, including even crude oil.

2. Sulfates are actively reduced when the oxidation-reduction potential of the surrounding medium is within the range of rH_2 = 6 - 10.

3. Reduced sulfur compounds such as hyposulfite and sulfides in a culture of *Thiobacillus thiooxidans* are oxidized under more oxidizing conditions with rH_2 from 10 to 16, the optimum being rH_2 = 16.

4. Molecular sulfur is oxidized in pure cultures of *Thiobacillus thiooxidans* at rH_2 values of 20-25.

Thus by determining the rH_2 under the conditions of nature, one can judge the degree to which the ecological conditions favor the activities of microorganisms in sulfur deposits.

2. THE PRINCIPAL TYPES OF SULFUR DEPOSITS

Geologists categorize all deposits of sulfur as sedimentary or volcanogenic. As the sedimentary deposits include more than 90% of the world's sulfur reserves, the discussion below will apply entirely to sedimentary sulfur deposits.

The genesis of sedimentary sulfur deposits is not yet sufficiently well known, even from the purely geological standpoint. Some researchers (Danov, 1936; Mursaiev, 1937; Drobyshev, 1930; and others) believe that the sulfur was precipitated simultaneously, or syngenetically, with the deposition of the surrounding rock, and is therefore to be associated with the sulfate-carbonate lagoonal deposits of ancient bodies of water. Other investigators, who adhere to the concept of the epigenetic, or secondary, formation of sulfur, believe that the sulfur originated from the reduction of gypsum and later oxidation of S^{2-} to S *in situ,* and that the calcite which usually occurs together with the sulfur is an *alteration* product of the gypsum.

A. S. Uklonskiy (1940) has analyzed the hypothesis of the secondary formation of sulfur in detail; he considers that sulfur deposits are always associated with oil, and that the formation of the sulfur is determined by the oxidation of the hydrogen sulfide that passes through fractures in the rocks from the oil deposit, as illustrated in Fig. 31.

Geologic data indicate that sulfur may be formed by both primary and secondary mechanisms, although geologists differ in their

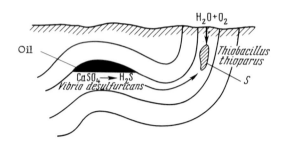

Fig. 31. Participation of various groups of
microorganisms in the formation of epigenetic sulfur deposits.

estimates of the role played by microorganisms in these processes.
Some information obtained from studies of the participation of
microorganisms in the formation and oxidation of the sulfur in
both types of deposits is presented below.

3. SOME MICROBIOLOGICAL DATA ON THE FORMATION
OF SULFUR IN SYNGENETIC DEPOSITS

Since the sulfur in syngenetic deposits is precipitated simultaneously with the formation of the surrounding rocks, its presence
often cannot be discerned visually or else is distinguishable only
as very thin interlaminations even when the sulfur content is as
high as 20% or more.

To judge the role played by microorganisms in the formation
of syngenetic sulfur deposits, one should find modern analogues
of ancient bodies of water in which sulfur and calcite were accumulated simultaneously. In such bodies of water the distribution of
sulfur in the sediments should be analyzed and the occurrence of
Vibrio desulfuricans and *Thiobacillus thioparus* should be studied.

Data on the simultaneous deposition of calcite, dolomite* and
molecular sulfur are available only for Lakes Balkhash (Sapozhnikov,
1951) and Tambukanskoye (Isachenko, 1927). These are shown in
Table 41. Although the amount of molecular sulfur deposited in
the oozes of these lakes does not exceed 0.25% of the dry weight
the data suggest that the sulfur and calcite may have been formed
simultaneously, as in the sulfur ores of syngenetic deposits. These
investigations, however, have not been accompanied by detailed
microbiological analyses.

---

* Editor's Note: Dolomite here may be Mg calcite.

Table 41

Mineral composition of the oozes in Lakes Tambukanskoye and
Balkhash
(% of dry substance of ooze)

Characteristics of ooze sample	Free sulfur	SiO_2	CaO	MgO	CO_2
Lake Tambukanskoye, surface ooze..	0.07	37.2	—	—	—
Lake Balkhash					
sandy ooze	0.05	53.99	10.51	2.58	8.04
	0.25	38.17	18.62	3.85	16.02
gray ooze	0.25	25.71	27.70	3.56	23.40
	0.21	27.50	25.81	3.55	21.48
white ooze	0.12	20.96	29.42	4.98	26.23
	0.11	14.41	26.95	11.61	31.52

Two ways in which microbiological processes may lead to the formation of sulfur in syngenetic deposits have been noted. One is the formation of molecular sulfur by bacteria in a bioanisotropic body of water rich in hydrogen sulfide. The sulfur then sinks into the lower layers of water, is deposited on the bottom, and is buried in calcareous sediments formed either by photosynthesis near the water's surface or by an exchange reaction between CaS and CO_2. The second possibility is that sulfides may be formed by the reduction of sulfates in the ooze deposits of the body of water, which diffuse to the surface layer of the ooze where it is oxidized to molecular sulfur by thiobacteria.

Up to the present time the literature has contained no conclusive data on bodies of water in which such a process may have taken place as described immediately above, although a number of bodies have been described in which molecular sulfur is being formed by the oxidation of the hydrogen sulfide that enters the lake from springs, and in which appropriate microbiological investigations have been carried out. These include the lakes of Cyrenaica in North Africa and Lake Sernoye in the Kuybyshev Oblast' of the USSR.

a) The Oxidation of Hydrogen Sulfide in Lake Water and the Accumulation of Sulfur in Bottom Sediments

The work reported by Butlin and Postgate (1953b, 1954), who investigated the microflora of the sulfurous lakes in Cyrenaica, is of great interest. These English microbiologists made a fairly detailed study of one of these lakes, Ain-es Sauya, whose water is brackish, with a mineral content of 25 g/liter. This lake is supplied with water from a deep spring, at a temperature of

34°C. The water in the lake contains hydrogen sulfide, and has a milky cloudiness created by the large amount of molecular sulfur being precipitated; the entire bottom is covered by a layer of deposited sulfur some 15 - 20 cm thick. This layer of sulfur on the bottom would doubtless be even thicker, were it not that the local Arab inhabitants have for a long time been extracting the sulfur, annually taking some 200 tons of sulfur from three lakes with a combined area of 20,000 m^2.

Butlin and Postgate found that sulfate-reducing bacteria were widespread in the ooze deposits and in the water of the lake, and thus concluded that the hydrogen sulfide in the lakes they investigated is formed from the reduction of sulfates by sulfate-reducing bacteria in the lake itself. They also call attention to the fact that an enormous number of purple and green sulfur bacteria, which are known to oxidize hydrogen sulfide to molecular sulfur, develop in shallow sulfur-forming lakes.

These observations prompted Butlin and Postgate to perform some quite interesting experiments with models, to discover the actual process by which the sulfur is formed in the lakes of Cyrenaica. Under laboratory conditions, sulfate-reducing bacteria and green and purple sulfur bacteria grew together in a medium with organic matter and yeast extract. Either gypsum or sodium sulfate was added to the medium as the only source of sulfur, and was reduced by the sulfate-reducing bacteria to hydrogen sulfide. Since colored sulfur bacteria were simultaneously present in the same dish, they oxidized this hydrogen sulfide to sulfur. In the experiments with cultures of *Chromatium,* the sulfur was precipitated within the cells of these bacteria; in the experiments with *Chlorobium,* however, an abundance of molecular sulfur was precipitated directly upon the walls and bottoms of the dishes. On the basis of their investigations, Butlin and Postgate came to the conclusion that both stages of the formation of sulfur in the lakes they observed involved the active participation of sulfate-reducing bacteria and colored sulfur bacteria.

The great importance of the work just described consists in the fact that it presents a thorough study of the only body of water thus far known in which there is an intensive deposition of molecular sulfur in the bottom sediments. But it seems to the present writers that Butlin and Postgate's assertion that the hydrogen sulfide is being formed in the lake itself lacks sufficient evidence. It is more likely that much of the hydrogen sulfide enters the lake already formed in the water from the spring. Butlin and Postgate quite convincingly demonstrated the subsequent role of the microorganisms in oxidizing the hydrogen sulfide to sulfur; unfortunately, however, these authors did not devote enough attention to the activity of the thiobacteria.

Similar conditions exist in Lake Sernoye in the Kuybyshev Oblast'. This lake is fed by the hydrogen sulfide waters of the Sergiyevskiye mineral springs, which contain 83 - 85 mg/liter of H_2S (Belkin, 1952). The deposition of molecular sulfur from the Sergiyevskiye waters is so intensive that in the time of Peter the Great, the molecular sulfur that settled to the bottom was collected and used to make gunpowder (Shilovtsev, 1952). At the present time abundant sulfur deposits cover the rocks where the springs flow out at the surface, and also the bottom of Lake Sernoye and of Molochnyy Creek, which flows out from the lake. As in the lakes of Cyrenaica described by Butlin and Postgate, the water in Lake Sernoye has a whitish-blue color from the molecular sulfur suspended in it.

As in the lakes of Cyrenaica, M. V. Ivanov (1957a) discovered numerous cells of *Chromatium* and *Chlorobium* in the bottom deposits and the encrustations on the rocks of Lake Sernoye. Nevertheless many of the overgrowths on the rocks contain no colored bacteria whatever, although subsequently the preparations made from them were literally filled with rodlike bacteria. Ooze and sulfur samples inoculated on Beijerinck's medium showed abundant thiooxidizing bacteria of the *Thiobacillus thioparus* type.

Hence, in Lake Sernoye, sulfides may have been oxidized to molecular sulfur by both the colored sulfur bacteria and the

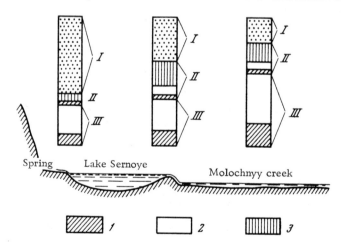

Fig. 32. Diagram showing the products and intensity of oxidation of sulfides of various points in Lake Sernoye:
I—unoxidized H_2S; II—oxidized to SO_4; III—oxidized to S; 1—abiogenic oxidation; 2—oxidation by thiobacteria; 3—oxidation by colored sulfur bacteria.

thiobacteria. To determine the specific roles played by each bacterial group, Ivanov (1957a, 1959) made some tests with the labeled sulfide Na_2S^{35}, which was added directly to a sample of lake water.

As will be seen from Fig. 32, these experiments established that the thiobacteria are the principal agents in the deposition of sulfur by the oxidation of hydrogen sulfide in Lake Sernoye; these oxidized 30% of the sulfides every twenty-four hours. The colored sulfur bacteria oxidized about 8% directly to sulfates, and about 17% of the sulfides were oxidized abiogenically to sulfur. These experiments also showed that each day about 120 kg of molecular sulfur is deposited in Lake Sernoye.

b) The Formation of Sulfur through the Oxidation of Hydrogen Sulfide Derived from the Reduction of Sulfates in Lake Ooze Deposits

The problem of the formation of the hydrogen sulfide in ooze deposits is closely associated with that of the genesis of medicinal muds. These processes have been thoroughly studied by B. L. Isachenko (1927), using the saline Lake Tambukanskoye as an example. He showed that there is a massive development of filamentous algae at the surface of the ooze in shallow lakes. After their death, putrefaction leads to the formation of a certain amount of hydrogen sulfide, so that anaerobic conditions are created beneath this layer. When sulfates are present in the surface layer

Table 42

Vertical distribution of desulfurizing bacteria in the bottom deposits of lakes (number of bacteria per gram of ooze)
(after S. I. Kuznetsov, 1952)

Depth from surface of ooze, m	Lake and its characteristics					
	Borovoye: mesotrophic fresh	Umreshevo: eutrophic brackish	Mogil'noye: eutrophic brackish	Maybalyk: mesotrophic saline	Repnoye: saline	Balpash-Sor: bitter-saline
0	0	1000	300	500	1,000,000	500
0.25	—	—	—	—	—	700
0.5	0	1000	100	30	—	500
1.0	0	—	10	60	100	—
2.0	0	—	0	100	100	—
3.0	—	—	—	—	1000	—
4.8	—	—	—	—	100	—
6.0	—	—	—	—	10	—
7.8	—	—	—	—	1	—

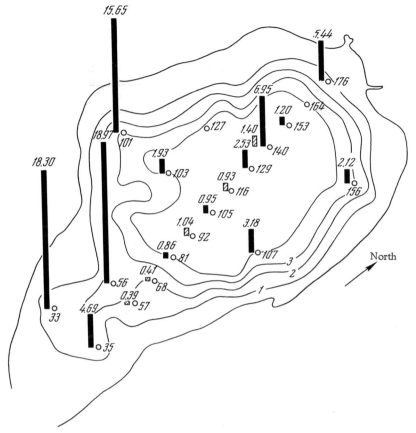

Fig. 33. Bathymetric map of Lake Solenoye. The columns indicate the intensity of the microbiological reduction of the sulfates in the surface layer of the ooze deposits (in mg of H₂S per kg of dry ooze). The black columns show the intensity of sulfate reduction at the end of July; the shaded columns show the same at the end of March; the circles show points at which ooze samples were taken for microbiological analysis; isobaths are drawn at one-meter intervals (after Ivanov and Terebkova, 1959b).

of the ooze, they are reduced where there is a sufficient amount of organic matter. A quantitative study of the distribution of *Vibrio desulfuricans* in various lakes (Kuznetsov, 1952, 1959a), presented in Table 42, shows that these organisms are abundant in brackish and saline lakes and occur in the surface layer of the ooze deposits. Experiments with radioactive isotopes by M. V. Ivanov and L. S. Terebkova (1959a and b) in Lake Solenoye have shown that the rate of sulfate reduction may be as high as 19 mg of H_2S per kg of ooze, as shown in Fig. 33.

Thus in the second type of formation of syngenetic deposits, the first stage of the process—the formation of hydrogen sulfide by the reduction of sulfates—occurs readily in the surface layer of the ooze in a number of lakes (Kuznetsov, 1952, 1959a; Ivanov, 1956) whose water contains fairly large quantities of sulfates.

Let us now examine the subsequent oxidation of hydrogen sulfide to molecular sulfur in the surface layer of the ooze deposits. This process, from all indications, ought to take place in the bioaniso-tropic Lake Belovod', which has been described in detail by G. I. Dolgov (1955). The results of analyses by G. A. Sokolova (1916) of the water and ooze from this lake are shown graphically in Fig. 34. The surface layers of the water in Lake Belovod' were

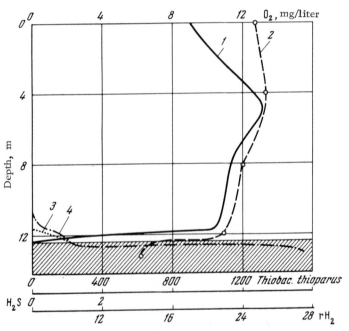

Fig. 34. Distribution of thiobacteria, hydrogen sulfide and oxidation-reduction potentials (rH_2) in the water and the surface layer of the ooze deposits of Lake Belovod':

1—dissolved oxygen; 2—rH_2; 3—hydrogen sulfide, mg/liter; 4—number of cells of *Thiobacillus thioparus* per ml of water or gram of ooze; cross hatching indicates ooze deposits.

saturated with oxygen, hydrogen sulfide was found only in the water layer next to the bottom, and the rH_2 values dropped sharply from the water to the ooze deposits. Thiobacteria were found in considerable quantities only in the surface layer of the ooze and the bottom layer of the water: this is quite consistent with the magnitudes of the oxidation-reduction potential.

Microscope studies of the surface layer of ooze established that new crystals of calcite (Fig. 35) were being formed; the calcite was precipitated in the oxidation of calcium sulfide and by the photosynthetic activity of the phytobenthos. On the other hand, the presence of molecular sulfur could not be established by direct analyses of these oozes. It must be supposed that molecular sulfur can be deposited in bodies of water of this type only when hydrogen sulfide is formed at a very high rate in the ooze deposits. The solution of this problem will require further investigations.

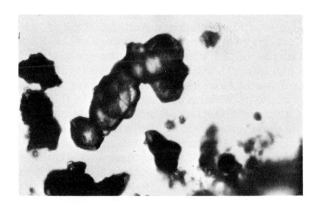

Fig. 35. Crystals of calcite from the surface
layer of the ooze in Lake Belovod'.

The origin of syngenetic sulfur deposits has been the subject of experimental studies by a group of Indian microbiologists, who investigated the sulfur deposits on the shores of the Gulf of Bengal (Iya and Srenivasaya, 1944, 1945a). Here the sulfur occurs in the sand-and-clay littoral sediments, which were flooded with sea water during the Mussonian period. The sulfur-bearing sediments are underlaid by a layer of black, hydrogen sulfide clay. The sulfur content is very high, in places up to 27 - 35% (Balasundaram, 1954). Active sulfate-reducing bacteria of the species *Vibrio desulfuricans* were found in the black clay underneath the sulfur-bearing sediments. The work of the Indian authors has provided the first incontrovertible proof of the participation of sulfate-reducing bacteria in the formation of sulfur deposits.

The example of the Indian deposits shows that the theory of the syngenetic formation of the sulfur deposits, which states that the sulfur could have been formed in marine basins simultaneously with the deposition of the surrounding sedimentary rocks, quite correctly reflects the actual conditions and processes that occur in nature. It is to be regretted only that the Indian microbiologists did not turn their attention to the bacteria that oxidize hydrogen sulfide to sulfur, but merely stated without any substantiation that this process is purely chemical.

All the above information testifies that the theory of syngenetic formation of sulfur is correct in principle, although separate publications are required to supply the necessary links in the chain of proofs of the theory of syngenesis that were lacking in earlier work. Lacking absolute examples of the present-day biogenic formation of sulfur in lakes, the adherents of syngenesis (Danov, 1936) had to fall back on the example of the Black Sea, in which the bottom layer of water contains hydrogen sulfide. This is not convincing, however, since the hydrogen sulfide content of the Black Sea water is small, and the initial condition for the creation of large sulfur deposits must be, above all, the intensive formation of hydrogen sulfide. The investigations described above were made in relatively small sulfur deposits which are clearly still in the stage of formation. Hence the participation of microorganisms in precipitating the sulfur in these cases was quite readily and clearly observed. But to determine the role of microorganisms in the genesis of larger deposits that may be of industrial value, investigations should not be limited to microbiological observations alone. Thorough analyses must also be made of the geological and hydrogeological data, to obtain the fullest possible picture of the actual geochemical environment in the deposit, both at the present time and in the past.

4. MICROBIOLOGICAL DATA ON THE FORMATION OF SULFUR IN EPIGENETIC DEPOSITS

A typical epigenetic sulfur deposit is located in the Shor-Su area. Here, according to Uklonskiy (1940), the sulfur was deposited by oxidation of the hydrogen sulfide in the ground water after the formation of the host rocks. Uklonskiy believes that both the formation of the hydrogen sulfide itself in a nearby oil deposit and its oxidation to molecular sulfur were abiogenic processes.

Ivanov (1957a and b) carried out a number of investigations to determine the possible role of microorganisms in the current formation of hydrogen sulfide and sulfur in the Shor-Su deposits. One of the most characteristic features of epigenetic sulfur deposits is their close connection with oil deposits and their emplacement in the open parts of the petroliferous structures. This rule is clearly followed in the Shor-Su deposits, where the sulfur formation is localized in the Lower Paleogene rocks of the second anticline, whose crest is fractured and crumpled. The rocks of the same age in the unbroken fourth anticline contain oil and sulfide waters.

As shown in the illustration (Fig. 36), *Vibrio desulfuricans* is present in the oil-bearing rocks of the fourth anticline, where the ecological conditions favor its existence. The oxidation-reduction potential rH_2 is 8 - 10, sulfates are present in the water, and the oil serves as a source of organic matter. Experiments with radioactive sulfur isotopes (Ivanov, 1957c) have shown that, although the salinity of the ground waters reaches 130 g/liter, hydrogen sulfide is now being formed at the rate of 0.2 mg/liter per day. The rocks are fractured, so that the sulfide waters, because of the gas pressure in the oil-bearing strata, rise to the open second anticline. Here they come into contact with the aerated surface waters descending along fractures in the rocks. The zone of contact contains favorable conditions for the development of *Thiobacillus*

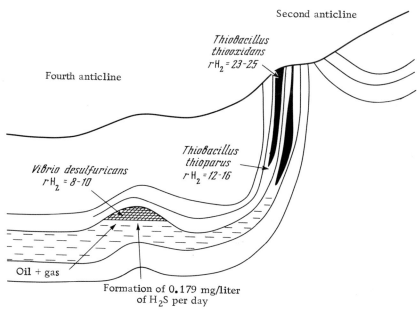

Fig. 36. Diagram illustrating the participation of various groups of microorganisms in the formation and decomposition of the Shor-Su epigenetic sulfur deposit.

thioparus: here the oxidation-reduction potential rH   rises to 12 – 16. Analyses reveal the presence of large numbers of *Thiobacillus thioparus* and of deposits of finely crystalline sulfur on the shaft walls, where the stratal waters trickle out (Fig. 37).

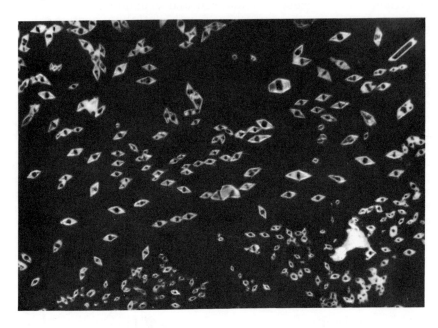

Fig. 37. Tiny crystals of native sulfur deposited on glass as a result of the oxidation of the hydrogen sulfide in the ground waters in the mine workings of the Shor-Su sulfur mine; × 200 (after Ivanov, 1957c).

Direct determination of the rate of oxidation of the sulfides, using the radioisotope method, has shown that every twenty-four hours about 50% of the sulfides in the stratal waters is oxidized to molecular sulfur. Of this percentage 30% is oxidized abiogenically and 20% by the thiobacteria.

Thus the role played by microorganisms in the formation of epigenetic sulfur deposits becomes clear. The data obtained from the study of the microflora in the Shor-Su sulfur deposit are of great theoretical interest, since the Shor-Su is itself a typical epigenetic deposit, which has served the adherents of the biogenic conception of sulfur formation as an example in their endeavor to create a theory of the mineral-reduction origin of sulfur (Uklon-skiy, 1940). Investigation of the microbiological processes occurring in this deposit has shown that the theoretical general course of these processes does not differ from that observed in bodies of water in the formation of syngenetic deposits. Table 43 shows the further transformation of microcrystalline sulfur and the formation of the large crystals that are encountered in caverns and cavities in limestones.

Table 43

The formation of large sulfur crystals

Stage		Nature of process
I	Formation of calcium sulfide by *Vibrio desulfuricans*	$CaSO_4 \rightarrow CaS$
II	Solution of colloidal and fine crystalline sulfur	$2CaS + 2H_2O \rightarrow Ca(OH)_2 + Ca(HS)_2$ $Ca(HS)_2 + 4S \rightarrow CaS_5 + H_2S$

III	Precipitation of large crystals	$CaS_5 + CO_2 + H_2O \rightarrow CaCO_3 + H_2S + 4S$
		                         ↓ ↓
		                Precipitation Precipitation
		                of secondary of large sulfur
		                calcite crystals

The category of epigenetic deposits also includes the very rich sulfur deposits in the caprock of the salt domes along the shores of the Gulf of Mexico. On the basis of their mass-spectrometer studies of the isotope composition of the sulfur, hydrogen sulfide and the sulfates gypsum and anhydrite, Thode and his co-workers (Thode, Wanless and Wallouch, 1954) concluded that bacteria have played a leading role in the formation of these sulfur deposits. Since the bacteria more readily reduce sulfates with the lighter isotope S^{32} than those with the heavier isotope S^{34}, the S^{32}/S^{34} ratio in the hydrogen sulfide of biogenic origin will be greater than in the initial sulfates. The American authors have shown, as seen in Fig. 38, that the molecular sulfur and the sulfides in every case had a higher S^{32}/S^{34} ratio than the sulfates in the same samples of caprock and, on the other hand, that the sulfate samples taken from the sulfur-bearing caprock has an S^{32}/S^{34} ratio lower than the norm, thus clearly indicating that the enrichment of these residual sulfates in the heavy sulfur S^{34} is due to the biological formation of "light" hydrogen sulfide. The hydrogen sulfide that is richer in S^{32} has, in turn, provided the material for the later formation of "lighter" sulfur.

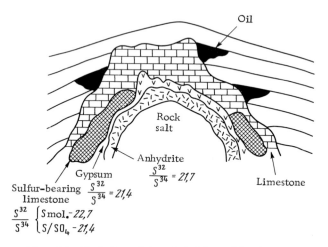

Fig. 38. Relationship of stable sulfur isotopes in different compounds of sulfur and in the caprocks of the salt domes along the coast of the Gulf of Mexico; for explanation see text.

5. THE ROLE OF MICROORGANISMS IN OXIDIZING THE SULFUR WITHIN DEPOSITS

Molecular sulfur, like the other reduced sulfur compounds hydrogen sulfide and metal sulfides, is among the minerals that are quite rapidly oxidized to the final product—sulfuric acid. The widespread occurrence of sulfuric acid in soils, mineral springs and deposits of sulfide minerals has been known for a long time (Vernadskiy, 1927).

In his investigation of the Karakumy sulfur deposits, A. Ye. Fersman (1926) found up to 4% sulfuric acid in a number of samples of sandy sulfur ore. Later, sulfuric acid and secondary sulfate minerals resulting from the reaction of the sulfuric acid with the sulfur-containing rocks were also found in other sulfur deposits (Danov, 1936; Uklonskiy, 1940). In the sulfur deposits in open structures this phenomenon is so clearly manifested that Uklonskiy (1940) suggested that secondary sulfate minerals be considered as a criterion in prospecting for sulfur.

The actual process by which sulfur is oxidized to sulfuric acid in nature was first discovered by soil microbiologists. Waksman and Joffe (1922) proved that the sulfur introduced as fertilizer into the soil is oxidized biologically. The same authors also isolated in a pure culture and described in detail the agent in this process, which they called *Thiobacillus thiooxidans*.

In subsequent years, papers by numerous microbiologists explained the role of this organism in oxidizing the sulfur compounds in different kinds of soils, in mineral springs, and recently also in deposits of sulfide minerals (Starkey, 1950). There have also been at least two attempts to discover *Thiobacillus thiooxidans* in the oxide zones of sulfur deposits; both, however, have been unsuccessful. L. D. Shturm and T. L. Simakova (1928) failed to find this bacterium in samples of Karakumy ore, which had a pH = 2.5. P. F. Samsonov and T. F. Merzhanova's study (1932) of specimens of Shor-Su sulfur ore also had negative results. It should be noted, however, that the authors of the latter paper committed a definite error in selecting the material for their investigation. Although they were attempting to determine the role of microorganisms in sulfuric acid weathering, they took samples of ore in which this process clearly had not taken place, as indicated by the neutral or slightly alkaline reaction of the samples studied (pH from 6.9 to 7.6). Finally, a systematic study of the role of *Thiobacillus thiooxidans* in oxidizing sulfur deposits in the Soviet Union was initiated in 1954 by the Institute of Microbiology of the USSR Academy of Sciences.

By now the distribution of these bacteria has been studied quite thoroughly. If oxidizing conditions are created in sulfur-bearing deposits, and the rH_2 of the water and rocks rises above 22, the sulfur may begin to be oxidized to sulfuric acid; the latter, reacting with the surrounding rocks, will form a whole series of secondary sulfate minerals that are characteristic of sulfur deposits (Uklonskiy, 1940; Korshunova and Pryanishnikov, 1935).

Sulfuric acid weathering is clearly manifested in one of the major sulfur deposits in the Soviet Union, located at Gaurdak in the Chardzhouskaya Oblast' of the Turkmen SSR. This is a very arid region, in which the annual atmospheric precipitation does not exceed 60 mm, mostly occurring during winter. The actual oxidation of the sulfur on the surface apparently takes place in the more humid part of the year, in spring. The active reaction on the site of sulfur-bearing tripolite limestone outcrops reaches pH 1. As one approaches the deposit, even at a distance one can discern by the lighter color the places where the acidic rocks are being formed on slopes (Fig. 39) (Ivanov, Lyalikova and Kuznetsov, 1958). To determine the role of the thiobacteria in weathering the sulfur-bearing limestones of the Gaurdak deposit, tests were made for acidity and for the presence of *Thiobacillus thiooxidans* in the ground waters and sulfur-bearing rocks. The resulting data are shown in Fig. 40, which shows that although the Kugitanskian limestones, which underlie the sulfur-bearing rock, have an alkaline reaction, the sulfur-bearing rocks themselves, where they form outcrops, show a very acid reaction, with pH from 0.4 to 4.0,

Fig. 39. General view of the first area of the Gaurdak sulfur deposit. The leached white rocks are visible where the sulfur-bearing deposits crop out at the surface.

which is well within the limits of acidity for the development of thiobacteria. The number of *Th. thiooxidans* in the places where the sulfur is oxidized varies from 1000 to 100,000 per gram of rock. The mine waters percolating through fractures in the ore body are also rich in acids and thiobacteria. A similar distribution of thiobacteria may also be observed in the upper part of the oxide zone of the Shor–Su sulfur deposit.

If, however, the sulfur-bearing limestones are isolated from the surface waters by dense, water-impermeable strata, the oxidation processes within them will be greatly retarded. Oxidation is prevented either by the complete lack of stratal waters, as in the Middle Volga deposits at Alekseyevka and Vodino, or else by the high content of hydrogen sulfide in the waters as, for example, at Rozdol or in the lower levels of the Shor–Su and Gaurdak sulfur deposits. In these cases the deposit is protected against the oxidizing action of the bacteria and is well preserved.

Sulfuric acid weathering begins to take place where sulfur-bearing rocks come into contact with the surface waters. This has been clearly demonstrated by G. I. Karavayko (1961), using the Rozdol sulfur deposit as an example. The data from his analyses

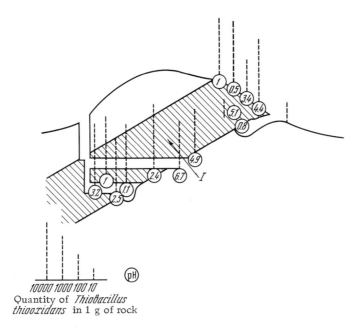

Quantity of *Thiobacillus*
thiooxidans in 1 g of rock

Fig. 40. Distribution of the pH and sulfur-oxidizing
thiobacteria in the rocks and waters of the Gaurdak
sulfur deposit. Figures in circles are the pH
values.
I—sulfur-bearing limestone.

are shown in Table 44, from which it is evident that the freshly
extracted ore does not contain *Th. thiooxidans;* in ore that has been
allowed to lie for two years exposed to the atmosphere and has
begun to be weathered, however, the number of *Th. thiooxidans*
increases sharply. In the first observation of the deposit in 1958,
Thiobacillus thiooxidans was virtually lacking in the ore body itself (Karavayko, 1959). Repeated observations made throughout the
year in which the ore stratum was exposed by mine workings
showed considerable increases in the number of sulfur-oxidizing
bacteria (Karavayko, 1961). It was noted at the same time that
the sulfur ore from the karst portion of the deposit had become
friable and crumbly, and showed signs of fusion on the sulfur-
fusion apparatus.

The general course of the oxidizing processes in the Rozdol
deposit is apparently the following: until they began to be worked,
the sulfur-bearing rocks of this deposit were saturated with
hydrogen sulfide waters, which prevented the occurrence of oxidizing processes. As the level of the hydrogen sulfide waters was

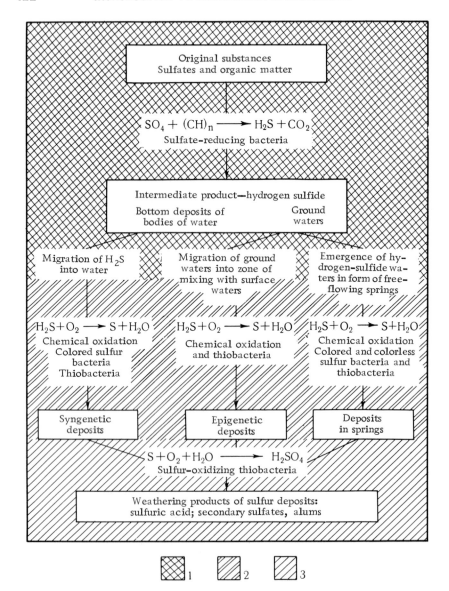

Fig. 41. The roles played by various groups of microorganisms in the formation and destruction of sulfur deposits of different types (after Ivanov, 1960a):
1—zone of pH values lower than 10; 2—zone of pH values from 10 to 18; 3—zone of pH values above 20.

Table 44

Propagation of *Thiobacillus thiooxidans* in freshly extracted ore and in ore that has been lying on the earth's surface for two years (after G. I. Karavayko, 1961)

Character of samples	pH of samples	Number of bacteria per gram of rock
Weathered blocks of sulfur-bearing limestone on an old stockpile	7.64	100
Clay from beneath ferruginous pebbles with white alum on pile of crushed rock	5.81	10,000
Fine crushed sulfur ore on an old stockpile	7.71	100
Clay with crushed sulfur ore	7.73	100
Corrosion patterns etched on blocks of sulfur-bearing limestone.	7.44	10
Alum-covered pebble with rock on block of sulfur-bearing limestone.	6.90	1000
Freshly mined ore.	7.50	0
Piece of sulfur-bearing limestone broken along fracture	7.20	0

lowered, surface waters and sulfur-oxidizing bacteria began to enter through the karst areas of the deposit. Thus the oxidation of the sulfur and the alteration of the ore took place first, and most intensively, in these karst areas.

Exposure of the sulfur-bearing stratum during the preparation of the deposit for open-pit exploitation still further intensified the contact between the sulfur and the oxidizing waters. When the ore, already contaminated with microorganisms, was crushed and carried out, the oxidation process was accelerated at an explosive rate. If one remembers that the amount of ore carried out is reckoned in hundreds of thousands of metric tons, it becomes clear that the loss due to oxidizing bacteria may be very great indeed.

Still greater danger is created by the possible development of oxidation processes within the ore body itself, since the exploitation of such an enormous deposit as the Rozdol requires several decades, and the loss of sulfur during the course of such a long period may also be very great. This indicates the very serious importance of this phenomenon and demands the further constant attention of geologists and microbiologists.

All the results of the study of the role played by microorganisms in forming and destroying sedimentary sulfur deposits are summarized in diagrammatic form in Fig. 41, which illustrates the activity of various groups of microorganisms in relation to the oxidation-reduction potential.

CHAPTER VIII

The Biogenic Oxidation of Sulfide Deposits

The drainage waters from bituminous coal mines, because of their high iron content and their acidity, are among the most disagreeable forms of industrial waste and have for a long time attracted the attention of investigators (Carpentor and Herndon, 1933; Hodge, 1937; Murdock, 1953). Carpentor and Herndon (1933) suggested that part of the sulfates in mine drainage waters might have been formed through the activity of bacteria, but the attempts of these authors to establish the biological nature of this acid formation did not meet with success.

The study of acid drainage waters by Colmer and Hinkle (1947) was far more successful. They observed that a characteristic rusty sediment was formed in colorless water taken from a mine shaft, after exposure to the air for two or three days. They had assumed earlier that this was the result of atmospheric oxidation of the ferrous sulfate. To determine whether this oxidation might be biological, Colmer and Hinkle carried out a number of experiments with antiseptics. To the water taken from the mine, they added mercuric chloride, phenol or formaldehyde in concentrations ranging from one part per thousand to one part per hundred trillion. Iron hydroxide was formed only in the controls or when a minimal amount of antiseptic was added. Mercuric chloride in concentrations of one part per million and phenol or formaldehyde in proportions of one per thousand completely prevented oxidation of the iron. Oxidation also failed to take place when toluene was added or when the water was sterilized by filtration through a Zeitz filter. Thus it was shown that the oxidation of the iron in the acidic drainage waters was due to biological causes. The water sterilized by filtration through the Zeitz filter was later used by Colmer and Hinkle as a nutrient medium for culturing a new iron-oxidizing bacterium, called *Thiobacillus ferrooxidans*. However, the properties of the new organism could be studied only after a culture had been isolated on a medium of definite known composition, since the complex and indeterminate composition of the mine water made it impossible to trace the changes taking place in it. Temple and Colmer (1951) suggested a synthetic nutrient medium consisting of a

0.1% solution of $MgSO_4 \cdot 7H_2O$, 0.05% $(NH_4)_2SO_4$ and $FeSO_4 \cdot 7H_2O$, added in various amounts from 2 to 26 g/liter to distilled water. The pH of the medium was adjusted with sulfuric acid to 2 - 2.5. Leathen and others (Leathen, McIntyre and Braley, 1951) used a more complicated synthetic medium, for which they proposed the following composition (g/liter of distilled water; final pH of 3.5):

$$(NH_4)_2SO_4 \quad 0.15$$
$$KCl \quad 0.05$$
$$K_2HPO_4 \quad 0.05$$
$$MgSO_4 \cdot 7H_2O \quad 0.50$$
$$Ca(NO_3)_2 \quad 0.01$$

To this medium was added 10 ml of a 10% solution of iron sulfate at pH 3.5, which was sterilized separately by filtration through an asbestos filter.

Later investigators for the most part used the Leathen medium, with some modifications. For example, Bryner and Jamerson (1958) added aluminum, manganese and sodium sulfates to this medium, and N. N. Lyalikova (1959) and Silverman and Lundgren (1959a) added a larger amount of ferrous iron, which was necessary in order to obtain a great mass of cells.

A pure culture of *Th. ferrooxidans* was obtained by repeated transfer of the colonies growing on a solid medium consisting of sterile mine water with 3% agar-agar. Other authors also managed to obtain pure cultures from individual colonies grown on Leathen medium plus agar or on silica gel plates impregnated with this medium. The latter method was more successful, since *Th. ferrooxidans* grows poorly on agar.

1. THE MORPHOLOGY AND PHYSIOLOGY OF *THIOBACILLUS FERROOXIDANS*, THE PRINCIPAL ORGANISM THAT OXIDIZES SULFIDES

a) Morphology

The organism isolated from acid mine waters is a short rod, usually separate, but sometimes grouped in pairs (Fig. 42A). In natural acidic waters they are 0.8-1 μ long and 0.4 μ wide. The bacteria are Gram negative and do not form spores (Colmer, Temple and Hinkle, 1949); they multiply by lateral division. Examination of the cells under a phase-contrast microscope clearly reveals polar bodies. Accumulations of chromatin-like substance in the centers of the cells were not discerned by examination with a phase-contrast microscope or by the use of special staining agents. The electron microscope at magnifications of 4500

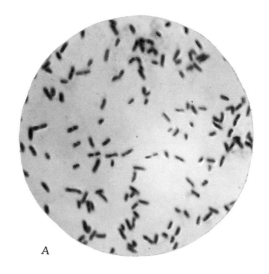

A

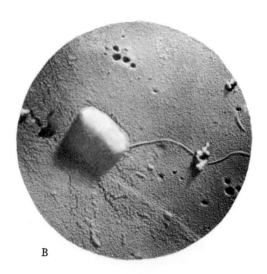

B

Fig. 42. *Thiobacillus ferrooxidans*
cells:
A—×1300; B—×15,000

clearly showed inclusions consisting of two or three round bodies
within the cells (Lyalikova, 1959); the nature of these inclusions
was not determined. The cells were stained with great difficulty,

and poorly absorbed such stains as methyl blue and erythrosine. Leathen studied their morphology by the use of the negative stain Congo red. Leathen's supposition that the cells move about actively by means of a single flagellum attached at the end was confirmed by examination of these bacteria under the electron microscope (Fig. 42B).

The bacteria form small colonies on mine water agar-agar. In dense cultures where the colonies are located close to each other, the amber-colored iron hydroxide sediment appears earlier than in well-isolated colonies. The sediment usually begins to be formed at the center of the colonies and spreads outward, sometimes forming lobes. The colonies of *Th. ferrooxidans* obtained by Leathen on a solid medium with silica gel had uneven edges and were elevated above the level of the silica gel; the young colonies had colors ranging from cream to rusty brown, whereas the older ones became granular and took on a dark-brown color.

Colmer and others (Colmer, Temple and Hinkle, 1949) observed the growth of iron-oxidizing bacteria on liquid and solid media with hyposulfite. The growth on a solid medium resulted in the formation of small colonies surrounded by some solid matter; the authors, however, believe that this solid material is not sulfur, which is separated out by *Thiobacillus thioparus* when it grows on a similar medium. In its remaining characteristics, the new iron bacterium was morphologically identical to the other thiobacteria, so that Colmer, Temple and others assigned it to the genus *Thiobacillus* and called it *Thiobacillus ferrooxidans*.

b) Physiology

For a proper estimate of the role played by an organism in nature, a knowledge of its physiology is essential. First of all, one must know which substrate can act as a source of energy for the growth of the given organism and the products that are formed as a result of the organism's action upon the substrate. To judge whether the organism occurs in an active state in nature, it is not enough merely to determine its presence; one must also establish the presence of a substrate favorable to its development and know the conditions under which the organism can carry out its vital activities. The development of *Th. ferrooxidans* in nature depends on the acidity of the medium, the oxidation-reduction potential, the presence of sulfides and ferrous compounds, and on other factors. Up to the present time, the data on the ecology and physiology of this organism have not yet been sufficiently generalized, so that it will be necessary to dwell in greater detail on these questions.

Th. ferrooxidans was isolated from acidic drainage waters as an organism capable of oxidizing ferrous iron in an acid medium.

The fact that it grows in a number of mineral media shows that it is a chemosynthetic autotroph—that is, an organism able to build up its body substance from carbon dioxide and certain salts, using chemical energy obtained by oxidizing inorganic materials. Autotrophic organisms in particular, inasmuch as they do not require organic substances, may play an important role in such biotopes as ore deposits of magmatic origin, which for all practical purposes are lacking in organic matter.

The establishment of the autotrophy of *Th. ferrooxidans* is not only important for determining its geochemical role; it is also of great theoretical significance because the existence of autotrophic iron bacteria has for many years been a subject of controversy. There have been two basic views of this problem. According to the opinion first expressed by S. N. Vinogradskiy (1888, 1922), the iron bacteria are a peculiar group of microorganisms capable of oxidizing ferrous iron and using the energy thus released for their life processes. In Molisch's view (1892, 1910) for example, the iron bacteria do not differ from the usual heterotrophic organisms in their nutrition and their means of obtaining energy, their only peculiarity being their habit of giving off a slimy substance in which is accumulated iron absorbed from the surrounding medium.

Any study of the physiology of the iron bacteria encounters great obstacles because in the air-exposed neutral or slightly alkaline medium in which the usual iron bacteria grow, the iron is readily oxidized by the oxygen in air; therefore it is difficult to estimate the role played by biological oxidation in this process. For this very reason, Meeham and Baas Becking (1927) denied their autotrophic nature because the iron bacteria developed in an alkaline medium. Iron bacteria are far easier to study in an acid medium, in which there is almost no chemical oxidation of the iron. Thus Leathen et al. (1956) found that the ferrous iron contained in acid mine waters in amounts of 200 mg/liter was completely oxidized by a young culture of *Th. ferrooxidans* in three days, whereas the chemical oxidation of a sterile solution of iron by atmospheric oxygen, at the same acidity in the medium, required more than two years.

The acid drainage waters from coal mines are an example of the existence in nature of a stable solution of iron not associated with organic matter. Pringsheim (1949), who did not know such waters actually existed, regarded their possible existence as being of great theoretical importance for the study of the autotrophy of iron bacteria.

Temple and Colmer (1951), studying the physiology of *Th. ferrooxidans*, cultivated this organism in a medium containing ferrous sulfate, magnesium sulfate and ammonium sulfate. This medium provided three possible energy sources: from contamination by organic matter, or by oxidation of the ammonia or iron. To eliminate any possible bacterial growth based on contamination by organic matter, chemically pure salts and water twice distilled with permanganate were used. The vessels used for the experiments were cleaned with hot concentrated sulfuric acid. The use of ammonia oxidation as a source of energy was prevented by the acid medium, in the first place; in the second place, calculations showed that even if all the ammonia in the medium were oxidized it could not have supported the growth of such a large amount of organic matter (as bacterial cells) as actually observed in the experiment. Moreover the development of bacteria, although somewhat retarded, could take place in a medium in which nitrates served as the only source of nitrogen. Chemical oxidation of iron through the action of nitrates, according to the reaction

$$6FeSO_4 + 2HNO_3 + 3H_2SO_4 \rightarrow 3Fe_2(SO_4)_3 + 2NO + 4H_2O,$$

could not explain the process taking place, since the amount of ferric sulfate formed in the medium in the presence of bacteria was twenty times greater than that which could have been formed by the above reaction.

Considering all the possible sources of energy in the medium in which *Th. ferrooxidans* was cultivated, and also the possibility of chemical oxidation of the iron, Temple and Colmer concluded that the iron was oxidized by the bacteria, which obtained their energy by oxidizing $FeSO_4$ according to the following reaction:

$$4FeSO_4 + 2H_2SO_4 + O_2 \rightarrow 2Fe_2(SO_4)_3 + 2H_2O.$$

The supposition that the oxidation process followed this reaction is supported by manometric studies (Beck, 1960) showing that the only source of carbon for the development of *Th. ferrooxidans* must have been the carbon dioxide in the air. When air from which the carbon dioxide had been removed with alkali was passed through the medium, neither oxidation of iron nor growth of bacterial cells was observed. Thus it was shown that *Th. ferrooxidans* is an autotrophic organism that obtains its energy by oxidizing ferrous iron. This has fully vindicated S. N. Vinogradskiy's conception of the existence of autotrophic iron bacteria, and has proved the theoretical possibility that other iron bacteria may also use the energy liberated in the oxidation of iron.

Temple and Colmer also made quantitative determinations of the oxidation of iron and fixation of carbon in a culture of *Th. ferrooxidans*. According to their data, the oxidation of 120 g of ferrous sulfate resulted in the fixation of 16.06 mg of carbon.

Temple and Colmer calculated the efficiency of energy utilization, assuming that the oxidation of iron yields 11.3 kcal/gram-atom, and that the fixation of 1 gram-atom of carbon requires 115 kcal. The efficiency of energy utilization thus computed amounted to 3.2%. This low percentage may be due to the fact that in their experiments Temple and Colmer used 17-day-old cultures, which used energy much less effectively than young, 2-day-old cultures. In such young cultures, according to N. N. Lyalikova (1958), the average efficiency of energy utilization was about 30%. The work of Silverman and Lundgren (1959b) confirms the high efficiency of energy utilization by a culture of *Th. ferrooxidans*. In experiments carried out with a Warburg apparatus, the effective use of free energy in the fixation of carbon amounted to 20.5 ± 4.3%.

Colmer, Temple and Hinkle (1949) believe that reduced compounds not only of iron but also of sulfur may be sources of energy for *Th. ferrooxidans*. In their experiments the bacteria oxidized hyposulfite to sulfuric acid, thus lowering the pH of the medium and causing the precipitation of sulfur by dissolving the hyposulfite. Some doubt has been cast on the data indicating that the same bacteria use both iron and hyposulfite. Leathen and Braley (1955) believe that the hyposulfite in Colmer and Temple's experiments may have been oxidized by a purely chemical reaction, and that the bacteria developed exclusively through the use of the ferrous iron introduced during inoculation. The organism which Leathen isolated from acid mine waters showed no morphological differences from *Th. ferrooxidans;* it oxidized iron at the same pH values, but failed to develop in a medium with hyposulfite. This bacterium was named *Ferrobacillus ferrooxidans* by Leathen, who assigned it not to the family Thiobacteriaceae, to which *Th. ferrooxidans* belongs, but to the family Siderocapsaceae, which includes many colonial iron bacteria.

The question of the possible use of reduced sulfur compounds is of great importance in determining the geochemical role of *Th. ferrooxidans*. If this organism is capable of oxidizing iron alone, this means that it cannot have contributed to the development of the great number of sulfide ore deposits in which iron is completely lacking.

Recently Beck's manometer experiments (1960) have shown that the organism which oxidizes iron in an acidic medium is also capable of oxidizing a slight amount of hyposulfite, and many authors (Beck, 1960; Bryner and Jamerson, 1958; Silverman and Lundgren, 1959b) who have carried out experiments with Leathen's bacterial strains have discovered that this organism, too, is capable of oxidizing molecular sulfur to sulfuric acid. The ability of *Th. ferrooxidans* to use reduced compounds of sulfur is also indicated by Lyalikova's experiments in the oxidation of sulfides such as antimonite and titanium disulfide—Sb_2S_3 and TiS_2—that do not contain iron.

Hence there can be no doubt that the same bacterial species is able to oxidize both ferrous compounds and reduced sulfur compounds. The lack of bacterial growth in a liquid hyposulfite medium is, in Temple and Colmer's opinion, to be explained by the loss of the ability of *Th. oxidans* to oxidize hyposulfite as a result of its long cultivation in a ferruginous medium.

The study of the autotrophic nutrition of *Th. ferrooxidans* and its distribution in nature gives rise to the question of the effect of various organic substances on its development. If many organic substances have a strong negative effect on *Th. ferrooxidans*, then this organism ought to occur mainly where there are no high concentrations of organic matter.

According to Leathen, Kinsel and Braley (1956), *Ferrobacillus ferrooxidans* described by them, which is in all likelihood identical to *Thiobacillus ferrooxidans*, is affected by organic matter. The presence of carbohydrates or peptone suppresses the oxidizing ability of this organism. A retarding effect on its growth is also exerted by the organic contamination existing in agar-agar, so that an agarized medium is capable of supporting the growth of this bacterium only after several inoculations.

Lyalikova (1959) and Bryner and Jamerson (1958) have also studied the influence of various organic substances on the oxidation of pyrite by pure cultures of *Th. ferrooxidans*. The results of these investigations are given in Fig. 43 and Table 45. The information represented in this graph and table shows that the retarding effect of most organic substances studied is exerted only at concentrations greater than 0.5%; formate and acetate retard the oxidation of iron at concentrations of 0.025%; and sugar generally has no retarding influence at all.

Such factors as the oxidation-reduction potential and the acidity of the medium are also of great importance for the development of these bacteria. It has already been mentioned that *Th. ferrooxidans* develops normally only in an acidic medium. The optimal conditions for the growth of this organism lie within the limits of pH 2 to 4, and growth ceases when the pH exceeds 4.5. Because of its ability to live under conditions of high acidity, *Th. ferrooxidans* can withstand the large concentrations of sulfuric acid that it forms as a result of metabolism. The bacterium transforms ferrous sulfate into ferric sulfate. This process causes alkalinification of the medium, since it requires two molecules of sulfuric acid:

$$4FeSO_4 + 2H_2SO_4 + O_2 \rightarrow 2Fe_2(SO_4)_3 + 2H_2O,$$

but this is followed by hydrolysis,

$$2\,Fe(SO_4)_3 + 12\,H_2O \rightarrow 2\,Fe_2(OH)_6 + 6\,H_2SO_4,$$

resulting in the formation of four more molecules of sulfuric acid than were required initially. The pH of the Leathen medium, which

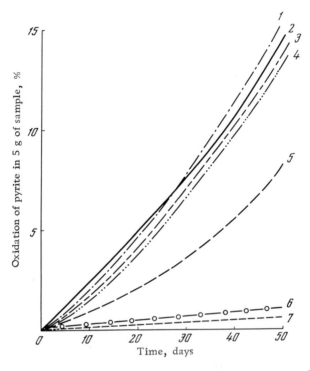

Fig. 43. Oxidation of pyrite in the presence of various organic substances (after Bryner and Jameson, 1958):
1—saturated solution of kerosene; 2—without organic substances; 3—0.4% glucose; 4—0.4% sucrose; 5—1% acetone; 6—saturated solution of benzene; 7—sterile control.

was originally 3.5, is lowered to 2-2.5 as a result of the bacterial growth. Acid is also formed in the oxidation of sulfides, especially pyrite, by the bacteria. Thus the bacteria themselves create a degree of acidity favorable to their development. This fact should be kept in mind in the investigation of ore deposits, and one should not assume, because of neutral pH values in the mine waters, that *Th. ferrooxidans* could not have played any role in oxidizing a given deposit. High acidity may be created in particular places where the oxidizing activity of these bacteria has been concentrated. In recently worked coal mines such foci of high acidity are very frequently observed.

Table 45

Effect of organic substances on the oxidation of iron by a culture of *Thiobacillus ferrooxidans* (after N. N. Lyalikova, 1959)

Organic substance introduced into culture	Concentration of organic substances, %	Effect on oxidation of iron
Glucose	0.05—1	None
Urea.	1	Retardation
Same	0.2	None
Peptone	0.5	Suppression
Same	0.1	None
Sodium acetate	0.025	Retardation
Same	0.05	Suppression
Sodium formate	0.025	"

To determine the most favorable oxidation-reduction conditions for the development of *Th. ferrooxidans*, Lyalikova (1959) measured the oxidation-reduction potential during the growth of a culture on Leathen medium. As Fig. 44 shows, the oxidation-reduction potential increases with increasing oxidation of ferrous and accumulation of ferric iron. The rH_2 range within which growth of *Th. ferrooxidans* was observed is fairly wide, varying from 16 to 30. *Th. ferrooxidans* develops best when the medium is well aerated, especially when air is blown through. This organism was also able to develop in low air concentrations, as in high-walled test tubes, but here its growth was slow. In this latter case the oxidation-reduction conditions of the medium after oxidation of the iron were as follows:

$$Eh = +715 \text{ mv}; \ pH = 1.95; \ rH_2 = 28.5.$$

These values are very close to those observed in the development of the organism in a thin layer of liquid* with good aeration:

$$Eh = +760 \text{ mv}; \ pH = 2.0; \ rH_2 = 30.4.$$

_____

*The average figures from two tests are given in both cases.

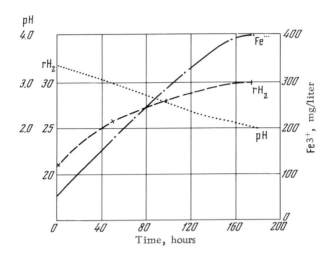

Fig. 44. Change in the oxidation–reduction potential (rH₂), the pH and the content of ferric oxide with the growth of *Thiobacillus ferrooxidans* in a culture.

In nature *Th. ferrooxidans* is active wherever sulfides are exposed to the earth's surface or where oxygen-rich waters come into contact with sulfides. Laboratory experiments have shown that oxidation of the iron by the oxygen in nitrates does not take place.

Study of the ecology of *Th. ferrooxidans* brings out the fact that this organism is little affected by copper and other heavy metals. For instance, Lyalikova (1959) isolated *Th. ferrooxidans* from mine waters in which the concentration of copper ions was 7.5 g/liter. The influence of copper ions was tested in laboratory experiments with cultures isolated from a spring in the Tula Oblast', whose water is free of copper, and from the Krasnogvardeyskoye ["Red Guard"] copper pyrite deposit in the Urals. A concentration of copper equal to 1 g/liter initially reduced the oxidation of iron by 60–70%, but all the iron was oxidized after several days. It is interesting to note that copper had the same effect on cultures isolated from different ecological environments.

Zimmerley et al. (1958) state that the resistance of *Th. ferrooxidans* to heavy metals may be increased by successive inoculation on media with progressively higher concentrations of the metals. For example, by gradual acclimatization it was possible to produce a strain that could withstand 17 g/liter of zinc, whereas the bacteria of the initial culture could grow only in the presence of less than 150 g/liter. Their resistance to copper was raised to a level of 12 g/liter.

Lyalikova's investigations showed that the *Th. ferrooxidans* culture isolated from the spring in the Tula Oblast', after 16 transfers on media with progressively higher contents of copper sulfate, acquired the ability to oxidize iron in the presence of 15 g/liter of copper, which corresponds to a 6% solution of copper sulfate. What are the reasons for this surprising resistance to copper? It is known that the toxic effect on microorganisms exerted by soluble compounds of copper, mercury and other heavy metals is due to their formation of mercaptides with the active sulfhydryl groups of oxidation-reduction enzymes. Monoiodoacetate is a specific inhibitor of the sulfhydryl groups. According to data from Temple and Colmer (1951), confirmed by Lyalikova's experiments, a concentration of only 1 millimolar iodoacetate completely suppresses the oxidation of iron by a culture of *Th. ferrooxidans*. Thus it may be supposed that copper fails to exert any great effect on these bacteria, not because the sulfhydryl groups of their enzymes occupy a specially closed position, but because the copper is unable to penetrate into their cells. This suggestion was confirmed by the following experiment, performed by Lyalikova. A pure culture of *Th. ferrooxidans* was grown in a medium with a 5 g/liter concentration of copper ion; thereafter it was centrifuged, and the resulting suspension was washed with water and centrifuged ten times to remove the copper that had been present in the medium. Thereupon rubeanhydride, a very sensitive reagent for copper which is capable of indicating its presence even in bacterial cells, was added to the medium. This reagent revealed no copper in the *Th. ferrooxidans* cells. When cells of *Pseudomonas* sp., which had been kept for two hours in a solution with the same concentration of copper and then washed in the manner described above, were treated with rubeanhydride, they showed the reddish-brown color that is indicative of copper. Thus cells that possess no resistance to copper revealed its presence, whereas the *Th. ferrooxidans* cells remained free of copper ions.

It is possible that the impenetrability of *Th. ferrooxidans* cells to high concentrations of copper has some specific connection with the acidity of the surrounding medium and the active acidity within the cells themselves. The possible existence of such a relationship is indicated by data of Starkey and Waksman (1943); these authors found mold fungi growing in a 4% solution of copper sulfate, whose pH was adjusted at 0.2-0.7. A connection between resistance to copper and low pH values and oxidation-reduction potentials within the cells was also shown by V. I. Uspenskaya (1939), who studied the ability of algae to withstand copper sulfate.

2. THE DISTRIBUTION OF *THIOBACILLUS FERROOXIDANS* IN NATURE

The main habitats of *Th. ferrooxidans* are the acid drainage waters in coal mines and in deposits of sulfide ores. These waters differ sharply from those inhabited by ordinary iron bacteria. The mine waters are characterized by higher total concentrations of salts, aluminum and manganese sulfates are present in large amounts, and there are still larger quantities of iron, present in the form of sulfates instead of the usual carbonates. Because of their high sulfuric acid contents, many mine waters are extremely acidic. Acid drainage waters occur especially often in the bituminous coal beds of Pennsylvania and Western Virginia; here the total content of pyritic sulfur in the coals is as high as 4.4-5.5% (Yurovskiy, 1948). Hodge (1937) cites the following series of pH values for the mine waters of Pennsylvania: 3.3, 2.0, 2.9, 1.7, 4.4, 2.1 and so forth, and of some three hundred coal mines only four gave alkaline reactions. In these regions of highly sulfurous bituminous coal, a number of investigators were able to isolate *Th. ferrooxidans* from samples of acid waters from the mines of Pittsburgh, Sewickley and Upper Freeport in Pennsylvania.

Fjerdingstad (1956) discovered this organism in the drainage waters of coal mines located in the western part of Denmark. Since the coal was mined by the open-pit method, bodies of water were formed in a number of abandoned mines; the water of these abandoned pits was reddish-brown, and the banks were covered with ochrelike iron deposits. *Th. ferrooxidans* was found not only in these waters, but also in a river into which part of the acid drainage waters flowed. Ashmeed (1955) isolated this organism from coal mines in Scotland.

In the Soviet Union, *Th. ferrooxidans* was found in coal mines in the Moscow Coal Basin, in the brown coal deposits at Kabarda and in samples of coal from the Pastukhovka mine in the Donets Basin (Lyalikova, 1959). This organism also occurs widely in the Kiselov Coal Basin, whose waters are highly acid and contain large quantities of iron sulfate.

A very intensive development of *Th. ferrooxidans* was observed when Leathen medium was inoculated with water from a forest spring in the Tula Oblast' quite likely genetically connected with those of the Moscow Basin. The water from this spring was highly mineralized, containing more than 1000 mg/liter of sulfates and 320 mg/liter of iron, and had a pH of 3.4. Because of the considerable content of ferrous iron and the acid reaction of the medium, the conditions were highly favorable to the development of *Th. ferrooxidans*.

N. N. Lyalikova has also found *Th. ferrooxidans* in a pure culture from the water of a stream flowing through the dam of a small pond (Borok, Yaroslavl Oblast'). This stream contained ferruginous growths that were found to consist of the usual filamentous iron bacteria. The water had small amounts of hydrogen sulfide and ferrous iron and a pH of 6.5. A more acidic medium probably existed in the microzones in which *Th. ferrooxidans* developed, and the iron, because of the presence of the hydrogen sulfide, was in the ferrous form.

The occurrence and distribution of this organism in the soil is indicated only by some indirect data obtained by Gleen (1950), who observed the oxidation of ferrous sulfate in soil columns. Gleen noted that the value of the lag phase preceding the oxidation depends on the nature of the soil, but he does not describe the soils used in his experiments.

Recently special attention has been devoted to the distribution of *Th. ferrooxidans* in sulfide ore deposits. The organism was isolated from the waters flowing out of copper mine tailings containing sulfide in Bingham Canyon in the state of Utah (Bryner, Beck, Davis and Wilson, 1954). Zimmerley et al. (1958) mention the existence of *Th. ferrooxidans* in mine waters at Chino, Mexico; and Bryner and Jamerson (1958) obtained a culture of this organism from the waters of the Cananea copper deposit, which is located in the state of Sonora in Mexico.

Inasmuch as the occurrence of *Th. ferrooxidans* has always been associated with the presence of acid waters having large contents of iron and sulfuric acid, there is some reason to suppose that it is also present in acid waters described by various other investigators, even though no special attempts might have been made to isolate it. An example of this is the waste waters from the Outokumpu copper mine in Northern Karelia, described by Rhyanen (1958). Large amounts of acid sulfate waters are also formed in the gold and coal mines of the Transvaal in South Africa (Butlin and Postgate, 1953a, b). The acidity of these waters is due to the oxidation of pyrite. Their discharge into rivers, whose pH is normally about 8, lowers the pH to 4.5 and in some cases to 3 or less. As these river waters are quite corrosive they require underground treatment with lime, at very great expense; moreover this treatment presents a new problem of what to do with the great volume of hard calcium sulfate-saturated water.

The occurrence of *Th. ferrooxidans* in ore deposits in the Soviet Union has been studied by N. N. Lyalikova (1959, 1960, 1961a, b) and by L. Ye. Kramarenko (1962). Their results are similar to those obtained by other authors; these data are summarized in Table 46.

Table 46

Occurrence of *Thiobacillus ferrooxidans* in nature

Habitat	Author
Bituminous coal mines of Pennsylvania and West Virginia, USA	Colmer, Hinkle, 1947 Temple, Delchamps, 1953 Leathen et al., 1953
Coal mines of Scotland	Ashmeed, 1955
" " " Denmark	Fjerdingstad, 1956
Moscow coal basin	N. N. Lyalikova, 1959
Lignite deposit in Kabarda	Same
Donets coal basin	Z. M. Zarubina, N. N. Lyalikova, Ye. I. Shmuk, 1959
Copper mines in Bingham Canyon, Utah, USA	Bryner et al., 1954
Cananea copper deposit, Mexico	Bryner, Jamerson, 1958
Akhtal'skoye polymetallic deposit, Armenian SSR	M. V. Ivanov, N. N. Lyalikova, S. I. Kuznetsov, 1958
Copper pyrite deposits of Middle Urals (Degtyarskoye, "Red Guard," "Third International" at San Donato)	N. N. Lyalikova, 1960a
Copper-nickel deposits of Kola Peninsula (Nittis-Kumuzh'ye, Kaula, Kammikivi)	N. N. Lyalikova, 1961
Rare-metal deposits of Central Kazakhstan	L. Ye. Kramarenko, 1962
Kounrad copper deposit, Kazakhstan	N. N. Lyalikova and G. A. Sokolova, 1962
Dzhezkazgan copper deposit, Kazakhstan	Same
Iron-bearing creek, Borok, Yaroslavl' Oblast'	N. N. Lyalikova, 1959
Creek in area of Moscow coal basin	Same
Borehole and lake at Gay Spa, Chelyabinsk Oblast'	"

3. THE ROLE OF BACTERIA IN THE OXIDATION OF PYRITE IN COAL DEPOSITS

Many coals may contain up to 10% sulfur, chiefly in the form of pyrite or marcasite. As the coal deposit is worked, air and water gain access to seams that contain sulfur minerals, and the sulfides are oxidized, resulting in the formation of enormous amounts of sulfuric acid. According to Davis's data (cited in Hodge, 1937), about 9000 tons of sulfuric acid annually enter the rivers of the Pittsburgh area. In 1932 the acid contamination of the Ohio River was equivalent to 3 million tons of concentrated sulfuric acid.

For a long time the formation of this acid was attributed to purely chemical oxidation of the iron sulfide, but with the isolation of the thiobacteria *Th. thiooxidans* and *Th. ferrooxidans* from the mines, scientists were struck by the possibility that bacteria might have contributed to the acid formation. Temple and Delchamps (1953), examining coal seams just previously opened, found that their stratal waters were neutral and that neither bacterial species was present. However, in the same areas after only a few days large numbers of *Th. thiooxidans* and *Th. ferrooxidans* were found and the stratal waters were highly acid.

For a final proof that bacteria play a definite role in the formation of acid, sulfur-bearing inclusions were separated from the coals and inoculated with the microorganisms. Leathen, Braley and McIntyre (1953) inoculated pyrite and marcasite, crushed to small particles some 1-2.3 mm in diameter with seven-day-old cultures of iron-oxidizing bacteria isolated from the drainage waters of the coal mines. The experiments were performed with the mineral medium proposed earlier by the same authors (Leathen, McIntyre and Braley, 1951), into which crushed pyrite, marcasite or "sulfur balls" (a type of sulfur-bearing inclusions) had been introduced as the only source of ferrous oxide. As compared to the sterile control, the bacteria in the experimental dishes sharply increased the acidity and the quantity of sulfates as they acted upon the marcasite and the "sulfur balls." The concentration of sulfuric acid and sulfates increased five times, while the pH in the experimental flasks dropped from 3.6 to 1.2. The pyrite, however, was not oxidized by the bacteria, according to these authors.

Temple and Delchamps (1953) have confirmed Leathen's data regarding the action of *Th. ferrooxidans* and *Th. thiooxidans* on sulfur-containing inclusions in bituminous coals. In the experiments that Temple and Delchamps carried out with "sulfur balls" obtained from the Pittsburgh coal seams, *Th. ferrooxidans* formed 0.1375 mole of sulfuric acid per liter; this figure is close to that of Leathen et al.—0.1268 mole per liter. The amount of sulfuric acid formed in the other experiments by Temple and Delchamps was considerably greater than that mentioned by Leathen and his coauthors. This may be due to the fact that Temple and Delchamps used special air-lift percolators, in which, because of the good aeration, oxidation was more rapid than in the flaks. Temple and Delchamps devoted particular attention to the oxidation of pyrite. In their experiments, as in Leathen's, *Th. thiooxidans* did not oxidize pure pyrite. *Th. ferrooxidans* always formed greater amounts of sulfates, whether acting upon pyrite concretions taken from the coals or upon a museum specimen of pure pyrite. Pyrite, in order to be biologically oxidized, must have a very small particle size.*

---

* Editor's Note: I have also noted this but then find it difficult to explain the oxidation of pyrite in formations where it is not finely divided into particles.

According to Temple and Delchamps, acid is formed in coal mines as follows: the first stage is chemical oxidation, in which the pyrite or marcasite is altered to ferrous sulfate:

$$FeS_2 + H_2O + 3\tfrac{1}{2}\,O_2 \rightarrow FeSO_4 + H_2SO_4. \qquad (I)$$

The ferrous sulfate is then oxidized to ferric sulfate:

$$2FeSO_4 + \tfrac{1}{2}\,O_2 + H_2SO_4 \rightarrow Fe_2(SO_4)_3 + H_2O. \qquad (II)$$

Since the chemical oxidation of iron ceases almost completely in an acidic medium, Reaction II is due primarily to the activity of *Th. ferrooxidans*. As it is formed, the ferric sulfate reacts with the pyrite that is present, so that the ferric sulfate is reduced and the pyrite is oxidized:

$$Fe_2(SO_4)_3 + FeS_2 \rightarrow 3FeSO_4 + 2S, \qquad (III)$$

$$2S + 6Fe_2(SO_4)_3 + 8H_2O \rightarrow 12FeSO_4 + 8H_2SO_4. \qquad (IV)$$

Part of the ferric sulfate is hydrolyzed to basic ferric sulfate:

$$Fe_2(SO_4)_3 + 2H_2O \rightarrow 2Fe(OH)SO_4 + H_2SO_4. \qquad (V)$$

Under actual conditions, the hydrolysis may go all the way to iron hydroxide $Fe(OH)_3$. The degree of hydrolysis depends on the ratio of ferrous to ferric oxide, the sulfate content, the acidity and the water's buffering capacity (Leathen, Braley and McIntyre, 1953). Reaction V is not included in Temple and Delchamps scheme. The molecular sulfur formed by the oxidation of the pyrite usually does not react with the ferric sulfate, but is oxidized to sulfuric acid by *Th. thiooxidans:*

$$S + 1\tfrac{1}{2}\,O_2 + H_2O = 2H^+ + SO_4^{--}.$$

It is hard to judge whether this scheme completely encompasses all the processes resulting in the high acidity of the mine waters; nevertheless it is of interest because it indicates the roles of both purely chemical oxidation and of *Th. ferrooxidans* and *Th. thiooxidans,* the constant inhabitants of drainage waters in coal seams with high sulfur contents.

Ashmeed (1955) undertook to determine how much of the acid is formed biologically, by studying the formation of acid in two coal mines in Scotland. The coal in these mines has a high sulfur content, up to 6 or 7%. The first mine, at a depth of 480 m, had already been worked for about fifty years. Its acid drainage waters had a pH of 2.8 and a high iron content—550 mg/liter. The drainage water from the second mine, located at a depth of 210 m and worked for only seven years, contained almost no iron (0.8 mg/liter) and had a pH of 7.2. In the last two years a steady rise in the iron concentration and a decrease in the amount of bases were noted in the waters of the second mine; and already in some places underground acid waters with a high iron content had accumulated. After a certain time the composition of the waters in the newer, second coal mine will evidently approach that of the waters in the first. Ashmeed carried out numerous experiments to determine the oxidation of iron disulfide and sulfurous coals from the two mines, both under sterile conditions and with the addition of mine water, which showed that *Th. thiooxidans* and *Th. ferrooxidans* were always present. These experiments convinced Ashmeed that for each ton of sulfuric acid formed by purely chemical means, four tons were formed by bacterial action. Thus bacteria play a very great part in forming the acid in mines. The practical significance of this bacterial activity will be discussed below, in a separate chapter.

4. THE OXIDATION OF SULFIDE ORES

Although the metallic sulfur compounds amount to no more than 0.001% of the earth's crust, they are of great interest as the principal raw material for the production of many nonferrous and rare metals such as zinc, lead, copper, nickel, cobalt, molybdenum, antimony and others. The genesis of the sulfide ores has been discussed above: it will be remembered that most sulfide ore deposits are of hydrothermal origin. The sulfides are precipitated from hydrothermal solutions at various temperatures and pressures to form replacement deposits or fracture fillings. Copper-nickel sulfide ores, which are usually associated with basic and ultrabasic intrusives, are segregated in the magmatic stage. There are also some sulfide ore deposits of sedimentary genesis, such as the cupriferous sandstones. In 1926 Bastin proposed his hypothesis explaining the effect of bacteria on the genesis of certain sedimentary sulfide ores. Sedimentary deposits of sulfide ores are classified as syngenetic, in which the ore is accumulated simultaneously with the sedimentation, or epigenetic, formed later, during diagenesis of the host rocks. Bacterial participation in forming epigenetic ores is especially likely.

Bastin (1926) called attention to the fact that in many places, particularly in Missouri, heavy bitumens and oils are associated with the sedimentary ore deposits. In his opinion, these oils may have been the source of carbon and energy for the bacteria which reduce the sulfates anaerobically to hydrogen sulfide. Hydrogen sulfide and sulfate-reducing bacteria have been discovered in the internal waters of this ore district and it is believed that the waters have been enriched in hydrogen sulfide by the bacterial activity. There the hydrogen sulfide waters coming into contact with metal-bearing solutions precipitate the metals as sulfides. In some deposits as observed by Bastin, when the sulfide ores are oxidized the metals are again dissolved and carried away. But since hydrogen sulfide waters are still present at the periphery of the deposit, the metals may be reprecipitated. Thus a "model" is created at the present time which reproduces, as it were, the conditions existing when the ores were first deposited. Although this scheme, as outlined by Bastin, is still hypothetical, it should be kept in mind in studying the genesis of sedimentary ores.

Many sulfides are not stable compounds as they are readily oxidized by the oxygen in surface waters. As a result of this oxidation the mineral and chemical composition of the ores in the upper parts of deposits is changed, forming an oxide zone which masks the nature of the initial sulfides.

The presence of oxidation products of sulfides is also of great economic importance, both in locating sulfide deposits and in exploiting known deposits, since in particular cases the oxidation may be very intensive. Thus numerous publications have been devoted to the oxidation of sulfide ores. One of the most valuable of these is S. S. Smirnov's classic monograph, "The Oxide Zones of Sulfide Deposits" (1955). In all these geological papers, however, the oxidation of the sulfide ores is considered as a purely chemical process, although at the present time it has been found that microorganisms do play a part. Before examining the role of bacteria in the formation of individual deposits, some discussion of laboratory experiments in the oxidation of various sulfides is needed, for the geochemical role of microorganisms can be determined only by a combination of field and laboratory research.

a) The Biogenic Oxidation of Sulfide Minerals in Ores under Laboratory Conditions

The oxidation of sulfide minerals by *Thiobacillus ferrooxidans* has been studied by Bryner, Beck, Davis and Wilson (1954). Their experiments were performed with a culture isolated from the mine waters of a copper deposit in Bingham Canyon. The experiments were carried out in percolators through which sterile air was passed under pressure, thus assuring constant circulation of the solutions (Fig. 45). In their first study, concerned with the action of bacteria on pyrite, a mixture comprising 20 g of crushed pyrite, 200 g of sand and a solution of salts placed in the percolator

was used. The sterilized experimental percolators were inoculated with bacteria.
The bacteria were able to accelerate the
rate at which the pyrite was oxidized by
some 20 times and the oxidation was accompanied by visible changes. The percolating liquid first took on a slightly
yellowish color which became more and
more intense as time passed. At the beginning of the experiment the pyrite had a
bright metallic lustre, but after a while became dark and dull. In the sterile control
percolators, by contrast, the solution remained transparent and colorless.

The biological oxidation of pyrite has
been confirmed by Bryner et al. (1954). In
his experiments the percolators were
heated or bactericidal substances added
(Fig. 46). After 35 days of bacterial growth,
one of the percolators was autoclaved, and
several milliliters of mercuric chloride
solution were added to another. In both
these percolators the biological oxidation
ceased and the pyrite began to be oxidized
at the same rate as in the sterile control.
The oxidation also ceased when air from
which oxygen and carbon dioxide had been
removed was passed through the percolator. When the percolators were placed in
ice, the amount of iron oxidized decreased 88% as compared to
the experiments at room temperature; after the percolators had
been removed from the ice, the rate of oxidation returned to
normal. Placing the percolators in total darkness also had a positive effect on the oxidation.

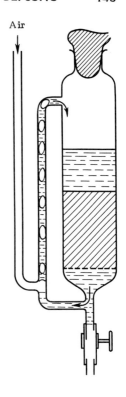

Air

Fig. 45. Percolator.

The same type of percolator was used to study the oxidation
of copper sulfide minerals. In experiments which made use of
a culture grown for some time in a copperless medium, special
methods were required to adapt the microorganisms to high copper
concentration. The culture was kept in a percolator containing
a mineral nutrient medium, pyrite and iron sulfate, to which
copper had been added up to a concentration of 500 mg/liter.
This special adaptation was not necessary in the case of the fresh
culture isolated from the waters of Bingham Canyon.

The results of the experiments showing the oxidation of
chalcopyrite are given in Table 47. The experimental percolator
was not inoculated with microorganisms until the 28th day; up to

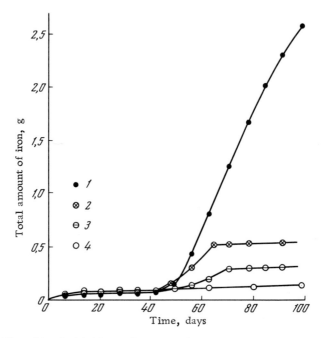

Fig. 46. Oxidation of pyrite by the bacteria in the
waters of Bingham Canyon:
1—inoculation by bacteria on 31st day after beginning of experiment; 2—inoculation on 28th day,
and on 63rd day percolator was sterilized in an
autoclave; 3—inoculation by bacteria on 35th day,
and on 70th day mercuric chloride was added to
percolator; 4—sterile control (after Bryner et al.,
1954).

that time, as the table shows, oxidation took place at the same rate
in both the experiment and the control. Other sulfide minerals besides chalcopyrite were also subjected to bacterial action; Table
48 gives the results of these experiments.

Thus Bryner and his co-workers showed that bacteria accelerate
the oxidation not only of chalcopyrite, but also of other copper
sulfide compounds. It is interesting to note the effect of the
bacteria on such minerals as covellite and chalcosite, whose
composition does not include iron. To test the ability of the bacteria
to grow on copper sulfide in the absence of iron, the same investigators experimented with pure copper sulfide. After 73 days
28.6% of the copper had gone into solution in the experimental
percolator containing bacteria, as compared to only 5.2% in the

Table 47

Biological oxidation of chalcopyrite
(after Bryner et al., 1954)

Time, days	Copper and iron dissolved, mg			
	Experiment		Control	
	Cu	Fe	Cu	Fe
14	9.4	1.0	8.1	1.0
28	16.4	1.3	16.4	1.4
42	68.8	2.3	20.9	1.5
56	160.8	20.0	25.0	1.8
70	192.8	36.0	26.2	2.0
84	229.8	43.4	23.1	2.4

control. The bacteria evidently must have utilized energy derived
from the oxidation of the low-valence sulfur to sulfate.

The chemistry of the oxidation of copper sulfide minerals is
discussed in S. S. Smirnov's monograph (1955). The copper sulfides may be divided into two groups, according to the manner of
their oxidation. The first group comprises the sulfides with insufficient sulfur to allow all the copper to go into solution, including bornite, chalcosite and tetrahedrite. The second group,
with a sufficient amount of sulfur, contains chalcopyrite, enargite and covellite.

Table 48

Biological oxidation of sulfide minerals
(after Bryner et al., 1954)

Time, days	Copper gone into solution, mg							
	Covellite (CuS)		Chalcosite (Cu_2S)		Bornite Cu_5FeS_4		Tetrahedrite $3Cu_2S \cdot Sb_2S_3$	
	Experiment	Control	Experiment	Control	Experiment	Control	Experiment	Control
7	13.5	4.6	12	6	15	0.8	0.8	0
14	39	10.1	23	12.8	23	2.2	1.7	0
21	79	14.1	52.4	19	31	2.6	2.1	0
28	112	17.7	83.4	26.6	38	3.9	2.9	0
35	126.4	20.5	91.4	41.4	41.4	4.17	2.9	0
42	134.8	22.4	99.6	39.2	46.1	5.1	2.9	0

Chalcosite is the most readily oxidized sulfide of the first group. Its oxidation involves the following reactions:

$$4\,Cu_2S + O_2 = 4\,CuS + 2\,Cu_2O,$$

$$Cu_2S + 2O_2 = CuSO_4 + Cu,$$

$$4\,Cu_2S + 9O_2 = 4\,CuSO_4 + 2\,Cu_2O.$$

Here, because of the lack of sufficient sulfur, not all of the copper goes into solution, and part remains as either native copper or cuprite. Chalcosite can also be oxidized by ferric sulfate:

$$Cu_2S + Fe_2(SO_4)_3 = CuSO_4 + CuS + 2\,FeSO_4.$$

Only copper and iron sulfates are formed in the presence of oxygen. The reaction involving ferric sulfate apparently did not take place in the laboratory experiments by Bryner and his colleagues, since these investigators used only pure chalcosite without any addition of pyrite.

Bornite is oxidized as follows:

$$Cu_5FeS_4 + 8\,\tfrac{1}{2}\,O_2 = 3\,CuSO_4 + FeSO_4 + Cu_2O.$$

If bornite is oxidized in the presence of water, the iron is converted to ferric hydroxide:

$$2\,Cu_5FeS_4 + 18\,O_2 + 3\,H_2O = 8\,CuSO_4 + Cu_2O + 2\,Fe(OH)_3.$$

The oxidation of tetrahedrite, whose composition for the sake of simplicity is given by the formula $3\,Cu_2S \cdot Sb_2S_3$, is accompanied by the formation of antimony trioxide:

$$2\,(3\,Cu_2S \cdot Sb_2S_3) + 27\,O_2 = 12\,CuSO_4 + 2\,Sb_2O_3.$$

Chalcopyrite, a very common mineral of the second group, is the most important ore of copper. Copper and iron sulfates are formed when chalcopyrite is oxidized atmospherically:

$$CuFeS_2 + 4\,O_2 = CuSO_4 + FeSO_4.$$

Chalcopyrite, however, is much more rapidly oxidized by ferric sulfate:

$$CuFeS_2 + 2\,Fe_2(SO_4)_3 + 2\,H_2O + 3\,O_2 = CuSO_4 + 5\,FeSO_4 + 2\,H_2SO_4.$$

The iron sulfate formed in these reactions can be oxidized chemically only in the absence of free sulfuric acid, but through the agency of *Th. ferrooxidans* the iron is readily altered to the ferric form in an acid medium as well. Ferric sulfate has a very strong oxidizing and dissolving effect on sulfides as shown by the reaction:

$$2RS + 2Fe_2(SO_4)_3 + 2H_2O + 3O_2 = 2RSO_4 + 4FeSO_4 + 2H_2SO_4,$$

where R is any given metal.

As Smirnov (1955) has written, "ferric sulfate may be considered one of the most significant factors in the transformation of sulfide material. Its importance in supplying oxygen to the various levels of the oxide zone, including the very deepest, is hard to exaggerate." This makes clear the magnitude of the role played by *Th. ferrooxidans*, which rapidly forms ferric sulfate in an acid medium, where its chemical formation scarcely takes place at all.

Ferric sulfate acts with different intensities upon the different sulfides. The sulfides are listed in decreasing order of their ability to react with a 0.1 N solution of $Fe_2(SO_4)_3$ as follows: pyrrhotite, tetrahedrite, galena, arsenopyrite, sphalerite, pyrite, enargite, marcasite, chalcopyrite.

Bryner and his colleagues (Bryner, Beck, Davis and Wilson, 1954) have also studied the effect of bacteria on the flotation concentrate from Bingham Canyon. After 98 days in the bacterially inoculated percolator, 25% of the copper and 17.7% of the iron present in the concentrate had gone into solution, as contrasted with 5% of the copper and 2.5% of the iron in the sterile control. They also observed that a considerable increase in the copper concentration, as well as of hydrogen ions (pH 1), greatly reduced the oxidation rate; this phenomenon is probably due to the toxic effect of these ions on the bacteria.

Bryner and Jamerson (1958) in their experiments in the oxidation of sulfide ores used pure cultures of *Th. ferrooxidans*, isolated from Bingham Canyon and from deposits of copper ores in Mexico. Bacterial strains isolated from different geographic localities appeared to have the same effect on the sulfide ores.

In addition to pyrite, the same authors studied the oxidation of molybdenite. Molybdenite—MoS_2—is one of the most stable of the sulfides. When subjected to bacterial action for two weeks an average of 0.6% of the MoS_2 was oxidized. The oxidation of molybdenite has been specially studied by Bryner and Anderson (1957), who showed that the action of *Th. ferrooxidans* resulted in the oxidation of seven times more molybdenite than in the sterile control. As the molybdenite was oxidized, molybdic and sulfuric acids were observed to form in the solution. The oxidation most likely took the following course:

$$2MoS_2 + 9O_2 + 6H_2O = 2H_2MoO_4 + 4H_2SO_4.$$

Since the molybdenite in the Bingham Canyon deposit occurs together with pyrite and chalcopyrite, Bryner and Anderson also studied the effect of these minerals on the oxidation of molybdenite. The addition of pyrite promoted the oxidation of molybdenite. The results obtained in these experiments are shown in Table 49, which reveals that in the presence of pyrite, bacterial action causes some 30 times more molybdenite to go into solution than in the sterile control. The addition of ferrous iron also hastened the oxidation of molybdenite. When bacteria were allowed to act upon a mixture of molybdenite and chalcopyrite, the oxidation of the molybdenite began only after all the copper sulfide had been fully oxidized.

Table 49

Biological oxidation of a molybdenite-pyrite mixture
(after Bryner and Anderson, 1959)

Time, days	Molybdenum and iron (dissolved), mg			
	Experiment		Control	
	Molybdenum	Iron	Molybdenum	Iron
7	1	8	1.5	1
14	9.4	364	2	3
21	27.4	834	2.5	4.5
28	48.2	1304	2.9	6
35	72.6	1599	3.1	7.2
49	93.6	1793	3.3	9
63	100.1	1897	3.5	10.8
77	103.4	1913	3.6	13

Experiments to show the bacterial oxidation not only of individual minerals, but of the ores from particular deposits, are of special interest from the standpoint of determining the geochemical activity of *Th. ferrooxidans* in ore deposits, since the conditions in the latter experiments are closer to those in nature. Lyalikova (1959) conducted some experiments on the oxidation of pyrite and chalcopyrite ores from the Degtyarskoye deposit. In each percolator were placed 20 grams of ore crushed to a particle size less than 1 mm; 250 ml of distilled water containing ammonium sulfate and potassium phosphate was then poured over the ore, and the pH was adjusted with sulfuric acid to 3.5. A culture of *Th. ferrooxidans* isolated from the Krasnogvardeyskoye ["Red Guard"] deposit was added to the experimental percolator. Thymol was added as an inhibitor to the control percolator, so that here only chemical oxidation could take place. The results are shown in Table 50. Toward the end of the experiment the ore in the experimental percolator lost its metallic lustre and was covered with a yellow encrustation of ferric oxide. Microscopic analysis of the solution from the experimental percolator showed that the number of bacteria had increased many times.

Table 50

Biological oxidation of copper-pyrite ore
by a culture of *Thiobacillus ferrooxidans*

Time, days	Copper and iron (dissolved), mg/liter					
	Experiment			Control		
	pH	Cu	Fe	pH	Cu	Fe
0	3.9	11		3.8	9	3.5
7	3.95	30	9.4	4.25	8.5	2.7
13	2.6	70	93	3.9	13	1.5
18	2.2	114	390	3.8	14	1.3
30	2.0	130	1150	3.8	16	2.3
37	1.9	140	1700	3.8	16	8.0

N. N. Lyalikova (1961a) also performed some experiments on the bacterial leaching of nickel and iron from the ores of the Nittis-Kumuzh'ye copper-nickel deposit on the Kola Peninsula. The ore here consists of pyrrhotite (FeS) [actually $Fe_{(1-x)}S$], pentlandite (FeNiS) [actually (Fe, Ni)S] and chalcopyrite, containing about 1% nickel, 0.5% copper and 13-15% iron. The experimental percolator was inoculated with a culture of *Th. ferrooxidans* isolated from the same deposit. After three months of the experiment, 58.75 mg of nickel and 133 mg of iron had been leached from 40 g of ore in the presence of the bacteria, whereas only 29 mg of nickel and 18 mg of iron were leached out in the sterile control. The concentration of dissolved nickel in the experimental percolator reached 400 mg/liter, but this was only two times greater than that in the control. The unexpectedly small difference in the nickel concentrations may be because the ore used in the experiment had lain for half a year after being brought to the surface and part was already oxidized. The large increase in the iron content in the solution in the presence of the bacteria, as compared to the control, shows that *Th. ferrooxidans* can oxidize pyrrhotite.

On the basis of the investigations described above regarding the bacterial oxidation of sulfides, it is possible to prepare a list of the minerals subject to oxidation by *Th. ferrooxidans;* this list is given in Table 51.

In addition to her experiments with ores, Lyalikova (1961b) made some studies of the biological oxidation by *Th. ferrooxidans* of chemically produced synthetic sulfides of titanium (TiS_2) iron (FeS), zinc (ZnS) and antimony (Sb_2S_3). Titanium sulfide does not occur in nature, but is nevertheless rapidly oxidized by the bacteria. After one month the pH in the experimental vessel dropped from 2.45 to 1.63, while the amount of sulfates increased by 1370 mg/liter SO_4-S as compared to the sterile control. The remaining sulfides used in these tests correspond to widespread minerals in nature—pyrrhotite (FeS), sphalerite (ZnS) [actually (Zn, Fe)S] and stibnite (Sb_2S_3). Since *Th. ferrooxidans* was able to oxidize these synthetic sulfides, it is probably also capable of oxidizing the corresponding minerals in nature, thus providing evidence in support of the bacterial oxidation of the pyrrhotite from the copper-nickel deposits on the Kola Peninsula.

These data on the oxidation of various minerals and ores indicate that *Th. ferrooxidans* can oxidize sulfide ores directly within deposits. Other thiobacteria probably also contribute to this process.

Table 51

Sulfide minerals subject to oxidation by
Thiobacillus ferrooxidans

Metallic element	Mineral	Formula
Iron	Pyrite Marcasite Pyrrhotite	FeS_2 FeS_2 FeS
Copper and iron	Chalcopyrite Bornite	$CuFeS_2$ Cu_5FeS_4
Copper	Covellite Chalcosite	CuS Cu_2S
Copper and antimony	Tetrahedrite	$3Cu_2S \cdot Sb_2S_3$
Molybdenum	Molybdenite	MoS_2

It has been shown that *Th. thiooxidans* accelerates the oxidation of marcasite; this organism oxidizes the sulfur formed in the oxidation of sulfides by ferric sulfate, as well as the sulfur formed in the leaching of covellite. The role of *Th. thioparus* in oxidizing sulfide ores within the deposits themselves has as yet been insufficiently studied, but these bacteria quite possibly do participate in oxidizing certain sulfides, especially when the internal waters circulating through the sulfide deposit are neutral or slightly alkaline. The contribution of this last organism to the oxidation of the rare-metal deposits of Kazakhstan has been mentioned by Kramarenko (1962).

b) Factors Affecting the Oxidation of Sulfide Ores in Nature

Many authors have studied the direct oxidation of sulfide ores in deposits. The results of their work have been summarized by Smirnov (1955) and are schematized in the first chapter of the present book. The facts summarized in this chapter are the basis for asserting that thiobacteria play a major role in oxidizing sulfide minerals. It is therefore worth while to consider what influence the factors affecting the intensity of oxidation in deposits may have upon the development of *Th. ferrooxidans* and *Th. thiooxidans*.

Smirnov (1955) believes that the oxide zone of sulfide deposits extends downward as far as the penetration of the oxygen-bearing ground waters. Since the penetration depth of surface waters in turn depends upon many conditions, such as the water permeability of the rocks, the amount of deposits and the degree to which they are fractured, all these factors will also affect the bacterial oxidation of ores.

Any discussion of the possible bacterial oxidation of a sulfide deposit must begin with some consideration of the mineral composition of the ores. The sulfide minerals that can be oxidized by *Th. ferrooxidans* have been listed above: moreover this organism is probably capable of oxidizing other minerals. Bacterial oxidation, like chemical oxidation, is greatly affected by the solubility of the resulting sulfate. The most highly soluble is zinc sulfate— 531.2 g/liter at $18°C$—whereas lead sulfate is almost insoluble— only 0.041 g/liter.

Smirnov (1955) classifies sulfide minerals according to their resistance to oxidation under natural conditions as follows: the most readily soluble are pyrrhotite, sphalerite and chalcosite; the least soluble are pyrite, galena and enargite; and the remaining sulfides occupy intermediate positions. At present, however, there is not enough information to arrange the sulfide minerals in the order to which they are subject to bacterial decomposition. An important factor in this problem is the peculiar properties of each bacterial strain and the degree of its adaptation to the particular sulfide: thus it is difficult to compare data obtained by different authors. On the basis of the experiments by Bryner and others (Bryner et al., 1954), copper sulfides may be arranged in order of increasing susceptibility to bacterial oxidation as follows: covellite, chalcosite, chalcopyrite, bornite and tetrahedrite. There is some discrepancy between the susceptibilities of sulfides to chemical and bacterial oxidation: chalcosite, for example, is readily oxidized chemically, but is more resistant to bacterial oxidation than covellite (see Table 48).

Far less susceptible to bacterial action than copper sulfides is molybdenite, whose oxidation in a mixture with chalcopyrite began only after all the latter had been consumed. Pyrite is a mineral differing sharply in its accessibility to chemical and bacterial oxidation. As one of the least readily soluble sulfides it is nevertheless easily oxidized by a culture of *Th. ferrooxidans,* especially if the bacteria cultured on it have been transferred several times. Thus in Lyalikova's experiments, some 130 mg/liter of iron out of 50 g of pyrite went into solution after ten days of bacterial action, whereas in experiments by Winchell, as described by Smirnov (1955), when 300 g of powdered pyrite was treated with air-saturated water for ten months, only 200 mg of the entire mass of the pyrite went into solution.

The amount of pyrite in a deposit is an enormous factor in determining the rate of oxidation since the alteration products of this mineral greatly accelerate the oxidation of the other minerals. The role of pyrite in the oxidation of sulfide deposits has been examined by Smirnov for two ore bodies of a lead-zinc deposit in the Eastern Transbaykal region. One of these, which has a large pyrite content and is located in a zone of intensive fracturing, was highly oxidized down to depths below 200 m. The other ore body, lacking pyrite, was only slightly altered; here the oxidation occurred only along a few random fractures to depths of no more than 10-15 m. Data on the presence of bacteria in these two ore bodies are lacking, inasmuch as microbiological investigations were not included in the study. *Th. ferrooxidans,* however, evidently took some part in oxidizing the pyrite-bearing ore body, since the occurrence of this organism in nature is very closely associated with the presence of pyrite. The oxidation of pyrite, a disulfide, results in the formation of a large amount of sulfuric acid and creates favorable conditions for the development of *Th. thiooxidans* and *Th. ferrooxidans.*

Apart from the significance of the acidity in the biological oxidation of sulfides, the conditions for such oxidation are also influenced by the character of the ground waters and especially the surrounding rocks. In such a case, if the host rocks, for example carbonates, neutralize the acids as they are formed, unfavorable conditions are produced for the development of *Th. ferrooxidans,* which is, to judge from all the available data, the principal organism that oxidizes sulfides.

It was mentioned earlier in the present book (Chapter I) that, according to Smirnov (1955), sulfide deposits are oxidized at different rates and intensities in different climates. Oxide zones are usually very distinct in tropical and temperate climatic zones and, as a rule, occur to only a slight degree in deposits located in polar areas. The slight manifestation of oxide zones in regions of polar climate that fairly recently have been glaciated, Smirnov believes, may be due to the fact that the oxide zones of sulfide deposits formed in preglacial times were perhaps cut off by the ice sheet, and new zones have not had the time to form in the brief interval after the last retreat of the continental glacier. A large factor in the lack of current oxidation in northern regions is low temperature, which retards both chemical and biological oxidation.

Recently Lyalikova (1961a) has obtained some direct experimental data that support the major role of low temperature. A culture of *Th. ferrooxidans* isolated from a copper-nickel ore deposit on the Kola Peninsula did oxidize ferrous iron at a temperature of + 4°C under laboratory conditions, but several times more slowly than at 20-30°. This relationship between the oxidation process and the temperature was observed even though the mine waters from which this bacterial strain was isolated had a constant temperature of 4°C.

The Kounrad copper deposit is an example of a deposit located in an area of arid climate. It lies in the northwestern part of the Balkhash region, where the total annual atmospheric precipitation is no more than 61-105 mm. The oxide zone of this deposit is so well developed that its ores, together with those from the secondary sulfide enrichment zone, are of industrial value, although the primary sulfide ores are not exploited. Despite the lack of water, the ores in the Kounrad open pit were very rapidly oxidized, in approximately two years after their exposure. Most of the oxidation very likely took place in the fissures in which the melt waters collected during the spring season. These fissures contain the minerals of the oxide zone—malachite, azurite and iron oxides. Analyses by Lyalikova and Sokolova (1962) have shown the presence of various thiobacteria in these places: *Thiobacillus ferrooxidans, Th. thiooxidans* and *Th. thioparus,* which have evidently contributed to the oxidation of the ores.

Fracturing of the surrounding rocks, and especially of the ore body itself, produces favorable conditions for the development of microorganisms not only by promoting the access of water, but also by creating larger surface areas for the microorganisms to act upon. The ore body of the Degtyarskoye copper pyrite deposit, in which bacterial oxidation is especially intensive, is highly fractured.

After considering the factors affecting the biological oxidation of ores, let us dwell in somewhat greater detail on the distribution of the bacteria and the significance of their activities in a number of different types of sulfide deposits.

c) The Biogenic Oxidation of Sulfide Ores in the Exploitation of Deposits

The widespread occurrence of *Thiobacillus ferrooxidans* in coal and sulfide ore deposits is the basis for studying its oxidizing activity directly within the deposits themselves. An example of a polymetallic deposit whose oxidation is chiefly due to bacteria is the Akhtal'skoye deposit in the Armenian SSR (Stepanyants, 1938). Usually oxidation of the ores within a deposit is intensified after the deposit has begun to be exploited industrially. The Akhtal'-skoye deposit has been worked since the end of the 18th century, and many parts of it have been exposed for a very long time, thus creating favorable conditions for both chemical and bacterial oxidation. The primary sulfides in the lower levels of the ore body are represented by sphalerite, pyrite, chalcopyrite, galena and bornite. The oxide zone occupies the upper levels. Its formation was facilitated by the ore body's location close to the earth's surface, thus allowing surface waters to penetrate readily along fractures and accumulate in considerable amounts in the deposit. These waters are drained by streams flowing from the worked and abandoned drifts. The water from the abandoned drifts contains large amounts of ferric oxide; its acidity varies from pH 1.4 to 4.9 (Fig. 47). Since almost no chemical oxidation of ferrous iron takes place at this high acidity, the ferric oxide evidently must have been formed through the agency of *Th. ferrooxidans,* which was present in all the samples of water studied (Ivanov, Lyalikova and Kuznetsov, 1958). The water taken at the entrances to the working drifts had a pH of about 6, but within, on the drift walls, streams of acid, rusty water were found with a pH of 2. *Th. ferrooxidans* was isolated from samples of copper, lead and zinc ore that had lain for about a year in piles on the surface. Ore that had been exposed for several years had undergone considerable alteration. The sulfides in this ore were oxidized to sulfates, and the host rock had been transformed into a soft, clayey mass. These facts indicate that the oxidizing activity of *Th. ferrooxidans* in the Akhtal'skoye deposit occurs where the infiltrating surface waters come into contact with the ore body, as well as in the mine tailings.

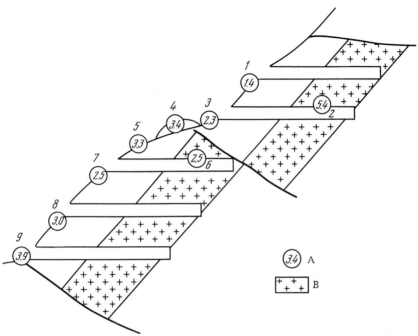

Fig. 47. Diagram of the Akhtal'skoye deposit of polymetallic ores. A—figures in circles are the pH values [figures outside the circles are the drift numbers]; B—ore bed is indicated by small crosses: 1—stream from drift No. 3; 2—seepage from roof of drift No. 2; 3—stream from drift No. 2; 4—mine tailings; 5—stream from mine tailings; 6—seepage from roof of drift No. 7; 7—stream from drift No. 7; 8—stream from drift No. 9; 9—stream from drift No. 14; *Thiobacillus ferrooxidans* was found in all samples.

Among the copper pyrite deposits of the Middle Urals, the most intensive bacterial oxidation has been observed in the Degtyarskoye and the Krasnogvardeyskoye deposits (Lyalikova, 1960a). The Degtyarskoye deposit is the largest of the copper pyrite deposits in the Middle Urals region. Like most other deposits of copper pyrite ores in this area, it is associated with the metamorphic rocks of the greenstone series, which extend throughout the length of the Ural Mountains. The Degtyarskoye ore consists primarily of pyritic sulfur and copper, containing an average of 0.9% copper, 1.38% zinc, 40.5% iron and 45.7% sulfur. Here, as in the Akhtal'skoye deposit, *Th. ferrooxidans* takes part in oxidizing the ores in the mine tailings; it has been found in the majority of samples investigated, in numbers from 1000 to 10,000 cells per gram of rock. These samples had a high acidity, with pH from 1.2 to

4.8. The mine waters are so highly acid that they have burned off all the vegetation along the drainage discharge channels. The ore body of the Degtyarskoye deposit has been exposed in shaft No. 2, at the 250-m level. The results of the analyses are presented in Fig. 48 and Table 52.

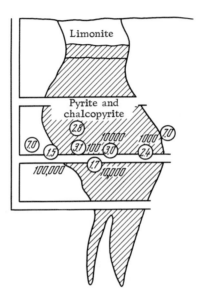

Fig. 48. Distribution of *Thiobacillus ferrooxidans* in the rocks and waters of the Degtyarskoye deposit. Figures in circles are pH values; the figures next to the circles are the numbers of bacteria per 1 ml of water or 1 gm of rock. The ore body is indicated by the shaded area.

The largest numbers of *Th. ferrooxidans* were found in the water filtering through the ore body. The bacteria were absent in freshly mined ore samples and in the water passing through the host rocks surrounding the ore body. *Th. ferrooxidans* occurred in 9 out of 14 samples from shaft No. 2.

The ecological conditions in the Degtyarskoye mine are extremely favorable for the development of *Th. ferrooxidans*. The deposit is highly flooded with an average annual influx of water exceeding 2.8 million m^3. Because of the large amounts of sulfuric acid formed during the oxidation of the pyrite and other sulfides, the mine waters are extremely acid, and thus promote the growth of *Th. ferrooxidans*. The sulfuric acid content in the waters of the second shaft reaches 1.35 g/liter and the copper content 1.27 g/liter.

Table 52

Distribution of *Thiobacillus ferrooxidans* in the Degtyarskoye deposit

Nature of sample	pH	No. of cells of *Th. ferrooxidans* in 1 ml of water or 1 g of rock
Water from fractures in quartz–albite porphyroids. . .	3.71	100
Water seepage at ore–rock contact	3.14	100
Water from fractures in host rock strata.		0
Water passing through ore body.	3.0	10,000
Water from borehole	2.86	
Water from horizontal borehole.	2.57	100
Water from borehole in ore body		1,000
Water flowing out along drift.	1.72	10,000
Water passing through ore body.	1.5	1,000
Water from fractures in ore body	2.43	1,000
Sample taken from boundary of ore body with rock. .		100
Freshly mined ore.		0
Ore from 130–m level		0
Freshly mined ore.		0

Laboratory experiments on the oxidation of the Degtyarskoye ores have shown that these ores may serve as energy for the development of *Th. ferrooxidans* and the amount of copper leached in the experiments to which bacteria had been added was approximately eight times that of the sterile control. Although the results of laboratory experiments which provide all the necessary conditions for bacterial growth cannot be applied directly to processes occurring in nature, it must be remembered that in nature the leaching takes place over a very long time, so that high concentrations of copper can be produced in the mine waters.

The Degtyarskoye deposit simultaneously contains large numbers of *Th. ferrooxidans,* a suitable substrate, and an ecological environment favorable for their growth—in other words, everything required for the activity of this organism. Hence it may justifiably be concluded that the large copper content and the high acidity of the mine waters have largely been produced by these bacteria. The amount of copper carried out annually with the drainage waters is so great that a special "Gidromed'' plant has been established at the Degtyarskoye mine to recover the copper from solution, using a special cementation apparatus in which the copper is precipitated in an exchange reaction with iron. The waters from the mine drifts flow into settling tanks some 2000 m² in area, in which pieces of ore and rock carried out with the water settle to the bottom. The water is then passed through a number of wooden troughs filled with iron scraps, where the metallic copper is precipitated out.

Table 53

Change in oxidation-reduction potential and acidity of medium in the process of cementation of copper

Collection point of sample	pH	Eh, mv	rH$_2$	Number of Th. ferrooxidans in 1 ml of water
From mine.	2.93	340	17.58	10,000
From settling tank	2.74			1,000
Between settling tank and contact with iron	2.62	605	26.1	
First trough with iron.	4.1	250	16.82	
End of trough with iron.	2.0	250	12.62	10,000

Lyalikova (1960a) has determined the oxidation-reduction potential, the acidity and the numbers of *Th. ferrooxidans* in the water at various stages of the "Gidromed" copper-extraction process. The results of her analyses are given in Table 53, which clearly shows the relationship between the oxidation-reduction potential and the changes in the ferrous iron concentration. The water entering from the mine shafts contains a large amount of ferrous iron and thus has a low oxidation-reduction potential. In the settling tank the oxidation-reduction potential rises and the ferrous iron becomes ferric. In the troughs containing the iron scraps, there is the reaction:

$$Fe + CuSO_4 = FeSO_4 + Cu,$$

resulting in the formation of ferrous iron, which again lowers the oxidation-reduction potential. Low potentials were also observed in young cultures of *Th. ferrooxidans,* in which no oxidation of iron had yet taken place. The high ferrous iron content and the acidity of the water in the cementation apparatus produced conditions so favorable to the development of *Th. ferrooxidans* that the content of this bacterium exceeded 1,000,000 cells per gram of copper concentrate.

Oxidation processes take place at the same rate in another copper pyrite deposit, the Krasnogvardeyskoye. The mineral composition of the ores in this deposit is the following: pyrite 65-80%, chalcopyrite 8-10%, and sphalerite 1-2%. Oxidation is so intensive in the highly sulfurous ore of the Krasnogvardeyskoye deposit that in a number of cases the ore has been spontaneously consumed (Yenikeyev and Sindarovskiy, 1947). The distribution of *Th. ferrooxidans* in this deposit was studied in areas where there is danger of fire. Table 54 shows the results of these analyses which indicate that *Th. ferrooxidans* was present in all samples taken from places where there had been spontaneous combustion of the ore. These bacteria may play some definite part in igniting the ore, since they accelerate its oxidation; at any rate, this question requires further study.

Table 54

Distribution of *Thiobacillus ferrooxidans* in the Krasnogvardeyskoye ("Red Guard") deposit

Sampling point	pH	Number of *Th. ferrooxidans* in 1 ml of water or 1 g of ore
304th level, 5th pillar, water from area silted up in extinguishing fire	1.55	100—1000
304th level, 3rd southern line, water and rusty incrustations on ore.	3.4	Present
244th level, main lens, 6th pillar, water from area beneath fire-protected area	1.7	10,000
237th level, main lens, 3rd pillar, burned ore. .	—	Present
244th level, main lens, 7th pillar, water from area beneath fire proofing	1.6	100,000

The Third International deposit differs from the two Middle Urals deposits just described above in its high zinc content. Two zones of this deposit—the 15th Anniversary of October and the Shmidt zones—contain copper-zinc ores, and only one zone, the Sernoye deposit, contains copper pyrite ore. The ores are both massive and dispersed; their mineral composition is as follows: pyrite 30%, sphalerite 23% and chalcopyrite 12% (Mazurin, 1955). Figure 49 shows the distribution of *Th. ferrooxidans* in this deposit. In a number of cases this organism was isolated from scrapings of fresh, slightly oxidized ores. Although the bacteria play some role in oxidizing a few isolated parts of the deposit, in general their importance in altering the ores of the Third International deposit is evidently negligible, as indicated by the small quantities of dissolved metals in the mine waters.

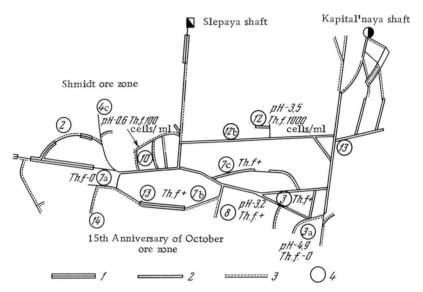

Fig. 49. Distribution of *Thiobacillus ferrooxidans* in the ore zone of the "Third International" deposit:
1—porphyroids; 2—albitophyres; 3—dispersed copper-zinc ore; 4—ore lenses.

The Nittis-Kumuzh'ye deposit is of the copper-nickel type: here the ecological environment does not favor microbial oxidation of the ores. This deposit is located on the Kola Peninsula, above the Arctic Circle, where the temperature in the underground mine is no more than 4°C. A particularly unfavorable factor for the development of *Th. ferrooxidans* is the complete absence of pyrite. For this reason, and because the ore veins are contained in a body of ultrabasic rocks, the mine waters are generally neutral. Although *Th. ferrooxidans* was found in 20 out of 23 samples, it was present in small numbers, reaching 1000 cells per ml of water only in two cases, in which the acidity of the water reached pH 3.8 (Lyalikova, 1961a). Thus the ore is very slightly oxidized, which is indicated by the fact that the nickel content in the mine waters usually does not exceed 15 mg/liter, and the copper content is only 2 mg/liter—almost a thousand times less than the copper content in the Degtyarskoye mine waters. It may be that the usual iron bacteria play some role in oxidizing the iron-containing minerals of the Nittis-Kumuzh'ye deposit. The neutral reaction of the mine waters and the low temperature create favorable conditions for the development of *Gallionella,* large numbers of which were found on membrane filters and culture dishes placed in the mine drift.

In contrast to the Nittis-Kumuzh'ye deposit, another copper-nickel deposit of the Kola Peninsula—the Kaula deposit—contains dispersed ores consisting of pyrrhotite, pentlandite, chalcopyrite and magnetite. Microbiological investigations in this deposit were made at the 6-m and 7-m levels in the mine, which are some 130-140 m above sea level. Additional samples were taken from the oxide zone in the open-pit workings. Table 55 shows the results of the analyses. *Th. ferrooxidans* was present in 7 out of 14 samples of the Kaula mine waters, but in even smaller numbers than in the Nittis-Kumuzh'ye deposit. There is almost no oxidation of the ores in the underground workings of the Kaula deposit. A discernible oxide zone exists only in the open-pit workings, and even here it is of very small thickness.

Table 55

Results of a microbiological survey of the Kaula deposit

Nature of sample	Number:		No. of samples in which *Th. ferroox.* was found in amounts (per gram):			Number of samples in which were found:	
	Of samples studied	Of samples in which *Th. ferroox.* was found	1 cell	10 cells	100 cells	*Th. thio-oxidans*	*Gallio-mella* sp.
Underground mine waters: pH = 7.1—7.8	14	7	3	3	1	2	3
Scrapings from ore	2	2	1	1	—	—	—
Samples of oxidized ore from open mine workings	12	5	2	3	—	1	1

The part played by *Th. ferrooxidans* in oxidizing the dispersed secondary sulfide ores of the Kounrad copper deposit in the arid northwestern part of the Balkhash region is of particular interest. This deposit has been studied in detail by a number of geologists; the latest summary is that of K. S. Gazizova (1957), who believes that the formation took the following course. Approximately during the Carboniferous period, a diorite complex some 5000 km² in area was intruded into Silurian sandstones overlain by extrusive diabases and diabase-porphyries. The intruded rocks consisted of granodiorites and quartz-diorite porphyrites. The emergence of the quartz porphyrites from the magma chamber was immediately followed by the segregation of magmatic solutions which caused the formation of secondary quartzites from the granodiorites and porphyries. The solutions traveled upward from the magma chamber through the granodiorite porphyries contained within the conical, ring-shaped structure, arrived at the screening surface of the extrusive porphyries and there spread out along the entire area of the extrusive rocks. Thus secondary quartzites were formed hydrothermally from both the extrusive and intrusive rocks.

The process of secondary quartz formation later was replaced gradually by ore deposition. The ore-bearing mineralized solutions most likely spread out along the same paths and fractures previously followed by the magmatic solutions. Thus the greatest accumulation of primary sulfide ores, as Fig. 50 shows, took

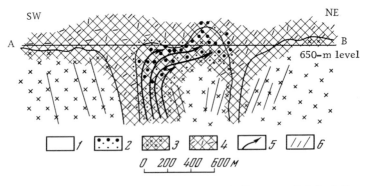

Fig. 50. Schematic section through the ore field of the Kounrad deposit (after Gazizova, 1957):
1—modern deposits; 2—distribution of primary ore mineralization; 3—granodiorites and granodiorite porphyries, in places altered to secondary quartzites; 4—secondary quartzites from extrusive porphyries; 5—main directions of movement of ore fluids; 6—directions of dip of conical fracture system.

place in the upper levels of the deposit. The formation of the copper-rich secondary sulfide ores began later; this process was perhaps the more intensive because the ore body was highly fractured, allowing the surface waters to penetrate readily and create an oxide zone. The copper and iron sulfides were, probably with the participation of the biological factor, oxidized to sulfates. As a result of the hot climate, the oxidation was rapid, but the soluble salts were not carried out of the deposit because of the even, flat relief of the locality. The ore-bearing solutions descended to deeper levels, entered a reducing environment and precipitated sulfide minerals, thus forming a zone of secondary sulfide enrichment.

At later stages in the development of the deposit, a gradual lowering of the base level of erosion occurred. This, in turn, caused the water table to be lowered. Thus the upper levels of the secondary sulfide zone were again brought into an oxidizing environment. Oxidation of the secondary sulfide ores may still be observed at the present time. In spite of the dry climate, water can be seen seeping out of fractures in the walls of the open-pit mine. These fractures are sharply distinguished by their yellowish color, which is due to the deposition of ferric iron. Large numbers of *Th. ferrooxidans* were found in the ferruginous deposits along the walls of fractures and in the water flowing out in the lowermost parts of the mine workings. Thus the oxidation of the secondary sulfide ores undoubtedly involves the direct participation of *Th. ferrooxidans*.

A summary of the studies of sulfide ore deposits in various climatic zones reveals some regular features in the distribution and the activities of *Th. ferrooxidans*. As a rule, this bacterium occurs widely in acid mine waters in the middle and southern latitudes, where it intensively oxidizes iron sulfides, as may be judged from the acidity of various mine waters. Examination of the stopes immediately after the ore has been blasted out, or of the walls of open-pit workings, permits direct observation of the fracturing of the ore body and the oxidation of the ore where water seeps out from the fractures. Inasmuch as analysis of freshly mined ore has shown the absence of *Th. ferrooxidans,* the propagation of this organism and the oxidation of the ore evidently follow the fracture systems in the rocks, wherever there is sufficient moisture and aeration. Both processes take place intensively as the deposits are exploited. Before the deposits are worked, however, oxidation involving *Th. ferrooxidans* probably occurs only in the zone of active water exchange. Sulfide ore deposits are capped by an "iron gossan," as in the Degtyarskoye, Kounrad and other deposits.

A necessary condition for the oxidizing activity of *Th. ferrooxidans* is the fracturing of the ore body. This supposition has been strongly confirmed by a study of the Verkhne-Pyshmenskoye deposit, in which the fracturing follows the contours of the host rocks alone, so that the surface waters have little contact with the ore body. Here *Th. ferrooxidans* is encountered only in rare cases at the interface of the ore body and the host rocks, and the mine waters are neutral.

Climate is also an important factor in the oxidizing activity of microorganisms, as readily seen in the examples of copper-nickel deposits above the Arctic Circle. As Lyalikova (1961a) has shown, despite the considerable occurrence of *Th. ferrooxidans*, there is almost no oxidation at the temperature of the mine waters, which approaches 4°C. The majority of the polar mine waters are neutral, another fact indicating the slight development of oxidation processes.

The Degtyarskoye copper mine provides an approximate quantitative estimate of the scale of bacterial oxidation. Since the yearly discharge of mine waters is about 2.8 million m^3, it may be calculated from the contents of copper and sulfuric acid in these waters that the bacteria annually dissolve about 2500 metric tons of copper and form about 2500 metric tons of sulfuric acid.

CHAPTER IX

The Role of Microorganisms in the Formation of Supergene Iron Ores

1. GEOCHEMICAL FACTORS DETERMINING THE MOBILITY OF IRON IN THE EARTH'S CRUST

Geological data indicate that iron-ore deposits were being formed on a very large scale as early as Archean and Algonkian times. M. N. Strakhov (1947b), who has studied all the information on the stratigraphy of the world's sedimentary iron ores in very great detail, summarized the material in the diagram illustrated in Fig. 51. This schematization shows that there have been iron-ore epochs and oreless epochs throughout the earth's geologic history. Of the two, the oreless periods were considerably longer; in other words, the epochs of iron-ore formation have been relatively short-lived episodes in the earth's history.

After studying the geographical distribution of iron ores, Strakhov came to the conclusion that these have arisen at the surface of the lithosphere only in specific regions, or "iron-ore provinces." Later (Strakhov, 1960), analyzing the areal distribution of continental iron-ore deposits, he dwelt upon the Pliocene-Quaternary and the present iron-ore epochs, since these provide the best evidence for the climatic conditions in individual regions. According to Strakhov, the accumulation of continental iron ores takes place exclusively in areas of humid temperate or hot climate; these occur, on the one hand, in the taiga-podzolic belt of Eurasia and North America and, on the other hand, in the subtropical areas of South America, Central Africa, India, the Malay Archipelago and Southern Australia.

2. THE FORMATION OF BOG IRON ORES

The general geochemical environment in the weathered crust of the taiga-podzolic belt favors the solution of iron. Solution is also promoted by the acidity of podzolic soil, which reaches pH = 3.8, since total precipitation of ferric iron as ferric hydroxide takes

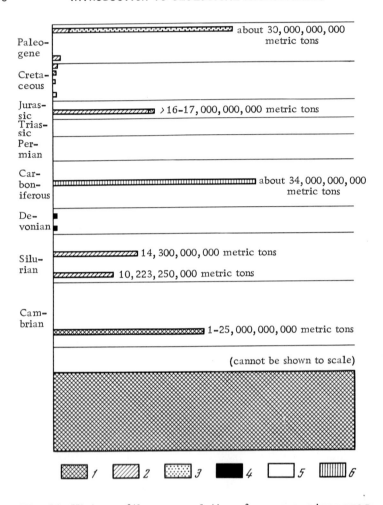

Fig. 51. History of the accumulation of supergene iron ores:
1—ores of jaspilite type; 2—ores of marine hydrogoethite-
chamoisite-siderite type; 3—continental ores (eluvial and
lacustrine-paludal, mainly hydrogoethites and siderites;
5—elastic ores; 6—siderites of littoral basins (after
Strakhov, 1947b).

place at pH = 5.5. The comparative lack of electrolytes in the
water and the presence of large amounts of humic substances that
combine with ferric iron to form complex soluble compounds all
facilitate the extensive supergene movements or migrations of iron
in the taiga-podzolic zone.

The migration process itself, according to Strakhov, takes place as follows. The iron, apparently in the form of a humic complex, is washed out of the A_1 and A_2 horizons in the podzolic soil and enriches the B horizon, where it is precipitated because of the greater alkalinity of the subsoil and the presence of Ca^{++} and Mg^{++} ions. Farther on, the migration of the iron may follow the contours of the relief, as illustrated in Fig. 52. Downward along the slopes, the level of the water table rises relative to the surface, and from the C horizon—the bedrock region—the ground waters gradually enter the B horizon. It is likely that when this horizon has considerable soil moisture and is rich in organic substances, bacterial life becomes active, and low oxidation-reduction potential values are produced (rH_2 about 14-16). Thus a large part of the iron salts goes into the ferrous form. Thereupon, says Strakhov, iron in the form of $Fe(HCO_3)_2$ is again diffused into the A_2 horizon, where its oxidation results in the formation of a hard pan. Farther down the slope, the $Fe(HCO_3)_2$ may be carried by streams into peat areas and here, becoming a layer of peaty oxide, form bog iron ore. The constant presence of filamentous iron bacteria of the genera *Leptothrix* and *Crenothrix* is probably evidence of their participation in the formation of the bog ore.

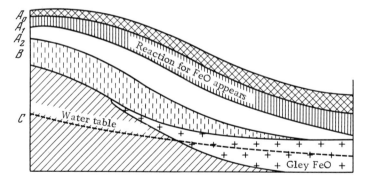

Fig. 52. Diagram showing the migration of iron in the soil profile. Explanation in text (after Strakhov, 1947b).

In ferrous form, the iron may be carried by surface waters from the weathering crust into rivers and lakes, or else it disappears beneath the drainage surface and is preserved within the earth's crust. In latter case the concentration of ferrous bicarbonate in the subsoil waters may reach 50-80 mg/liter, as found at a number of points in the taiga-podzolic zone, particularly in the Martsial'nyy waters in Karelia, at Palyustrov, in the vicinity of

Leningrad and elsewhere. According to Rode's calculations for one of the soils in the Leningrad Oblast', the total amount of iron removed from all the soil horizons is 344 metric tons per hectare for the entire Postglacial period, or 26 kilograms per hectare annually.

Microorganisms play a dual role in the formation of bog iron ore. In the first place, they contribute to the creation of a general reducing environment in the subsoil, promoting the transformation of fixed ferric iron into the mobile ferrous form. In the second place, the oxidation of $Fe(HCO_3)_2$ to $Fe(OH)_3$ in the oxidizing zone and the formation of the bog ore involve the participation of filamentous iron bacteria.

After studying all the available information on continental iron-ore accumulation, Strakhov (1947b) concluded that, from the Late Paleozoic to the present, these ores have been formed under the conditions of humid climates with moderate or high temperatures, and have nowhere been formed in arid zones or in polar and tropical climatic regions.

3. THE FORMATION OF LAKE IRON ORES

The ooze deposits of iron-ore lakes in Sweden have been recently investigated in detail; the results are set forth at length in a summary by Lundqvist (1927). As a rule, the lower layers of the oozes are rich in calcium carbonate. Similar accumulations of lacustrine chalk were found by V. V. Kudryashov (1924) some 5 m below the surface of the ooze in the deposits of Lake Chernoye at Kosino, and by L. L. Rossolimo (unpublished) in Lake Glubokoye in the Moscow Oblast'. In the upper ooze layers, the lime content decreases to zero, so that in iron-ore lakes the surface layers of the ooze contain large amounts of ferric oxide, in a number of cases leading to the formation of lake iron ore. Figure 53 diagrammatically shows the occurrence of the lake ore in the Swedish lakes. This distribution of calcium carbonate and ferruginous formations Strakhov explains on the basis of the evolution of the eluvial process in the soil mantle (Fig. 54).

In the taiga-podzolic zone, the soil formation begins with an alkaline phase, designated as Stage I. In this stage sulfates, chlorides and carbonates are leached out of the matrix rock; at the same time the aluminosilicates are hydrolyzed and the bases leached out. The iron, going into solution, immediately coagulates in the soil eluvium. The carbonates, on the other hand, particularly calcium carbonate, accumulate in lake basins as lacustrine chalk and marl, forming the calcareous layers of the lake deposits.

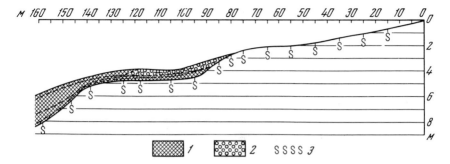

Fig. 53. Occurrence of iron ores in the section through the modern sediments of one of the lakes in Sweden: 1—fine detrital gyttja (ooze); 2—diatomaceous ochre and deposits of ferric hydrate; 3—sand (after Lundqvist, 1927).

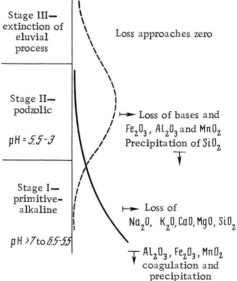

Fig. 54. Diagram showing the evolution of the eluvial process in the soil mantle in areas of humid climate (after Strakhov, 1947b). Explanation in text.

In this process the absorptive complex of the soil formed from the matrix rock combines with the Ca^{2+} and Mg^{2+} ions, whose place is taken by hydrogen. The soil solution becomes acidic, and the iron sesquioxides begin to be leached out. If the iron migration develops far enough, favorable conditions are created for the formation of iron ore, represented by concretions ranging from 5 mm to 10—15 cm in size (Fig. 55).

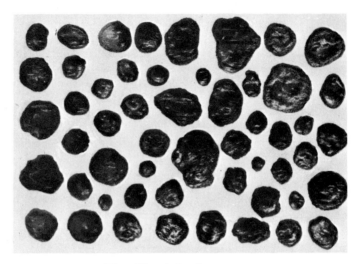

Fig. 55. Lake iron ore.

At the present time, lake iron ores are accumulating primarily in the northern part of the taiga-podzolic zone. The matrix rocks on which the soil mantle is formed may be either iron-rich igneous rocks and crystalline schists, or normal sedimentary rocks. The only requirements for lakes and swamps to form are conditions favoring the removal of iron from the soil, a hilly topography and a slight amount of surface runoff and poor drainage. Under these conditions topographic depressions provide the sites for the formation of bog or lake iron ores, while the iron is eroded from the higher areas separating them.

The lake ores are formed in a relatively narrow littoral zone some 100-300 m wide, at depths from 1 to 3-5 m. Only in very small and shallow lakes is the ore deposited over the entire area of the water. The ore does not accumulate throughout the littoral areas of oligotrophic lakes, but only in isolated spots. In Lake Yenis-Yarvi the ore-bearing areas are concentrated along the swampy shores and shallow bays with gently sloping bottoms (Fig. 56). According to Aarnio (1915) and Naumann (1922, 1927), the formation of lake ores is associated with the presence of sandy, water-permeable soils through which the lake can be supplied with iron-bearing ground waters.

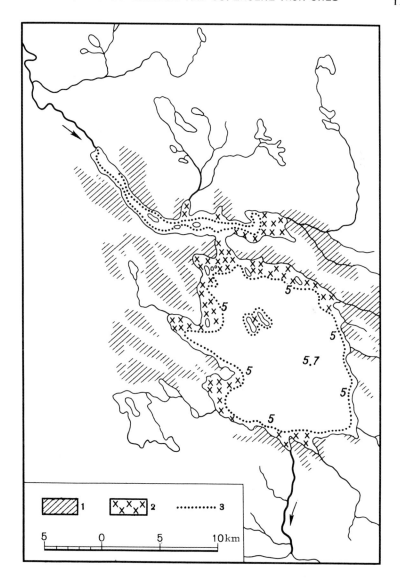

Fig. 56. Map showing the distribution of iron ores
in Lake Yenis-Yarvi
(after Strakhov, 1947b):
1—peat bogs; 2—lake ore; 3—five-meter isobaths.

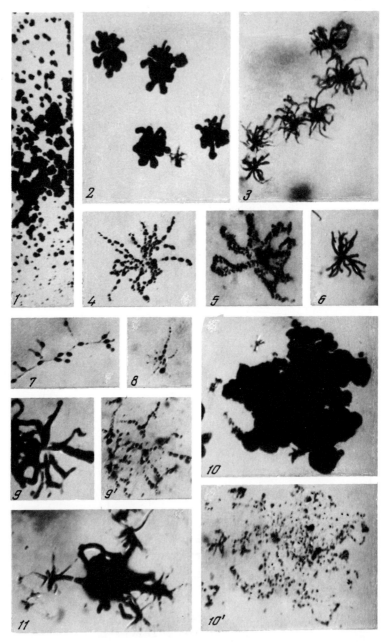

Fig. 57. A new manganese- and iron-oxidizing microbe,
Metallogenium personatum Perf., gen. et sp. nov., the

The question of microbial participation during the formation of lake iron and manganese ores has aroused great controversy and has been the subject of considerable literature. As early as 1877, A. A. Inostrantsev proposed a physicochemical theory to account for the formation of lake iron ores. Molisch (1910), in his monograph on the iron bacteria, cites analyses of about 60 samples of bog iron ores, of which iron bacteria were found in only four. Aarnio (1915) and Naumann (1922) also concluded that iron bacteria play no part in iron-ore formation in lakes.

This view is shared by Strakhov (1947b), who decided, after analyzing the available materials on the role of bacteria in lake ores, that there is no factual basis for the idea that the great mass of lake ores was formed biogenically. He believes that the biogenic hypothesis is supported only by a few doubtful occurrences of bacteria in lake ores, and is contradicted by the great number of unsuccessful searches for bacterial structures in ores of various origins. In Strakhov's opinion, in most cases the conditions under which lake ores are deposited do not favor the growth of iron bacteria.

The hypothesis of the biogenic formation of iron ores, which gives the iron bacteria the chief role in the ore formation, was put forth by Aschan (1907), and later supported by Ya. V. Samoylov and A. G. Titov (1917–1918), V. I. Vernadskiy (1923), K. M. Deryugin (1924) and Baier (1937). This hypothesis was based on the fact that iron-bearing concretions had been found to contain not only bacterial cells, but also the ferruginous sheaths of iron bacteria.

The first papers mentioning the discovery of iron bacteria in ooze deposits and ferruginous concretions in connection with ore

---

principal ore-forming agent in a number of lakes in Karelia:

1—microzonal growth of *Metallogenium* microcolonies in the canal of a pelloscopic capillary ($\times$ 70); 2, 3—trichospheric stage of *Metallogenium* in various phases of ore mineralization; 4, 5, 8—structure of the trichospheric stage of *Metallogenium* from gemmate cells emerging after treatment with oxalic acid and staining with gentian violet ($\times$ 1000 and $\times$ 1300); 9—($\times$ 1000); 10—($\times$ 500)—microcolonies up to and including 9′ and 10′—microcolonies after treatment with gentian violet; 6, 11—formation of round reproductive cells at the ends of radiating filaments and their growth into trichospheric microcolonies ($\times$ 600); 7—structure of *Rhodomicrobium* (after Perfil'yev and Gabe, 1961).

formation were those of B. V. Perfil'yev (1926, 1927). From the ooze of one of the dystrophic lakes in the vicinity of Lake Seliger, he isolated an organism which he called *Sphaerothrix latens*. This bacterium formed regular, fairly flattened colonies of concentric structure, made up of a mass of branching threads permeated with ferric hydrate. The surfaces of the colonies revealed individual, radially arranged cells 0.6 × 1.5 or 2 μ in size. The dichotomous branching of the *Sphaerothrix* filaments closely resembles the similar appearance of *Gallionella*. B. V. Perfil'yev believed that the iron-manganese concretions were gigantic colonies of *Sphaerothrix latens*. This view, first of all, called for re-examination of the assertion that microbes were absent in the concretions. It seemed possible that all previously unsuccessful attempts to find microorganisms in the concretions had failed because the microbes occurred only at the very surfaces of the concretions and had thus escaped the notice of the investigators. By direct microscope examination, Perfil'yev found cells resembling those of *Sphaerothrix* and *Gallionella* on the surfaces of lake ore concretions. In later laboratory experiments with a purely mineral liquid nutrient medium, he observed the formation of solid, hemispherical colonies of this organism up to 2.5 mm in diameter.

Perfil'yev's very important work (1952, 1961), using capillary microscopy, showed the presence in the ooze deposits of a new species of iron bacterium, *Metallogenium personatum* Perf. (Fig. 57), whose widespread occurrence has been noted by K. A. Guseva (1955), G. A. Sokolova (1959, 1961a) and other authors. Perfil'yev believes that this organism is the principal ore-forming agent in a number of lakes of Karelia. By the method of capillary microscopy, he also discovered the separate stages of development of this organism. Until the time of his work, it had been impossible to observe the cellular structure of this microorganism, which Perfil'yev in 1952 named *Metallogenium invisum*, alluding to its invisibility.

Thus weighty arguments do exist for considering the formation of iron ore in lakes to be a biogenic process, although this problem has not yet been definitively solved. As to Strakhov's views, it may be said that there are fewer data in support of the physicochemical theory of the formation of individual iron concretions than there are to support their biological origin.

4. THE ROLE OF MICROORGANISMS IN THE FORMATION OF IRON ORES IN MARINE BASINS

N. M. Strakhov (1947b), studying the geographic distribution of iron deposits of marine origin, proceeds from the assumption that all the iron in the sea has been carried in from the continents by rivers, and that the iron entered the river water from the weathering of rock outcrops, according to the scheme set forth above. Marine iron ores are apparently not being formed at the present time; they were formed only in earlier geologic periods, before the Jurassic. For this reason interpretations of their genesis must be tentative.

Sideritic ores of marine origin as a rule are closely associated with coal seams (Fig. 58). Usually they are closely contiguous, very large concretions which sometimes merge together into a continuous thin stratum. Reconstruction of the environment in which the coals were formed suggests that these formations arose in low flatlands near the shore, which were sometimes covered by a shallow sea and at other times emerged from them.

In the area of true marine deposits, the most typical are oolitic hematite-chamoisite-siderite ores. Beginning with a zone of pure sand facies, they grade into clayey sand and thence into shell-limestone deposits. Here they reach their maximum volume, thereafter wedging out into ooze or carbonate sediments. These ores, as in the Kerch deposits, may spread out in area for distances up to 100 km longitudinally and 20 km in width. All this also indicates that the marine ores were formed in the shallow zone of the sea immediately adjacent to the shoreline. Strakhov completely denies their biogenic origin, and believes rather that the iron was carried in from the continent and simultaneously deposited because of its decreased solubility in sea water.

V. S. Butkevich (1928) has studied the biogenic role in the formation of marine ores and attributes the formation of the ferruginous concretions in the White Sea to the activity of *Gallionella tortuosa*. The concretions, he believes, were formed as follows: The iron humates or their ferrous compounds, carried in by rivers, are oxidized together with manganous compounds directly upon their arrival in the sea. The ferric or manganic hydrozides settle to the bottom where they enter a reducing environment and, in the presence of sufficient carbon dioxide, become ferrous or manganous carbonates. The constant supply of ferrous carbonate salts from the ooze and the presence of oxygen from the overlying water create the most suitable conditions for the development of ore-forming organisms in the surface ooze layer. B. V. Perfil'yev and V. S. Butkevich believe that the formation of lacustrine and marine iron ores is due to autotrophic iron bacteria, utilizing the chemical energy derived from the oxidation of ferrous to ferric oxide.

Another view is held by V. O. Kalinenko (1946), who generally denies that bacteria can use the chemical energy from the oxidation of individual elements for their assimilation of free carbon dioxide. He considers rather that the formation of the ferruginous concretions results from the deposition or adsorption of ferric

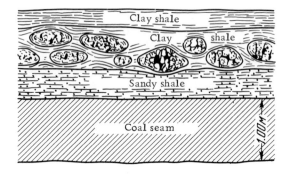

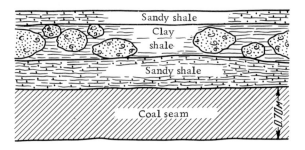

Stratum of shaly iron ore

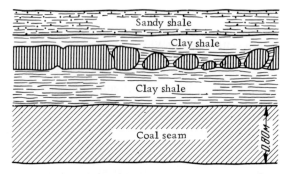

Fig. 58. Structure and composition of a
deposit of siderite ores of marine origin
(Ruhr basin) (after Strakhov, 1957b).

hydrates in the mucous membranes of *Bacterium precipitatum*.
Proceeding from this concept, Kalinenko decided that only heterotrophic organisms could contribute to the formation of the iron and
manganese concretions in the seas and lakes. Therefore, throughout all of his investigations, in obtaining cumulative cultures of
bacteria that deposit iron in their mucous membranes, he used sea

or lake water with the addition of 0.1% iron citrate. Pure cultures were isolated on meat-peptone agar to which KNO_3 and 0.5-0.1% iron citrate were added.

From the ferruginous microconcretions in the Kara Sea, Kalinenko isolated a pure culture of bacteria, which consisted of rods some 5 x 0.5 μ in size. In peptone water with iron citrate this organism forms flocs of adhering cells. Iron salts are precipitated on the surfaces of these flocs, and at small magnifications the external appearance of these colonies resembles the microconcretions from the Kara Sea ooze.

Kalinenko (1946) described the organism he had isolated as a new species, which he named *Bacterium precipitatum* n.sp. Kalin., and to this species he attributed the ability to form marine ferruginous concretions. A second bacterial species which Kalinenko (1952) used in his experiments was isolated on the same organic media and identified as *Leptothrix ochracea*. The use of organic nutrient media for isolating iron bacteria naturally resulted in the isolation of heterotrophic organisms. This aspect of the study has been analyzed in detail by A. S. Razumov (1957), who showed that Kalinenko in his experiments was dealing with heterotrophic varieties of *Sphaerotilus*, which he erroneously identified as *Leptothrix ochracea*. Observations of the growth of this organism in a liquid nutrient medium with 0.5% iron citrate have established that in the surface film of the liquid the bacteria form individual colonies, in whose vicinity amorphous flocs of iron accumulate; these later become consolidated into spherical formations.

Thus Kalinenko has shown that a number of heterotrophic bacteria in organic media containing from 0.1 to 0.5% iron citrate are able to form concretions of ferric hydrates. This still does not mean, however, that these particular organisms participate in forming the concretions of iron or manganese ores. In nature even organically contaminated waters do not contain such high concentrations of organic iron compounds as Kalinenko added to his nutrient media. Moreover, as N. I. Semenovich has shown (1958), the water of Lake Punnus-Yarvi, where iron ore is being deposited, has a total iron content, both suspended and dissolved, not exceeding 0.2 mg/liter with a dissolved oxygen content of about 2 mg O_2/liter.

From the available data on the formation of iron-manganese concretions in oligotrophic lakes and in the sea, it appears that the best hypothesis is that proposed by Perfil'yev (1926) and Butkevich (1928): that autrophic iron bacteria are the chief agents in this process. The autotrophs develop in the uppermost, surface layer of the bottom sediments, utilizing energy obtained by oxidizing the ferrous carbonates that diffuse toward the surface from the deeper layers of the ooze deposits. On the other hand, the question of bacterial participation in the formation of marine siderite ores still requires further study.

CHAPTER X

The Role of Microorganisms in Forming the Chemical Composition of Ground Waters

It was stated earlier in this book that the formation of the chemical composition of ground waters follows certain definite laws. As a rule, the zone of active water–exchange contains mostly hydrocarbonate waters, sulfate waters predominate in the zone of retarded water exchange, and finally the zone of standing water has a predominance of brines with high concentrations of calcium or magnesium chlorides. V. A. Sulin (1948) believes that this distribution of the salt compositions of internal waters is wholly determined by physical laws; according to Baas Becking (1938), L. Ye. Kramarenko et al. (1956) and M. S. Gurevich (1958, 1961), there is no longer any doubt that the chemical composition of ground waters may be changed not only by inorganic processes, but also by the activities of microorganisms. These authorities state that the participation of microorganisms in forming the chemical composition of ground waters typically characterizes a particular stage in the geochemical history of the ground waters in the biosphere. The role of microorganisms is most clearly manifested by the metamorphism of the waters in the zones of active and retarded exchange, and applies especially to carbon and sulfur compounds.

Microbial activity under stratal conditions is closely regulated by the oxidation–reduction environment of the medium, and by the presence of organic matter and of sulfates or sulfides. The presence of strongly reducing conditions, sulfates and organic substances creates the most favorable conditions for the activity of *Vibrio desulfuricans*. Under these circumstances the sulfates may be completely reduced to sulfides or free hydrogen sulfide. N. V. Tageyeva's experimental investigations (1955) showed that bicarbonates begin to accumulate in the water, the calcium and magnesium ions are precipitated, and the chemical type of the water changes. Finally, acid waters containing large quantities of ferric sulfate and free sulfuric acid are formed on a large scale when the water table is lowered artificially during the exploitation of coal and ore deposits, in the course of which *Thiobacillus ferrooxidans* causes the oxidation of pyrite inclusions in the coals or lignites, or of the pyrites in sulfide deposits. Some examples of the geological activity of microorganisms leading to changes in the chemistry of internal waters are discussed below.

1. THE FORMATION OF HYDROGEN SULFIDE BY THE REDUCTION OF SULFATES

Even the very first microbiological studies of oil deposits, made by Bastin (1926), revealed the presence of sulfate-reducing bacteria in the stratal waters. Laboratory investigations by V. O. Tauson and V. I. Aleshina (1932) then confirmed the fact that hydrogen sulfide begins to be formed in cultures of desulfurizing bacteria with oil as the only source of organic matter. Later these observations were supported by quantitative data in a paper by V. A. Kuznetsova, K. B. Ashirov et al. (1957). Table 56 shows that more than 200 mg of H_2S per liter may accumulate in three months in cumulative cultures of *Vibrio desulfuricans,* in which the only source of organic matter was oil. Before the oil hydrocarbons can be used by the desulfurizing bacteria, the oil apparently must first be broken down by other species, since up to now no formation of hydrogen sulfide has been observed in a medium with oil when the experiment is performed with pure cultures of *Vibrio desulfuricans* or *Vibrio aestuarii* (Shturm, 1958).

From thermodynamic considerations and from the ecology of the sulfate-reducing bacteria, Tauson and Aleshina concluded that these bacteria oxidize the volatile hydrocarbons completely and the heavy hydrocarbons only partially. In this process the hydrocarbons may be polymerized along with the formation of cyclohexane derivatives. These authors believe that naphthene oils are the final product of bacterial transformation of paraffin-base oils. ZoBell (1943, 1946a, b, c) also attributed great importance to the activity of desulfurizing bacteria in the oil stratum.

It was said earlier that the question of whether this group of bacteria transforms the oils directly within the deposit still requires further study. Recently, however, sufficient proof has been obtained that the presence of large amounts of sulfides and free hydrogen sulfide in the stratal waters is due to the reduction of sulfates by desulfurizing bacteria. The data in Table 57 show that in the Kalinovka oil deposit, bacterial counts of *Vibrio desulfuricans* on various media revealed up to 100,000 desulfurizing bacteria per ml of stratal water. That the sulfates are reduced within the deposit itself can be seen from the fact that the total amount of sulfur in the sulfates and sulfides does not fluctuate as strongly as does the quantity of hydrogen sulfide.

Table 56

The formation of hydrogen sulfide by cultures of desulfurizing
bacteria in a mineral medium with oil from the Kalinovka
deposit
(after V. A. Kuznetsova, K. B. Ashirov et al., 1957)

No. of well from which culture was taken	Duration of experiment, days	Amount of hydrogen sulfide formed, mg/liter	Remarks
452	94	229.5	*Vibrio desulfuricans* culture
528	94	231	isolated in medium with
550	210	365.5	lactate
550	210	241.8	*Vibrio desulfuricans* culture
550	210	247.3	isolated in medium with oil

The activity of the desulfurizing bacteria is manifested especially
clearly in oil fields where fresh or sea water has been pumped in
to flood the oil stratum in the secondary recovery of oil. The
Pokrovskoye deposit is of particular interest in this regard: this
oil deposit began to be worked in 1950; the first analyses (Ekzertsev
and Kuznetsov, 1954) showed no hydrogen sulfide or desulfurizing
bacteria in the stratal waters. Areal flooding of the oil-producing
stratum was begun in 1954. Figure 59, prepared from Ashirov's
data (1961) on the Bashkirian stage in the southern part of the
deposit, shows that hydrogen sulfide was rapidly formed in the
flooded stratum. After four months had passed between two
analyses, there was an increase in the amount of hydrogen sulfide
throughout almost the whole stratum; the quantity of H_2S reached

Table 57

Contents of hydrogen sulfide, sulfates and desulfurizing bacteria
in the stratal waters of the Kalinovka oil deposit

Area of deposit	S/H_2S	S/SO_4	Total sulfur in sulfides and sulfates	Number of desulfurizing bacteria in 1 ml of stratal water, computed for media with different organic substances		
	(mg/liter)			Lactate	Acetate	Oil
Southwestern . . .	963	1543	2506	0	10,000	10,000
	883	1954	2837	100,000	10	0.2
	666	1913	2579	0	10	10
Southeastern . . .	520	2100	2620	10	10	0.2
Central.	762	1188	1950	10	10,000	10,000
Northern	240	1760	2000	10	1,000	10

120 mg/liter in individual wells, corresponding to an increase of 1 mg/liter per day. A similar situation was observed by M. V. Gasanov (1961) in the "Artem" oil field of the Baku district, where the producing stratum was flooded with sea water.

Laboratory experiments by V. T. Malyshek and M. V. Gasanov (1959) showed that sulfates are reduced readily in a mixture of

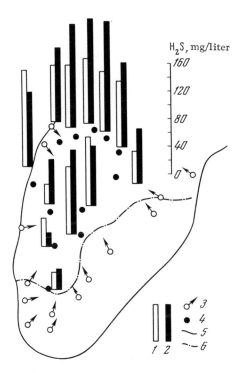

Fig. 59. Increase in the amount of hydrogen sulfide in the ground waters of the Bashkirian stage in the Pokrovskoye deposit as the stratum was flooded for the secondary extraction of oil (after Ashirov, 1961):
1—amount of hydrogen sulfide in July; 2—amount in November; 3—pressure wells; 4—production wells; 5—contour of oil-bearing area at beginning of exploitation in July; 6—contour of oil-bearing area in November.

stratal and sea water in the presence of oil as the only source of organic matter (Table 58). These authors concluded that the intensity of the sulfate reduction depends on the amount of organic matter, the pH of the solution, the quantity of sea water introduced and other factors. The sulfates were especially rapidly reduced when oil from the "Artem" oil field was used and when the ratio of stratal to sea water was 4 : 1.

Table 58

The formation of hydrogen sulfide in stratal water upon the
addition of water from the Caspian Sea
(after V. T. Malyshek and M. V. Gasanov, 1959)

Experimental conditions				Sulfate, mg/liter		Amount of H_2S formed, mg/liter
No. of volumes of		Organic matter	Duration of experiment, days	At beginning	At end	
Sea water	Stratal water					
1	1	Calcium lactate	46	1620	48	272.8
1	1	Oil	141	1620	464	233.0
2	8	"	46	647	324	122.0

Gasanov (1961) studied the acceleration of the reduction of sulfates directly under stratal conditions in the Kosha-Naur oil field. Table 59 shows the data from repeated analyses made in the

Table 59

Contents of hydrogen sulfide and sulfate-reducing bacteria
in the stratal water of the Kosha-Naur oil field as
the stratum was flooded with sea water
(after M. V. Gasanov, 1961)

Well No.	First sampling of water			Later samplings of water		
	Date	No. bacteria per ml	H_2S mg/liter	Date	No. bacteria per ml	H_2S mg/liter
118	16.III	24	19.8	3. VI	130	163.5
931	16.III	23	38.8	3. VI	120	89.7
1008	1.IV	110	211.2	3. VI	150	257.4
1067	1.IV	40	39.1	20. VI	100	100.9
1040	8.IV	69	8.5	10. VI	75	33.8
1185	15.IV	110	8.3	22. VI	150	61.8
1086	15.IV	72	173.3	30. VI	90	252.7
2475	11.V	130	37.3	11. VII	200	85.1
2053	11.V	50	95.5	11. VII	120	154.9

same oil wells, indicating that the hydrogen sulfide content rose by 140 mg/liter after 2.5 months in some parts of the oil-bearing stratum. Analyses also showed increases in the hydrogen sulfide content of the stratal waters corresponding to the movement of the stratal water contours as sea water was pumped in.

2. THE BIOGENIC TRANSFORMATION OF THE TYPES OF GROUND WATERS

Many authorities believe that hydrocarbonate-chloride-sodic waters are formed from sulfate-chloride-calcic waters by the reduction of sulfates and simultaneous formation of hydrocarbonates. In alkaline media the hydrocarbonates precipitate calcium and magnesium ions and form carbonates, leading to the appearance of sodium carbonate and raising the alkalinity of the solution. According to Sulin (1948), this process takes the following course: sodium sulfate is reduced by *Vibrio desulfuricans* or *V. aesturarii*, and sodium bicarbonate is formed:

$$Na_2SO_4 + 2C_{org} + 2H_2O \rightarrow 2NaHCO_3 + H_2S.$$

The sodium bicarbonate reacts with the alkaline earth salts; calcium and magnesium carbonates precipitate out from the water to enrich the rock, while sodium chloride accumulates in the water:

$$2NaHCO_3 + CaCl_2 \rightarrow 2NaCl + CaCO_3 + H_2CO_3.$$

Thus the waters are changed from the sulfate-chloride-calcic to the hydrocarbonate-chloride-sodic type. Such reactions will continue until all the sulfates and chlorides of the alkaline earths have been used up.

In the case of magnesium chloride waters of marine origin, which contain sodium and magnesium chlorides and magnesium and calcium sulfates, as the alkaline-earth sulfates are reduced they are precipitated as calcium and magnesium carbonates, and in this manner the waters are changed to the chloride-sodic type.

Depending on the nature of the waters and the surrounding rocks, bacterial reduction of the sulfates may result in the formation of chloride, hydrocarbonate-sodic or hydrocarbonate-calcic waters from sulfate waters. These waters are most often encountered in oil deposits in which there is an excess of organic matter, and the sulfates are reduced with particular intensity in the crest of the domical structure (Fig. 60A). According to N. T. Lindtrop (1947), at the contacts between the stratal waters and the oil in the Groznyy oil fields, the sulfates decrease rapidly and the amount of bicarbonates simultaneously increases.

The formation of ground waters of alkali–chloride–hydrocarbonate-sodic composition by the biogenic reduction of sulfates is, in M. S. Gurevich's opinion (1961), one of the most common and likely origins of such ground waters. The rate of reduction of the sulfates in stratal waters, according to Z. I. Kuznetsova (1959), depends on the presence of sulfates and dissolved organic matter, and within the Terek–Dagestan oil province is frequently limited by the excessively high temperature of the stratal water.

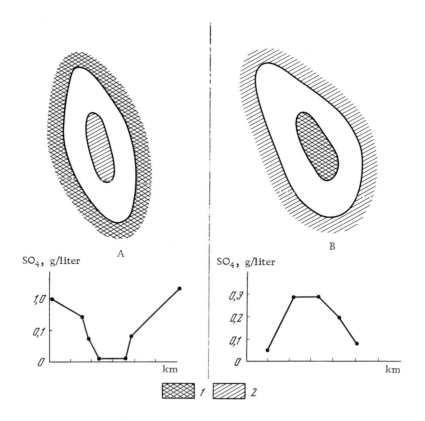

Fig. 60. Chief types of distribution of sulfates in ground waters of oil deposits:
A—sulfateless marginal waters (a number of deposits of the Urals–Volga region); B—marginal waters with high sulfate contents through oxidation of hydrogen sulfide (Surakhanskoye deposit); 1—amount of sulfates more than 0.3 g/liter; 2—amount of sulfates less than 0.1 g/liter.

3. THE BIOGENIC FORMATION OF SULFATES IN OIL STRATAL WATERS

Sulfates may be formed in underground waters through the oxidation of sulfides by thiobacteria. As indicated by S. I. Kuznetsov's and G. A. Sokolova's laboratory experiments (1960), *Thiobacillus thioparus* readily oxidizes calcium sulfide or free hydrogen sulfide, which are practically always present in hydrogen sulfide stratal waters. Oxidation occurs when the oxidation-reduction potential of the surrounding medium is in the range of $rH_2 = 12$-22.

It should be stressed that analysis of this group of bacteria must take the form of observing the turbidity of the organisms in the nutrient medium and the formation of a sulfur film at the contact surface between the liquid medium and the air. Estimates of growth from the amount of hyposulfite consumed can lead to errors, especially if *Thiobacillus thiooxidans* is counted on a medium with hyposulfite at an initial pH lower than 4.5. In this case the hyposulfite may be dissolved chemically in the acid medium and molecular sulfur produced, which will be included in titrating the hyposulfite and interpreted as bacterial development. The possibility of such errors casts doubt on the data regarding the occurrence of *Thiobacillus thiooxidans* in the stratal waters of Turkmenia at a depth of 1800 m.

Studies of the distribution of *Thiobacillus thioparus* in oil stratal waters have been made by Z. A. Kolesnik (1955), Z. I. Kuznetsova (1959, 1961), T. L. Simakova and co-workers (1958), Ye. N. Dutova (1959), G. A. Sokolova (1961b) and others. V. A. Kuznetsova's study (1961b) of the oxidation-reduction potentials of deep stratal waters has shown that the rH_2 fluctuates between 5 and 12.5—that is, in most cases it occurs within the range in which *Thiobacillus thioparus* does not oxidize sulfides.

To determine the distribution of *Thiobacillus thioparus* in stratal waters, Sokolova (1960) investigated a large number of samples of stratal waters from oil fields in the Kuybyshev Oblast', taking account of possible penetration of surface waters into the oil strata. Her analyses are presented in Table 60, which shows that *Thiobacillus thioparus* was encountered in the stratal waters of open deposits with some degree of exchange of stratal waters, or else in deposits that had been artificially flooded for the secondary recovery of oil. As a rule, *Thiobacillus thioparus* was not found in closed deposits. All the waters of these deposits contained some amount of sulfates, but it is hard to say whether these are secondary sulfates formed by the oxidation of sulfides.

A classic example of water of high sulfate content in the crest of an oil-bearing structure and of low sulfate content in the waters along the periphery is the Surakhan structure shown in Fig. 60 B

Table 60

Distribution of *Thiobacillus thioparus* in stratal waters as
related to the manner of exploitation of the stratum
(after G. A. Sokolova, 1961b)

Nature of deposits	H_2S content in stratal water, mg/liter	Number of samples	
		Investi- gated	In which *Th. thioparus* found
Open, with flow of fresh water.	12—1261	49	22
Open, without flow of water.	0—348	7	3*
Closed, with flow of fresh water.	25—100	9	7
Closed, without flow of fresh water . . .	Not determined	16	2*

* *Th. thioparus* found only in samples taken with sludge pump.

(Gurevich 1961). Gurevich states that the high sulfate content may
be caused either from the supply of internal waters entering through
disjunctive dislocations in the crest of the structure, or else from
the hydrogen sulfide which diffuses from the lower part of the structure and is oxidized to sulfates by thiobacteria. The progressive
changes in the sulfate content of the water, according to N. A.
Volodin (1935), can be readily traced across the trend of the
Surakhan structure. From this standpoint there is some interest
in the data cited by V. T. Malyshek and A. A. Maliyants (1932), in
which large numbers of thiobacteria in the stratal waters of the
Surakhan structure were found. Although the reasons for the
development of sulfur purple bacteria in these waters must still
be guessed at, the growth of the thiobacteria may very well be due
to the introduction of oxygen into the stratum as a result of the com-
pressed air method of secondary recovery which was used.

4. THE BIOGENIC FORMATION OF ACID WATERS IN COAL AND SULFIDE ORE DEPOSITS

From the acid waters of a coal mine, Colmer and Hinkle (1947)
isolated and described the organism *Thiobacillus ferrooxidans*,
which is one of the thiobacteria. As previously mentioned in
Chapter VIII, Temple and Delchamps (1953) suggest the following
scheme for the oxidation of the pyrites in coal mines. They believe
that the first stage in the oxidation of pyrite to ferrous sulfate is
a purely chemical reaction:

$$FeS_2 + 3\frac{1}{2}O_2 + H_2O \rightarrow FeSO_4 + H_2SO_4.$$

The subsequent oxidation of ferrous to ferric sulfate involves the participation of *Thiobacillus ferrooxidans,* since chemical oxidation of ferrous sulfate by atmospheric oxygen for practical purposes does not take place in an acid medium:

$$2FeSO_4 + \tfrac{1}{2}O_2 + H_2SO_4 \rightarrow Fe_2(SO_4)_3 + H_2O.$$

The ferric sulfate that is formed again reacts chemically with the pyrite, to form ferrous sulfate and molecular sulfur:

$$2FeS_2 + 2Fe_2(SO_4)_3 \rightarrow 6FeSO_4 + 4S.$$

The molecular sulfur is oxidized to sulfuric acid by *Thiobacillus thiooxidans,* whereas *Th. ferrooxidans* oxidizes the ferrous sulfate. Thus the whole cycle of biological and chemical reactions is repeated. The chalcopyrite in hydrothermal copper sulfide deposits is similarly oxidized.

According to Bryner, Beck, Davis and Wilson (1954), Lyalikova (1959) and others, the bacterial oxidation of pyrite and chalcopyrite is many times faster than purely chemical oxidation and ceases immediately upon sterilization of the ore or coal.

The pyrite in coal seams begins to be oxidized if the surface waters percolate through the coal seam along fractures and become enriched in ferrous oxide. Later, as these waters travel through finely comminuted, pyritized coal under good aeration conditions in the mine, the pyrite is rapidly oxidized by *Thiobacillus thiooxidans* and *Th. ferrooxidans.* Thus large amounts of ferric hydrates accumulate in the water tanks and clog the pipes, while great quantities of free sulfuric acid are concentrated in the mine waters, lowering the pH to 1-2 and strongly corroding the mining equipment (Table 61). Table 62 presents the results of analyses of

Table 61

Chemical composition of mine waters in a coal deposit (mg/liter)
(after Ashmeed, 1955)

Deposit	Solid residue	SO_4^{2-}	Cl^-	Total Fe	Fe^{2+}	NH_4^+	Ti
Coal mine in England	2990	2100	220	558	74	100	30

acid mine drainage waters, showing that microorganisms may radically alter the chemical composition of the surface waters as they travel through sulfide ore deposits. The formation of acid sulfate waters in deposits of sulfide ores has been observed by Bryner, Beck, Davis and Wilson (1954), Ashmeed (1955), Lyalikova (1959, 1960) and others.

Table 62

Chemical composition of mine waters in some sulfide ore
deposits (in mg/liter)

Deposit	pH	Cu	K + Na	Ca	Fe^{2+}	Fe^{3+}	SO_4	Cl	Zn
Copper ore, USSR	2.45	276	2	276	175	885	6,551	0	339
Same	1.96	5,123	499	510	1,556	14,240	59,160	0	3,465
"	2.73	67	38	124	25	10	1,018	5	50
"	1.07	6,350	172	335	43,830	140	123,000	90	167
Copper, Mountain View	—	45,633	48	307	49	8	71,053	17	411
Copper, E. Tennessee	—	41	13	238	1.3	186	2,068	2	54
Copper-zinc, St. Louis	—	59	50	39	154		2,672	13	852
Lead-zinc, Alabama	—	4	50	345	474		6,153	3	2,412

In copper deposits, copper in the form of $CuSO_4$ may accumulate up to 1-2 g/liter in the mine waters. The oxidation of chalcopyrite is probably similar to that of pyrite, involving the reactions:

$$FeS_2 + 3\frac{1}{2}O_2 + H_2O \rightarrow FeSO_4 + H_2SO_4 \text{ (chemically)}$$

$$2FeSO_4 + \frac{1}{2}O_2 + H_2SO_4 \rightarrow Fe_2(SO_4)_3 + H_2O \text{ (Th. ferrooxidans)}$$

$$CuFeS_2 + 2Fe_2(SO_4)_3 \rightarrow 5FeSO_4 + CuSO_4 + 2S \text{ (chemically)}$$

$$2S + 2H_2O + 3O_2 \rightarrow 2H_2SO_4 \text{ (Th. thiooxidans)}$$

$$2FeSO_4 + \frac{1}{2}O_2 + H_2SO_4 \rightarrow Fe_2(SO_4)_3 + H_2O \text{ (Th. ferrooxidans)}$$

Thereafter the entire cycle of chalcopyrite oxidation is repeated.
Microbiological analyses by Lyalikova and Sokolova (1962) have revealed the presence of large numbers of *Th. thiooxidans* and *Th. ferrooxidans* in the oxidized ore and in the waters passing through the ore body of the Kounrad copper deposit, which is being mined by the open-pit method. Acid waters with large contents of iron and copper salts are formed if the ore body is fractured and the surface waters passing through the fractures oxidize the iron sulfides. This may be seen very readily on the walls of the open-pit copper mine at Kounrad. Here the host rocks are granodiorites and granodiorite porphyries, which in some places have been altered to secondary quartzites (Gazizova, 1957). Inspection of the walls of the Kounrad copper mine reveals the clearly visible, highly fractured ore body. Deposition of pyrite is observed along the fractures in the rock, and in the dry areas this pyrite in the fractures is preserved without alteration (Fig. 61). As the ore is

broken away, one can readily see that the pyrite lies mainly in the planes of the fractures.

In the wet areas of the mine, the surface waters seep through the fractures in the ore body, crop out as streams at the surface, and again disappear into fractures in the rock. In these places it can be seen that the entire system of seams, as well as the rock surface, is covered with ferric oxides formed in the oxidation of the pyrite. Frequently the whole slope of the host rocks is colored green or blue by the malachite and azurite formed.

Fig. 61. Distribution of ferric oxide deposits along the fractures in the ore body of the Kounrad deposit.

Chalcopyrite and chalcosite are oxidized by the above chemical reactions to copper sulfate, which accumulates with the mine water in settling tanks in the deepest part of the open pit. This water is expelled from the deposit through pipes.

Approximately the same process is followed by the oxidation of the chalcopyrite in the Degtyarskoye copper deposit of the Middle Urals. Mine waters containing 1-2 g/liter of copper are pumped from water collectors into settling tanks and thence into the "Gidromed" plant, where the metallic copper is recovered by exchange reactions with scraps of iron.

CHAPTER XI

Methods of Regulating the Geochemical Activity of Microorganisms for Economic Purposes

Study of the geological activities of microorganisms in deposits of oil, sulfur and sulfide ores has revealed many of the laws governing the course and intensity of particular processes altering economic minerals or their host rocks, as well as the scale on which these processes take place. Hence it has become possible to accelerate the useful activities of microbes or to hinder their harmful effects, especially those that may occur through insufficient attention to the importance of microbiological processes in the exploitation of economic mineral deposits.

1. ATTEMPTS TO USE THE ACTIVITY OF MICROORGANISMS TO INCREASE THE SECONDARY RECOVERY OF OIL

The first suggestions regarding the use of microorganisms to increase oil production were made by Beckmann (1926). Much time passed, however, before the suggestions were actually put to practical use. As mentioned earlier, study of the microflora in oil strata has shown that the sulfate-reducing bacteria are the most widespread group in oil stratal waters. Thus the first attempts to separate oil from the reservoir rocks were made with the use of enrichment cultures of this very group of microorganisms. ZoBell (1946a, 1947a), in devoting his attention to the use of bacteria for increasing the secondary extraction of oil, performed a number of laboratory experiments. On the basis of the results he took out a corresponding patent (1946). The chief conclusions of ZoBell's work are that secondary oil extraction may be increased in one of the following ways: 1) by the bacterial formation of acids, particularly carbonic acid, which facilitate the movement of oil by increasing the pore spaces in the limestone rocks; 2) by the formation of gases which, being dissolved in the oil, increase its mobility; 3) by the destruction of high-molecular hydrocarbons and the formation of more mobile compounds with short carbon chains; 4) by the destruction of surface-active substances by bacteria.

In his laboratory experiments ZoBell (1947a) showed that these requirements are met by the sulfate-reducing bacteria, particularly *Desulfovibrio hydrocarbonoclasticus* and *Desulfovibrio halohydrocarbonoclasticus*. He suggests preliminary culturing of these organisms on a nutrient medium with sodium lactate, at temperatures approximating those in the oil stratum, which range from 21 to 82°C. The cultured organisms may be then introduced into the stratum. These laboratory experiments were repeated by Updegraff and Wren (1954), who attempted to separate oil from sand. They used 38 different enrichment cultures of desulfurizing bacteria, and simultaneously added various organic substances to the nutrient medium. These authors finally concluded that not one of their cultures was suitable to bring about secondary separation of oil through injection into the oil stratum under actual field conditions. Other experiments were carried out with moderate success by Mackenzie (1952), Updegraff and Wren (1954) and others, a summary of which may be found in Davis and Updegraff (1954) and in Birstekher [Beerstecher] (1957).

Experiments carried out in the field by Beck (1947a), who obtained his initial culture of *Desulfovibrio* from ZoBell, did not show any increase in the liberation of Bradford oil from the oil stratum. Neither was the Bradford oil separated from the reservoir rock in laboratory experiments. Later on a patent for a bacterial method of increasing oil production was taken out by Sanderson (1953), who proposed the introduction of a culture of *Clostridium sporogenes, Cl. histolyticum, Cl. lentoputrescens* or *Pseudomonas fluorescens* into the oil stratum.

Investigations of the oil microflora in the Middle Volga region, made by Ekzertsev (1956, 1960), have shown that the oil deposits also contain a widespread group of bacteria capable of destroying oil to form gaseous products. As a result of these laboratory studies, an attempt was made to decrease the viscosity and increase the mobility of oil under stratal conditions by introducing an enrichment culture of these bacteria into the stratum.

Kuznetsov (1955a) has suggested that introduction of an active culture of bacteria may, by breaking down the oil directly within the stratum, increase the gas pressure and thereby decrease the viscosity of the oil. In this connection G. A. Vorob'yeva isolated a cumulative culture of bacteria which decomposed oil under anaerobic conditions to form combustible gases, and could also be grown on molasses. Field tests were made in the Sernovodsk oil field. Some 54 m^3 of the culture, which had multiplied in a solution containing 4% molasses, was injected into the oil stratum at a depth of about 1000 m. The oil well was sealed off for six months, on the assumption that the bacteria would multiply, first consuming all the molasses and then beginning to break down the

Sernovodsk oil, which has a very high viscosity. When the well was opened, an increase of 1.5 atm in pressure was observed at the well-head. Before these experiments, the well discharged 37 metric tons per day with a water content of 7.5%; after bacterial injection the well produced 40 tons of oil per day with a water content of 5-6%. Four months later, the daily oil yield decreased to 36.4 metric tons with a water content of 4%. The gas factor remained at a level of 16 m^3/ton, instead of the 11-15 m^3/ton that it had been for five years before the above experiments. Bacteriological analysis of the stratal water showed the presence of the bacteria that were introduced into the well at the beginning of the experiment. Analysis of the gas revealed an increase in the nitrogen content to 35%, instead of the previous 20%, as well as increased amounts of carbon dioxide and propane and a decrease in methane. The dynamic viscosity of the oil rose from 40.3 to 49.3 centistokes.

Although this experiment did not yield positive results, in the sense of lowering the oil's viscosity, it did show that introduction of a bacterial culture directly into the stratum could accelerate breakdown of the volatile components in the oil. Similar results were obtained when the same culture was introduced into the oil stratum in the Berezovka oil deposit. This indicates the value of carrying out further experiments.

2. MICROBIOLOGICAL PROSPECTING FOR OIL AND GAS DEPOSITS

Study of the distribution in the subsoil of bacteria which oxidize gaseous hydrocarbons was the basis for elaborating microbiological prospecting methods for oil and gas deposits (Mogilevskiy, 1938, 1940; Bokova et al., 1947; Luchterowa, 1953a and b; Kuznetsov, 1959b; Dostalek, 1953a, b, c).

A number of different biological prospecting methods have been proposed, both in the Soviet Union and the United States of America. Microbiological methods of surveying deposits have been most extensively carried into practice in the Soviet Union (Mogilevskiy, 1953; Kuznetsova, 1947). The principal bacterial prospecting methods are summarized in Table 63; of these, the most commonly used are the soil and water bacterial surveys. A very simple method of analysis is used; it is represented diagrammatically in Fig. 62.

Water samples were taken for study from all the streams and wells in the area, placed in small glasses with a Muentz mineral nutrient medium, and exposed to an atmosphere consisting of air and methane. After two weeks' incubation in a thermostat,

Table 63

Principal bacterial methods of prospecting oil and gas deposits

Basis of method	Method of computation	Type of survey
Counting of bacterial population growing in soil or water or gas	1. Determination of intensity of growth of particular species of bacteria in laboratory on mineral medium with gas mixture. Medium inoculated with water or soil sample to be tested.	Soil- water-bacterial
	2. Determination of numbers of particular species of hydrocarbon-oxidizing bacteria. Solid mineral medium inoculated with sample to be tested; incubation in atmosphere with radioactive carbon added. Colonies counted by radioautographic method.	Soil-radioautographic
	3. Determination of intensity of absorption of oxygen from oxidation of hydrocarbon gas in differential respirometer.	Soil-gas
	4. Determination of absorption of oxygen dissolved in water through oxidation of bubble of methane or propane introduced into isolated sample of water to be tested.	Water
Calculation of gas flow from deposit	1. Determination of intensity of development of particular species of bacteria in mineral nutrient medium within vessel placed in borehole.	Bacterial-debit

the intensity of bacterial development in the individual samples was recorded and plotted on a chart. The areas of distribution of the key index microorganisms, with the rates of growth above certain background values, were contoured on a map, as illustrated in Fig. 63, which provides a schematic comparison of the results of water-microbe surveys in 1946 and 1949 with the data from subsequent drilling. It will be seen that the distribution of the hydrocarbon microflora agrees closely with the contours of the gas-bearing areas.

Soil-microbiological survey was similarly carried out. Samples for microbial analysis were taken at a depth of 2 m from the subsoil horizon, placed with the mineral medium in dishes and incubated for the same length of time in an atmosphere of methane and air.

The application of microbiological methods to oil prospecting was begun in the USSR in 1943; since then, more than sixty different structures and areas have been surveyed microbiologically. Water-bacterial surveys were first undertaken in 1947 and, as G. A. Mogilevskiy (1953) has stated, areas totaling more than half a million km^3 have been surveyed by this method.

Within the areas characterized by soil-microbe survey data, 16 structures were subsequently drilled. In ten of these the presence of industrial oil and gas deposits was established; in three, gas and oil shows of no commercial value were found; in three the prognoses of the microbiological survey were not confirmed. In none of the areas characterized negatively by the microbial survey data, did subsequent drilling reveal any signs of oil or gas occurrence.

This initial period of exaggeratedly optimistic valuation of bacterial survey methods was followed by a period in which these methods were denied any value at all. On the basis of later major researches (Mogilevskiy, 1953; Slavnina, 1958; etc.) combining

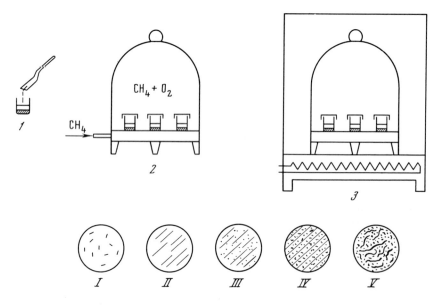

Fig. 62. Diagram of microbiological analysis of soil or water in microbiological oil and gas prospecting (after Mogilevskiy, 1953): 1—inoculation of soil or water; 2—filling of bell jar with methane and air; 3—cultivation in thermostat. Estimate of bacterial growth: I—turbidity of medium, bacteria discernible only microscopically; II—thin transparent film; III—semitransparent, slightly pigmented film; IV—solid smooth pigmented film; V—solid, wrinkled pigmented film.

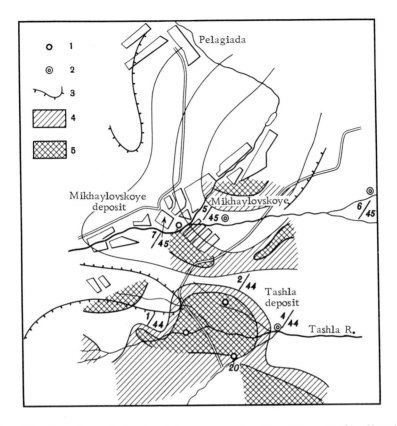

Fig. 63. Results of bacterial survey in the Stavropol' district
(after Mogilevskiy, 1957):
1—wells with gas; 2—gasless wells; 3—limits of occurrence of
hydrocarbon microflora in soil waters; 4—zones of medium population density of subsoil hydrocarbon microflora; 5—zones of high
population density.

these methods with geochemical, gas and seismic surveys, and
also taking account of the geological data on the regions in question, the prospects of the microbiological survey methods may be
more accurately and properly evaluated.

Microbial and geochemical methods must be used in combination. From the standpoint of both economy and rapidity in surveying,
the water-bacterial type of survey seems to afford the best prospects. Such a survey can be used to determine whether a given
district justifies more detailed investigation by more expensive
deep geophysical methods and by exploratory drilling. Soil-bacterial

survey methods may turn out to be especially useful in areas where seismic surveys fail to reveal the geologic structure, as has happened in the Stavropol' Kray. Radioautography (Romanenko, 1959; Davis, Raymond and Stanley, 1959) apparently also has good prospects for future use.

3. ATTEMPTS TO INHIBIT THE BIOGENIC FORMATION OF HYDROGEN SULFIDE IN STRATAL WATERS

When sulfates are present in oil stratal waters, they are usually accompanied by certain amounts of sulfides and free hydrogen sulfide. Often the sulfates may be completely reduced to hydrogen sulfide. Microbiological investigation has shown that the hydrogen sulfide here is formed by sulfate-reducing bacteria. Its presence, however, causes strong corrosion of the rods, clamps and bulbs of the deep pumps (Kuznetsov, 1957b). Investigations by Beck (1947b) and Plummer and Walling (1946) have shown that 10 to 50 mg/liter of formaldehyde is toxic to sulfate-reducing bacteria and quite adequately protects the metal against the corrosion induced by these organisms. Their data were confirmed by V. A. Kuznetsova and others (1957).

In this connection V. A. Kuznetsova, K. B. Ashirov and others (1957) carried out field experiments in the suppression of sulfate reduction directly within the oil stratum in the Kalinovka oil field of the Kuybyshev Oblast'. Some 2.5 metric tons of formalin (27% formaldehyde solution) were introduced into the drill hole through which water was pumped to flood the oil stratum. The formalin was added in a thin stream along with the water in such a manner that its concentration in the water upon entering the oil stratum was 40 mg/liter.

The spread of the water through the oil stratum was observed by the fluorescence method and by analysis of the chlorides in the stratal water of the working wells located around the water-pumping well. After two weeks the water had moved 100-150 m along the stratum in a specific direction. Microbiological analyses showed that the growth of the desulfurizing bacteria was suppressed in the formalin-water mixture that entered the oil stratum from the well and that these bacteria were absent in the stratal water for two or three weeks after the formalin had ceased to be added. The hydrogen sulfide content in the water was simultaneously reduced.

The same authors made similar tests on a larger scale in the Novostepanovo oil field. Twenty-five metric tons of 40% formalin were pumped into the oil stratum in the course of its flooding. This measure sharply decreased the number of breakdowns due to corrosion and breaking of the pumping rods in this oil field.

Measures taken to inhibit sulfate-reducing bacteria can be especially valuable where sea water is used to flood the oil stratum
to increase the secondary extraction of oil (Gasanov, 1961) or
where sulfate-rich water is pumped in, as at Pokrovka in the Kuybyshev Oblast' (Ashirov, 1961).

These experiments in suppressing sulfate reduction have also
solved a problem of theoretical significance by showing that the
introduction of antiseptics can cut short the activities of the
sulfate-reducing bacteria directly within the deposit. The problem
that remains is to find antiseptics that are less expensive and
more readily reconvertible than formalin.

4. THE FORMATION OF HYDROGEN SULFIDE IN THE CARPATHIAN SULFUR DEPOSITS

A characteristic feature of the Carpathian sulfur deposits is
the presence of hydrogen sulfide in the ground waters. The question of the origin of this gas is important both for determining the
genesis of the deposits in this area, and for the economic exploitation of the sulfur in the Carpathian region. From the standpoint of the genesis of the sulfur, study of the formation of hydrogen
sulfide is important because this very substance is the "raw
material" from which the sedimentary sulfur deposits are formed.
Thus a knowledge of the conditions favoring H_2S formation at the
present time may allow one to understand the geochemical processes that have led to the creation of the enormous sulfur deposits
of the Carpathians in the geologic past. The practical value of
studying the formation of hydrogen sulfide in the ground waters
lies in the fact that exploitation of the Carpathian sulfur deposits
by the open-pit method must first be preceded by drainage of the
sulfur-bearing stratum through a system of water-lowering
wells.

The fact that hydrogen sulfide occurs in all the waters draining
out of the Upper Tortonian deposits along the zone of contact between the southwestern margin of the Russian platform and the
Ciscarpathian marginal basin is quite thoroughly known in the
hydrogeological literature (Saydakovskiy, 1955; Kudrin, 1953; Gayun,
1956; Gonsovskaya–Goleva, 1957). Nevertheless there are questions
that have not yet been studied, such as how the hydrogen sulfide
content will be changed when the water is removed from the sulfur-
bearing limestones through the water-level-lowering wells, or
whether there will be a renewal of hydrogen sulfide in the waters
entering the deposits from the alimentation region. There is no
knowledge of the agency by which hydrogen sulfide is formed in
the ground waters of this region. Although the majority of

hydrogeologists have assumed a microbiological origin for the hydrogen sulfide in the ground waters within the Upper Tortonian deposits (Kudrin, 1953, 1957; Gayun, 1956; Gonsovskaya–Goleva, 1957), there has been no actual proof that this view is correct.

To cast some light on this problem, M. V. Ivanov (1960b) studied the distribution of sulfate-reducing bacteria in the waters and rocks of the Rozdol, Yazov, Nemirov and Lyuben'skoye sulfur deposits. The bacterial counts were parallelled by studies of the oxidation-reduction potential and certain hydrochemical properties of the waters investigated and by a determination of the rate of formation of hydrogen sulfide from the sulfates.

Study of the distribution of sulfate-reducing bacteria in ground waters of various types showed these bacteria to be common in all the waters investigated; they could not be found only in five out of 96 samples analyzed. The number of living cells of sulfate-reducing bacteria varied from 200 to 10,000 per liter of water, fewer cells as a rule being found in the hydrocarbonate waters outside the peripheries of the deposits and the numbers increasing as the waters approached closer to the deposits themselves. These bacteria were most numerous and widespread in the porous and highly fractured Upper Tortonian rocks, through which the hydrogen sulfide waters circulate.

The source of the sulfates required by the sulfate-reducing bacteria to form hydrogen sulfide are the gypsum-anhydrite deposits which generally underlie the sulfur-bearing beds in all the deposits of the Carpathian region (Sokolov, 1958). The very lack of sufficient sulfates in the hydrocarbonate-calcic waters filling the source region of the aquifers in the Rozdol and Yazov deposits retards the microbiological formation of hydrogen sulfide in these waters. Analyses have shown that, despite the presence of sulfate-reducing bacteria, hydrogen sulfide occurred in almost no samples of hydrocarbonate-calcic waters. On the other hand, even the presence of sulfates together with a high oxidation-reduction potential failed to cause any intensive formation of hydrogen sulfide. This is clear from wells drilled down to the aquifer stratum in the gypsum-anhydrites of the Rozdol and Yazov deposits.

Although enough sulfate-reducing bacteria and sulfates were present in all these waters, hydrogen sulfide formation either did not occur or was very slight, as indicated by the low concentration of H_2S in the water from these wells. The explanation must lie in the high oxidation-reduction potential, $rH_2 = 14.9-17.2$; these high values are not conducive to the active life processes of strictly anaerobic sulfate-reducing bacteria. By contrast, all the typical sulfate-calcic waters in the Carpathian deposits with large hydrogen sulfide contents have oxidation-reduction potentials of rH_2 12 or lower.

The hardest task was to determine the third component—organic matter—required for the reduction of sulfates to hydrogen sulfide. Most authorities who have studied the formation of hydrogen sulfide and sulfur in the Carpathian deposits are inclined to believe that the reduction of the gypsum-anhydrites, both in the geologic past and in the present, has occurred through a reaction with gaseous hydrocarbons migrating from a basin containing large natural gas occurrences (Sokolov, 1958). Without denying the possible migration of gas from the basin into the zone of the sulfur deposits, the present writers must nevertheless point out that this cannot be of use in deciphering the genesis of the sulfur and hydrogen sulfide in this region. Actually the chemical reaction between sulfate and methane can take place only at temperatures above 700°C, and microbiological reduction of sulfates by the use of methane does not occur at all (Rubenchik, 1947; Sorokin, 1957).

Proceeding from these observations, M. V. Ivanov (1960c) and V. N. Ryzhova and M. V. Ivanov (1961) performed a number of experiments to identify the organic matter needed for the reduction of the sulfates within the sulfur-bearing limestone itself. Some authors (Saydakovskiy, 1955; Kudrin, 1953) have assumed that the hydrogen sulfide is formed through the use of organic substances leached out from the host rocks themselves, while a paper by A. S. Sokolov (1958) mentions the presence of small amounts of bitumen in the Rozdol sulfur-bearing deposits. Ivanov and Ryzhova used cultures of sulfate-reducing bacteria and a mineral medium without any traces of organic matter for the experiments. As the only source of organic matter for the sulfate reduction process, sulfur-bearing ore was taken from a longitudinal trench in the Rozdol sulfur mine. After two weeks the quantity of hydrogen sulfide in some experiments rose to 200 mg/liter or more. Since no organic matter had been provided in the nutrient medium, the increased amount of hydrogen sulfide can only be due to the fact that the organic component necessary for sulfate reduction had been introduced together with the sulfur-bearing rock.

Thus the above observations and the results of experiments testify that all the necessary conditions for the reduction of the sulfates exist within the stratum of sulfur-bearing limestones, and hence that the sulfate-reducing bacteria, which are widespread in the ground waters of the Carpathian sulfur deposits, do actively form hydrogen sulfide from the sulfates.

All these facts, however, merely bear witness to the possibility that hydrogen sulfide is currently being formed in the ground waters of the sulfur deposits in the Carpathian region. But incontrovertible proof of the present formation of hydrogen sulfide in these waters is furnished by the results of experiments to determine the intensity of sulfate reduction, using tagged atoms, in the Rozdol and Yazov deposits (Tables 64 and 65). These data show that in certain parts of these deposits, microbiological formation of hydrogen sulfide during summer takes place at a rate of 2-3 mg per liter every twenty-four hours. Comparison of the intensities of sulfate reduction, as determined by experiments in spring and summer, reveals that during the summer this process takes place in the waters of almost all the boreholes at rates exceeding those in spring by 4-10 times or more.

Table 64

Intensity of sulfate reduction in waters of Rozdol sulfur deposit

Well No.	March–April, 1959			July, 1959		
		Hydrogen sulfide, mg/liter			Hydrogen sulfide, mg/liter	
	rH_2	Content	Intensity of formation in days	rH_2	Content	Intensity of formation in days
9	11.3	37.4	0.089	10.2	38.9	0.579
8	11.6	49.3	0.101	10.1	49.7	0.017
16	12.3	36.7	0.069		33.3	0.270
23	15.5	16.3	0.002	12.6	17.0	0.022
1c	12.4	37.4	0.015	11.9	18.7	0.207
31	11.6	30.9	0.009	12.4	19.7	1.675
32	10.3	51.3	0.031	11.6	51.0	3.232
5	11.0	18.9	0.045	—	—	—
29	18.0	20.3	0.021	—	—	—
25	14.5	27.7	0.003	—	—	—
37	—	—	—	13.5	29.9	0.024
26	—	—	—	11.6	28.9	0.073
2c	12.9	50.1	0.007	—	—	—
Source in trench	—	—	—	—	38.0	0.056

The hydrogen sulfide concentration in the waters investigated is affected principally by two processes: by the removal of hydrogen sulfide waters through the water-level-lowering wells and dilution of the hydrogen sulfide stratal waters by waters lacking hydrogen sulfide drawn in from the region of alimentation, and by the continuous microbiological formation of hydrogen sulfide from sulfates in the water medium. If one recalls that during the entire period of observation, from June, 1958 to November, 1959, the amount of water lacking hydrogen sulfide that flowed into the stratum each month to dilute the hydrogen sulfide stratal waters was approximately constant, it becomes clear that the cessation of the gradual decrease in the hydrogen sulfide content of the Rozdol waters at the beginning of summer can be due only to intensification of microbial sulfate reduction.

Table 65

Intensity of sulfate reduction in waters of central part of Yazov sulfur deposit

Well No.	April, 1959			August, 1959		
	rH_2	Hydrogen sulfide, mg/liter		rH_2	Hydrogen sulfide, mg/liter	
		Content	Intensity of formation in days		Content	Intensity of formation in days
1241	10.8	67.6	0.075	9.6	63.3	1.350
1281	10.2	74.8	0.021	9.9	77.9	3.820
Group 5	10.0	80.0	0.065	8.6	81.4	1.059
1174	10.5	79.5	0.030	9.1	82.2	0.691
1295	9.6	113.1	0.005	9.0	116.9	0.823
1293	9.5	118.8	0.012	8.6	121.6	3.019
1297	10.6	117.5	0.005	8.8	142.1	3.612
12B	9.0	80.6	0.005	9.0	83.6	2.030
15B	10.5	117.5	0.005	8.6	121.7	1.052

Thus direct study of the intensity of sulfate reduction by means of labeled atoms and analysis of the hydrogen sulfide content in the waters removed from the deposits reveals the seasonal changes in the intensity of hydrogen sulfide formation within the Rozdol sulfur deposit. Similar data on the seasonally changing intensity of sulfate reduction were obtained from studies of the ground waters in the Yazov deposit (Table 65).

A summary review of all the information on the formation of hydrogen sulfide in the Carpathian sulfur deposits suggests the following conclusions:

1. Surface waters penetrate into the aquifer strata where there is no screen of clay shales; the surface waters, traveling gradually along the aquifer beds, leach organic matter from the surrounding rocks, thereby decreasing the value of the oxidation-reduction potential in the water.

2. After these waters have crossed the contours marking the boundaries of the gypsiferous deposits, they contain sufficient amounts of sulfates for the microbiological formation of hydrogen sulfide to begin immediately.

3. Since all the conditions needed for microbiological sulfate reduction (sulfate-reducing bacteria, organic matter and sulfates) are present within the sulfur ore itself, removal of the static internal waters does not free the sulfur-bearing beds from hydrogen sulfide. New hydrogen sulfide is formed in the fresh supply of water arriving from the region of alimentation, with particular rapidity during the summer months.

4. The system of water-level-lowering pipes installed within the sulfur-bearing rocks at Rozdol to drain the deposit cannot eliminate the hydrogen sulfide. As long as water can enter the deposit, hydrogen sulfide will continue to be formed.

5. To prevent the formation of new portions of hydrogen sulfide along the stratum, measures must be undertaken to stop the penetration of water into the ground-water-saturated gypsum-anhydrites that underlie the sulfur deposit.

5. THE BIOGENIC OXIDATION OF SULFUR ORE

Studies of the role of microorganisms in the gensis and weathering of sulfur deposits, made by M. V. Ivanov (1957b, c, 1958, 1959, 1960a, b), have shown that the chief reason for the preservation of the sulfur deposits at Shor-Su, Gaurdak, Rozdol and other localities is the presence of free hydrogen sulfide in the stratal waters that saturate the sulfur-bearing rocks. One of the necessary conditions for the industrial exploitation of sulfur deposits by underground or open-pit mining methods is the lowering of the level of hydrogen sulfide waters to the bottom of the working stratum. Depending on the depth and manner of penetration of the oxygen-saturated atmospheric waters, during this process some degree of oxidizing conditions will be created within the deposit, with the attendant possibility of further oxidation of the sulfur and formation of secondary gypsum. Oxidation may be especially intensive in sulfur ore extracted from the deposit and stored at the earth's surface.

The oxidation of sulfur, accompanied by the formation of secondary gypsum, is still more intensive in ore that has been exposed to the atmosphere for about a year. As G. I. Karavayko, M. V. Ivanov and B. I. Srebrodol'skiy (1962) have indicated, the sulfur is oxidized through the direct participation of *Th. thioparus* and *Th. thiooxidans*. The number of bacteria here reaches hundreds of thousands of cells per gram of rock. The oxidation takes place in the very surface layer, 5-10 mm thick, of the individual ore lumps, where the content of secondary gypsum during a year's storage of the ore may reach 20%, although the total gypsum content in the ore as a whole is no more than 1-2%. Such formation of secondary gypsum greatly hinders extraction of the sulfur in the autoclaves.

The examination of the problem of the oxidation of sulfur ore suggests that, from the microbiological standpoint, the following measures are needed to counteract this process: 1) in working the sulfur deposits one must see that the level of the hydrogen sulfide waters is only lowered shortly before the ore is mined from a given part of the deposit; 2) after extraction the ore must not be stored in the open, where it is exposed to atmospheric precipitation, but if possible should be taken directly from the mine to the refining plant. The problem of how to store the already extracted sulfur ore over long periods of time needs further study by chemists and microbiologists. Fundamentally, this requires creation of such storage conditions as will be most unfavorable to the development of *Th. thioparus* and *Th. thiooxidans.*

6. THE ROLE OF *THIOBACILLUS FERROOXIDANS* IN FORMING ACID DRAINAGE WATERS IN COAL DEPOSITS AND MEASURES TO COUNTERACT THEIR FORMATION

The geochemical activity of *Th. ferrooxidans* takes place in coal mines and in deposits and storage piles of sulfide ores. Such activity is often harmful, so that the task arises of limiting or entirely eliminating its damaging effects. On the other hand, the oxidizing capacity of these microorganisms can be utilized in industry.

In some regions of the USA there is a very serious problem of pollution by acid drainage waters from bituminous coal mines. Because of their sulfuric acid content, the drainage waters are corrosive even in the mines themselves, where they do considerable damage to rails, pipes and other equipment. The corrosive action of acid waters in the coal pits of Scotland has been mentioned by Ashmeed (1955). In the Soviet Union, acid mine waters are present in the Kizelov coal basin. According to verbal communication from V. V. Smirnov and P. A. Kolevatov, staff scientists of the Perm Scientific Research Institute for Coal, the acid mine waters contain much iron, which is deposited in the pipes as hydroxides, thus sharply reducing the pipe diameters and hindering the flow of water. Precipitated ferric hydroxide also clogs the sides of the channels into which the mine waters drain.

When the acid mine waters enter the rivers, the dissolved oxygen in the river water is taken up in oxidizing the ferrous sulfate, and this result along with the large amounts of iron salts and the high acidity in these rivers kills all the vegetation and animal life. In Leathen's opinion (Leathen et al., 1956), *Th. ferrooxidans* can, however, play a positive role in the purification of water reservoirs, since if oxidation of ferrous sulfate were to take place only through a slow chemical process, many bodies of water would be completely barren of life throughout. The iron–oxidizing bacteria rapidly oxidize the iron and cause most of the ferric sulfates to be precipitated in the stream not far from the source of contamination and thereby limit the area of river water in which oxygen is lacking.

Acid mine waters do great damage even when they enter large rivers. Bridges, sluices and dams suffer from the gradual corrosion caused by constant contact with weak sulfuric acid. The additional chemical treatment of the water used for drinking and industrial purposes becomes much more expensive. To give some notion of the losses caused by the effects of sulfuric acid, most of which is formed in mines by bacterial activity, the following figures may be cited: in Pittsburgh, three million dollars are spent annually for purification of the drinking water, and corrosion of pipes causes a loss of five hundred thousand dollars annually in West Virginia alone. The annual losses due to corrosion and expenditures for additional water purification were estimated at ten million dollars for the states of the Ohio River basin (Hodge, 1937). Since the sulfuric acid is formed by the oxidation of the iron sulfide present in the coals, some mine operators in the USA decided to shut off the access of oxygen into the mines, so as to prevent oxidation and thus counteract the appearance of acid drainage waters. In an extensive program of closing off abandoned mines carried out over three years, more than 47 thousand mine openings were sealed off, decreasing acid formation in these regions by 25%, and in some localities by 80%. Murdock (1953), however, believes that closing off abandoned mines is of no practical value. In four of the sealed-off mines he made weekly chemical analyses of the waters. Although there was a small decrease in the amount of acid one year after the mines had been closed, the acid concentration in the mines fluctuated violently and showed almost no average decrease.

Chemical neutralization measures have been adopted to eliminate the acids in mine waters. In a mine that produces typical acid waters, a channel was constructed into which five metric tons of finely crushed limestone were placed. After the mine water had been in contact with the limestone for one hour, less than 50% of the acids were neutralized. Hence the method of prolonged contact between water and limestone was considered to be unsuitable, and it was decided that the waters should be neutralized in special reservoirs, in which the water and limestone were placed and violently agitated to mix them together. Four hours were required to neutralize water containing 400 g of sulfuric acid, but since in this process iron hydroxide was precipitated over the limestone, subsequent neutralization took much longer. Since neutralization of this type requires considerable time and expenditure, chemical treatment was abandoned as unsuitable.

Murdock believes that the quantity of acid emanating from a mine does not correspond to the total amount of acid formed there, but depends on the volume of water flowing through the mine. The formation of acid and contamination of streams are related to the degree of water-saturation of the mines; therefore it should be possible to get rid of the acid waters by decreasing the flow of water into the mines to a minimum. Murdock considers that the most rational method of combating the formation of acid waters is to prevent the surface waters from entering the mines and to remove the ground waters from coal seams with high contents of pyritic sulfur. Since bacteria greatly accelerate acid formation from sulfur inclusions in the coals, and about four fifths of all the acid is formed by bacteria (Ashmeed, 1955), it should ultimately be possible to counteract acid waters by working out methods based on the action of antibacterial substances. Bufton (1958) writes that at Johns Hopkins University in the USA, experiments are being carried out on the treatment of mines with such chemicals as phosphates and chromates, in order to stop the oxidation of sulfur-containing materials.

7. THE IMPORTANCE OF *THIOBACILLUS FERROOXIDANS* IN DESULFURIZING COAL

Sulfur-containing coals are usually of lower quality. Therefore the oxidation of the sulfurous inclusions in rock coal not only causes the formation of sulfuric acid, but also frees the coal from sulfur. Z. M. Zarubina, N. N. Lyalikova and Ye. I. Shmuk (1959) have performed some experiments in the desulfurization of coal by bacteria. Samples of both high-sulfur and low-sulfur coals, with a predominance of pyritic sulfur, were placed either in percolators with uninterrupted circulation of liquid, or in a moist atmosphere in desiccators. A culture of *Th. ferrooxidans* isolated from the highly oxidized coal of the Donets Basin was added to the experimental coal samples. The controls consisted of the same coals, with a culture of bacteria previously killed with mercuric chloride. Table 66 gives the results of some of these experiments.

These results form the basis for concluding that bacteria considerably accelerate oxidation of the pyrite in coal. In one month they removed 23-30% of the sulfur, transforming it from the pyrite form into soluble sulfate. Further study has shown that desulfurization of the coal may be promoted by pulverizing the coal, as well as by the use of younger cultures of bacteria. The removal of pyrite from the coal was also hastened when a concentrated suspension of cells was used, instead of a culture containing an average of 30 million cells per ml. Nevertheless the microbiological desulfurization of coal is too slow a process to be used in this form for industrial coal purification. It may be, however, that this method can be used in combination with others for coals that do not yield readily to purification.

Table 66

Liberation of Class 3-0 mm coal from sulfur by treatment with *Thiobacillus ferrooxidans* culture

Mine from which coal taken	Initial content of total sulfur, %	Duration of experiment, days					
		10		20		30	
		Total sulfur, % of coal weight	% of sulfur oxidized to sulfates	Total sulfur, % of coal weight	% of sulfur oxidized to sulfates	Total sulfur, % of coal weight	% of sulfur oxidized to sulfates
Krasnoarmeyskaya TsFO	3.70				Experiment		
		3.43	7.3	3.23	12.7	2.73	26.2
					Control		
		3.69	0.27	3.70	0	3.70	0
Abakumov	2.41				Experiment		
		—	—	2.12	12.05	1.76	27.0
					Control		
		—	—	2.40	0.41	2.40	0.41
Novo-Dzerzhinsk	3.95				Experiment		
		3.47	12.2	3.46	12.43	3.02	23.5
					Control		
		3.95	0	3.95	0	3.95	0
Yasinovskaya, coal concentrate from 3/5 shaft	3.26				Experiment		
		2.79	14.4	2.78	14.70	2.51	23.0
					Control		
		3.26	0	3.26	0	3.22	1.23
Nikitovskaya	2.80				Experiment		
		2.53	10	2.49	14.30	1.96	30.0
					Control		
		—	—	2.70	3.60	2.66	5

8. THE USE OF *THIOBACILLUS FERROOXIDANS* IN THE LEACHING OF COPPER FROM LOW-GRADE ORES

The use of bacteria for purifying low-grade sulfide ores appears to have much better prospects for practical application. As the richer deposits are gradually exhausted, it will become necessary in the future to obtain metals from low-grade ores. The results of bacterial leaching of ores have been given earlier in this book. In experiments by Bryner, Beck, Davis and Wilson (1954), about 25% of the copper was leached out after 90 days of bacterial action. Thus this process, like the bacterial desulfurization of coal, is too slow to be used in ore-purification plants. But bacterial leaching can be used directly in mines where acid water containing bacteria passes through the ore storage piles. Since this type of leaching does not involve expenditure for installations and equipment, it may be economically feasible, and the long time required for the leaching is of no particular significance.

Such leaching is actually carried on in many mines, but the importance of bacterial activity in this process is usually not recognized, since it is believed that the ores are oxidized purely chemically. An example of the leaching of low-grade ores is the installation at the Cananea deposit in Mexico (Weed, 1956). Over several years of mining, some 40 million tons of ore, containing an average of 0.2% copper, were accumulated around the mine. The principal copper mineral was chalcosite. The ore storage piles were subjected to leaching action by water passing repeatedly through the ore. The water, containing up to 3 g/liter of copper, was then collected in underground reservoirs, where the copper was recovered by an exchange reaction with iron. This leaching yielded an additional 650 tons of copper per month. Weed (1956) makes no mention of any role of bacteria in this process, but Bryner and Jamerson (1958) isolated cultures of *Th. ferrooxidans* and *Th. thiooxidans* from the leaching solution, and laboratory experiments convinced them that the leaching at Cananea is a biological process.

Copper can be leached from the ore not only in the storage piles, but also within the mines themselves. Extraction of the ore always involves losses, varying from 5 to 20% depending on the different systems of extraction. The ore remains in the worked sulfide deposits, in which further ore extraction by mining methods is impossible because the ore body has been destroyed, or impracticable because of the low copper content. According to V. A. Aglitskiy and S. Ye. Dyn'kina (1956), the copper remaining in this abandoned ore amounts to thousands of tons. The only possible method of recovering copper that is not accessible to mining operations is by artifically induced underground leaching, in which three quarters of the calculated copper losses may be saved. Artificial underground leaching has been used with great success in the USA, where some 29% of all the copper reserves was leached out in half a year in one of the mines in Arizona; in this leaching process the copper content in the solution reached 9.2 g/liter.

In the Soviet Union, artificial underground leaching has been undertaken in the worked-out portions of the Degtyarskoye, Belaya Reka and other mines in the Urals. Fresh water or the waste water from the mine installations was used for the leaching, better results being achieved in the latter case. This may be due to the fact that, besides containing large quantities of ferric sulfate and sulfuric acid, which promote solution of the copper sulfide minerals, the waste waters from the mines also contain many bacteria. In the installations at the Degtyarskoye and Krasnogvardeyskoye deposits, for instance, according to the present writers' analyses, *Th. ferrooxidans* numbered 10,000 cells per ml. In artificial underground leaching, as in the leaching of ore storage piles, bacterial activity must be taken into account and favorable conditions created, for example by the addition of nitrogenous salts. Thus the leaching process will probably be accelerated.

Bacterial leaching of sulfide ores is excessively slow, but can be speeded up by the use of ferric sulfate, which causes the metal to go into solution from the ore, the oxidation of the sulfides being accompanied by conversion of the iron to the ferrous form. This method of leaching has long been known, but its widespread application has been hindered because the reduced iron must be regenerated before the cycle can be repeated. The chemical oxidation of iron under acid conditions is very difficult. Passing air through the solution does not help, so that some oxidizing agent such as sulfur gas must be used, thereby greatly complicating the leaching process. In 1958 the Kennecott Company, in connection with the extraction of copper (Zimmerley et al., 1958), obtained a patent for the oxidation of a solution of ferrous iron by a culture of *Th. ferrooxidans*. It was shown that bacteria, by direct action on pyrite, can produce leaching substances—$Fe_2(SO_4)_3$ and sulfuric acid. Of particular value is the rapidity with which the bacteria-containing solution can be regenerated by simple aeration, without expensive equipment and complicated procedures (Zimmerley et al., 1958). The bacterially regenerated solution again comes into contact with the ore; this constitutes the cycle in the process diagrammatically illustrated in Fig. 64. Copper and zinc ores can be leached in this manner. In the case of mixed sulfide and oxide ores, both leaching and flotation can be used. By leaching, the copper can be separated from a mixture of molybdenite and copper minerals and a high-grade molybdenum concentrate obtained.

The patent also proposes a method for obtaining chromium and titanium concentrates from iron ore containing these valuable

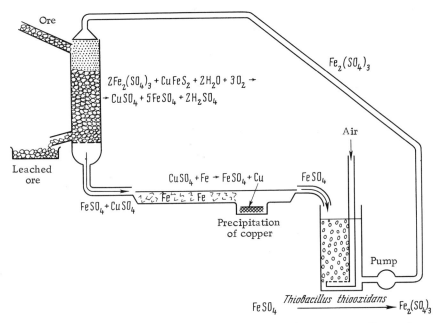

Fig. 64. Diagram of apparatus for extracting copper from low-grade ore with use of bacteria to regenerate solution of ferrous sulfate (after Zimmerley et al., 1958)

metals. The ore is reduced in a furnace with coke, after which the metallic iron is leached out.

9. MICROBIOLOGICAL PROSPECTING FOR SULFIDE ORES

In the USSR, the All-Union Geological Institute (VSEGEI) is carrying out a program of study of the specific microflora in ore deposits. L. Ye. Kramarenko, I. I. Prizrenova and R. I. Teben'-kova (1959), after studying the microflora of the Shalgiy molybdenum deposit in Central Kazakhstan, established the presence of the thiobacteria *Thiobacillus denitrificans* and *Th. thiooxidans* in the deposits above the ore body. Further investigations (Kramarenko, 1962) showed that the waters of the hydrochemical anomalies above the deposits could be distinguished from the general regional ground water by the intensity of development of particular bacterial species. Thus by determining the particular groups of ground-water bacteria involved in the sulfur cycle in nature, microbiological analysis can be used to supplement hydrochemical methods of locating ore deposits. Neither microbiological nor hydrochemical methods can be used if the waters altered chemically and microbiologically by the ore body are greatly diluted by other waters. The prerequisite conditions for the application of the hydrochemical method have been described by A. A. Brodskiy (1957). The microbiological prospecting method needs to be further developed; in particular, the frequency with which thiobacteria may be encountered in waters not associated with economic mineral deposits must be determined.

These possibilities for the practical utilization of autotrophic bacteria justify the hope that microorganisms taking part in geochemical processes may ultimately be widely used in economic geology.

References

AARNIO, B., 1915. O Vypadenii Okislov Zheleza i Alyuminiya v Peschanykh i Shchebenchatykh Pochvakh Finlyandii [The Precipitation of Oxides of Iron and Aluminum in the Sandy and Gravelly Soils of Finland]: Pochvovedeniye, Nos. 2 & 3.

ABELSON, P. H., 1956. Paleobiochemistry: Scientific American, v. 195, pp. 83–92.

AGLITSKIY, V. A., and S. Ye. DYN'KINA, 1956. Podzemnoye Vyshchelachivaniye Medi [The Underground Leaching of Copper]: Gornyy Zhurnal, No. 11, p. 35.

AL'TOVSKIY, M. Ye., 1958. Fiziko-khimicheskiye Protsessy v Formirovanii Podzemnykh Vod [The Physicochemical Processes in the Formation of Underground Waters]: Trudy Lab. Gidrogeol. Problem, im. Akad. F. P. Savarenskogo, v. 16.

AL'TOVSKIY, M. YE., Z., Z. I. KUZNETSOVA and V. M. SHVETS, 1958. Obrazovaniye Nefti i Formirovaniye Yeye Zalezhey [The Genesis of Oil and the Formation of Its Deposits]: Moscow, Gosnauchtekhizdat.

ANDREYEV, P. F., 1955. K Voprosu o Bakterial'noy Gipoteze Genezisa Tipov Neftey [On the Problem of the Bacterial Hypothesis of the Genesis of the Types of Oil]: Trudy Vses. Neft. Geol.-Razved. In-ta, No. 83.

ANDREYEVSKIY, I. L., 1959. Puti Ispol'zovaniya Neftyanoy Mikrobiologii v Neftedobyvayushchey Promyshlennosti [The Ways of Utilizing Oil Microbiology in the Oil Extraction Industry]: Trudy VNIGRI, No. 131, Geol. Coll. No. 4.

ASCHAN, O., 1907. Die Bedeutung der wasserlöslichen Humusstoffe für die Bildung der See- und Sumpferze: Z. prakt. Geol., v. 15.

ASHIROV, K. B., 1959a. Usloviya Formirovaniya Neftyanykh Mestorozhdeniy Kuybyshevskogo Povolzh'ya [The Conditions Determining the Formation of the Oil Deposits in the Kuybyshev Part of the Volga Region]: Trudy In-ta "Giprovostokneft'," No. 2.

ASHIROV, K. B., 1959b. Tsementatsiya Prikontaktnogo Sloya Neftyanykh Zalezhey v Karbonatnykh Kollektorakh i Vliyaniye Yeye na Razrabotku. Geologiya i Razrabotka Neftyanykh

Mestorozhdeniy [The Cementation of the Contact Layer of Oil Deposits in Carbonate Reservoir Rocks and Its Effect on their Exploitation. The Geology and Exploitation of Oil Deposits]: Trudy In-ta "Giprovostokneft'," No. 2.

ASHIROV, K. B., 1961. Mikroorganizmy kak Indikator Svyazi Plastovykh Vod s Neftyanymi Zalezhami [Microorganisms as Indicators of the Connection between Stratal Waters and Oil Deposits]: Trudy In-ta Mikrobiol., No. 9. Coll. "Geologicheskaya Deyatel'nost' Mikroorganizmov" [The Geological Activity of Microorganisms].

ASHIROV, K. B., and S. P. MAKSIMOV, 1958. Usloviya Gazonosnosti Mestorozhdeniy Kuybyshevskogo Povolzh'ya [The Conditions of Gas Occurrence in the Kuybyshev Volga Region]: Geologiya Nefti, No. 2.

ASHMEED, D., 1955. The Influence of Bacteria on the Formation of Acid Mine Waters: Colliery Guard., v. 190, p. 694.

BAARS, J. K., 1930. Over Sulfatreductic Door Bacterien: Delft.

BAAS BECKING, L. D. M., 1938. On the Cause of High Acidity in Natural Waters, Especially in Brines: Proc. Konikl. Nederl. Akad. Wet., v. 58, pp. 1074-1085.

BAAS BECKING, L. D. M., 1959. Geology and Microbiology. Contribution to Marine Microbiology: New Zealand Dept. of Sci. and Ind. Res., Inform. Ser., No. 22. New Zealand Oceanograph. Inst. Mem., No. 3, pp. 48-64.

BAAS BECKING, L. D. M., I. R. KAPLAN and D. MOORE, 1960. Limits of the Natural Environment in Terms of pH and Oxidation-Reduction Potentials: J. Geol., v. 68, No. 3.

BAAS BECKING, L. D. M., and E. J. F. WOOD, 1955. Biological Processes in the Estuarine Environment. I. Ecology of the Sulphur Cycle: Proc. Konikl. Nederl. Akad. Wet., v. 58, pp. 160-181.

BAIER, C. R., 1937. Die Bedeutung der Bakterien für die Bildung oxydischer Eisen- und Manganerze: Geol. Meer-und Binnengewasser, v. 1, Nos. 2-3.

BAKIROV, A. A. et al., 1955. Proiskhozhdeniye Nefti. Sb. Sostavlen Gruppoy Nauchn. Sotrudn. Ryada Otrasl. i Akademich. Institutov SSSR [The Origin of Oil. A Collection of Papers by a Group of Scientific Workers in a Number of Branches and Academic Institutes of the USSR].

BALASUNDARAM, M. S., 1954. Occurrence of Sulphur near Kona, Krishna District, Madras: Indian Minerals. v. 8, p. 2.

BARANIK-PIKOWSKY, M. A., 1927. Über den Einfluss hoher Salzkonzentration auf die Limanbakterien: Zbl. Bakteriol., Abt. II, v. 70, pp. 373-383.

BARKER, H. A., 1956. Biological Formation of Methane: Ind. Eng. Chem., Part I, v. 38, No. 9, p. 1438.

BASTIN, E. S., 1926. The Presence of Sulphate-Reducing Bacteria in Oil Field Waters: Science, v. 63, No. 1618, pp. 21-24.

BASTIN, E. S., and F. E. GREER, 1930. Additional Data on Sulphate-Reducing Bacteria in Soils and Waters of Illinois Oil Fields: Bull. Amer. Assoc. Petrol. Geologists, v. 14, pp. 153-159.

BECK, J., 1960. A Ferrous-Oxidizing Bacterium: J. Bacteriol., v. 79, No. 4.

BECK, J. V., 1947a. Penn Grade Progress on the Use of Bacteria for Releasing Oil from Sands: Producer's Monthly, v. 11, No. 11, pp. 13-19.

BECK, J. V., 1947b. Prevention of Microbial Growths in Water Flood Operations: Producer's Monthly, v. 11, No. 12, pp. 13-19.

BECK, Th., and H. POSCHENREDER, 1958. Über die Artenmässige Zusammensetzung der Mikroflora eines sehr sauren Wald-moorprofils: Zbl. Bakteriol., Abt. II, v. 111, Nos. 21-25, pp. 672-683.

BECKMANN, J. W., 1926. The Action of Bacteria on Mineral Oil: Ind. Eng. Chem. News, Ed. 4 (Nov. 10), 3.

BEERSTECHER, E., 1954. Petroleum Microbiology: New York, Elsevier Press.

BEGAK, D. A., and N. M. BELIKOVA, 1934. Kolichestvo i Ras-predeleniye Mikroorganizmov v Verkhovykh Torfyanikakh [The Number and Distribution of Microorganisms in the Upper Layers of Peat Bogs]: Trudy N.-I. In-ta Torf. Promyshl., No. 14.

BEIJERINCK, M. W., 1904. Über die Bakterien, welche sich im Dunkeln mit Kohlensäure als Kohlenstoffquelle ernähren können: Zbl. Bakteriol., Abt. II, v. 111, pp. 593-599.

BELIKOVA, N. M., 1931. K Voprosu o Gumifikatsii v Iskusst-vennykh Usloviyakh [On the Concentration of Free Hydrogen Under Artificial Conditions]: Torf. Delo, No. 6.

BELKIN, A. D., 1952. K Voprosu o Kontsentratsii Svobodnogo Serovodoroda v Istochnike i Vannakh Kurorta Sergiyevskiye Mineral'nyye Vody [On the Concentration of Free Hydrogen Sulfide in the Spring and the Bathing Pools of the Sergiyevskiy Mineral Waters Spa]: Trudy Kurota "Sergiyevskiye Miner. Vody," v. 1.

BELOUSOV, V. V., 1937. Ocherk Geokhimii Prirodnykh Gazov [A Survey of the Geochemistry of Natural Gases]: ONTI.

BIRSHTEKHER, E., 1957. Neftyanaya Mikrobiologiya [Oil Micro-biology]: Moscow, Gostoptekhizdat [translation of Beerstecher, 1954, to Russian].

BOKOVA, Ye. N., 1947. Izucheniye Osnovnykh Svoystv Bakteriy, Okislyayushchikh Zhidkiye i Gazoobraznyye Uglevodorody, Vydelennykh iz Glubinnykh Sloyev i Podpochvennykh Otlozheniy, i Vyyasneniye Nekotorykh Usloviy, Ogranichivayushchikh Ikh

Razvitiye [A Study of the Principal Properties of the Bacteria that Oxidize Liquid and Gaseous Hydrocarbons Extracted from Subsoil Deposits and Deeper Strata, and a Determination of Certain Conditions that Limit Their Development]: Izv. Glav. Upr. Geol. Fondov, No. 3.

BOKOVA, Ye. N., 1953. Obrazovaniye Metana Pri Mikrobial'nom Razlozhenii Nefti [The Formation of Methane in the Microbial Decomposition of Oil]: Polevaya i Promyslovaya Geokhimiya, No. 2. Moscow, Gostoptekhizdat.

BOKOVA, Ye. N., 1954. Okisleniye Etana i Propana Nekotorymi Vidami Mikrobakteriy [The Oxidation of Ethane and Propane by Certain Species of Microbacteria]: Mikrobiologiya, v. 23, No. 1.

BOKOVA, Ye. N., V. A. KUZNETSOVA and S. I. KUZNETSOV, 1947. Okisleniye Gazoobraznykh Uglevodorodov Bakteriyami kak Osnova Mikrobiologicheskoy Razvedki na Neft' [The Oxidation of Gaseous Hydrocarbons by Bacteria as a Basis for Microbiological Oil Prospecting]: Doklady AN SSSR, v. 56, No. 7.

BONYTHON, C. W., 1956. The Salt of Lake Eyre—Its Occurrence in Madigan Gulf and Its Possible Origin: Trans. Roy. Soc. S. Australia, v. 79, p. 66.

BONYTHON, C. W., and D. KING, 1956. The Occurrence of Native Sulphur at Lake Eyre: Trans. Roy. Soc. S. Australia, v. 79, pp. 121-129.

BRODSKIY, A. A., 1957. Gidrokhimicheskiy Metod Poiskov Rudnykh Mestorozhdeniy [The Hydrochemical Method of Prospecting for Ore Deposits]: Moscow, Gosgeolizdat.

BRUYEVICH, S. V., 1949. Skorost' Osadkoobrazovaniya Donnykh Otlozheniy v Mirovom Okeane [The Rate of Deposition of the Bottom Sediments in the World Ocean]: Trudy In-ta Okeanologiy, v. 3.

BRUYEVICH, S. V., 1953. Khimiya i Biologicheskaya Produktivnost' Chernogo Morya [The Chemistry and Biological Productivity of the Black Sea]: Trudy In-ta Okeanologiy, v. 7.

BRYNER, L., and R. ANDERSON, 1957. Microorganisms in Leaching Sulfide Minerals: Ind. and Eng. Chem., v. 49, p. 1721.

BRYNER, L., J. BECK, D. DAVIS and D. WILSON, 1954. Microorganisms in Leaching Sulfide Minerals: Ind. and Eng. Chem., v. 46, No. 12, p. 2587.

BRYNER, L. C., and A. K. JAMERSON, 1958. Microorganisms in Leaching Sulfide Minerals: Appl. Microbiol., v. 6, No. 4.

BUFTON, A. W., 1958. Industrial and Economic Microbiology in North America: Published by DSYK Dept. of Sci. and Indust. Res.

BUTKEVICH, V. S., 1928. Obrazovaniye Morskikh Zhelezo-Margantsevykh Otlozheniy i Uchastvuyushchiye v Nem

Mikroorganizmy [The Formation of Marine Iron-Manganese Deposits and the Microorganisms Participating in This Process]: Trudy Morsk. Nauchn. In-ta, v. 3.

BUTLIN, K. R., and J. R. POSTGATE, 1953a. The Economic Importance of Autotrophs: 4th Sympos. Soc. Gen. Microbiol.

BUTLIN, K. R., and J. R. POSTGATE, 1953b. The Microbiological Formation of Sulphides and Sulphur: Sympos. on Microbiol. Metabolism, Rome, 126.

BUTLIN, K. R., and J. R. POSTGATE, 1954. The Microbiological Formation of Sulphur in Cyrenaican Lakes: Biology of Deserts, Inst. Biol. London, 112.

CARPENTOR, L., and L. HERNDON, 1933. Used Mine Drainage from Bituminous Coal Mines: West Virginia Univ. Engin. Exptl. Sta. Res. Bull., No. 10.

COLMER, A. R., and M. E. HINKLE, 1947. The Role of Microorganisms in Acid Mine Drainage: Science, v. 106, p. 253.

COLMER, A., K. TEMPLE and M. HINKLE, 1949. An Iron-Oxidizing Bacterium from the Drainage of Some Bituminous Coal Mines: J. Bacteriol., v. 59, p. 317.

DANOV, A. V., 1936. Ob Usloviyakh Obrazovaniya Mestorozhdeniy Sery v Sredney Azii [The Conditions Governing the Formation of Sulfur Deposits in Central Asia]: ONTI.

DAVIS, J. B., 1956a. Symposium on Petroleum Microbiology: Bacteriol. Revs., v. 20, No. 4.

DAVIS, J. B., 1956b. Microbial Decomposition of Hydrocarbons: Ind. and Eng. Chem., Pt. I, v. 48, No. 9.

DAVIS, J. B., H. H. CHASE and R. L. RAYMOND, 1956. Mycobacterium paraffinicum n. sp., a Bacterium Isolated from the Soil: Appl. Microbiol., v. 4, No. 6.

DAVIS, J. B., R. L. RAYMOND and J. STANLEY, 1959. Areal Contrasts in the Abundance of Hydrocarbon-Oxidizing Microbes in Soil: Appl. Microbiol., v. 7, No. 3.

DAVIS, J. B., and D. UPDEGRAFF, 1954. Microbiology in the Petroleum Industry: Bacteriol. Revs., v. 18, pp. 215-238.

DERYUGIN, K. M., 1924. Barentsovo More po Kol'skomu Meridianu [The Barents Sea along the Kola Meridian : Trudy Severn. Nauchn. Promysl. Eksp., No. 19.

DOBRYANSKIY, A. Ya., 1948. Geokhimiya Nefti [The Geochemistry of Oil]: Moscow, Gostoptekhizdat.

DOLGOV, G. I., 1955. Sobinskiye Ozera [The Soba Lakes]: Trudy Vses. Gidrobiol. Ob-va, v. 6, 193-204.

DOSTALEK, M., 1953a. Uhlovodikové Bakterie v Pudách Naftoyých Oblasté [Hydrocarbon Bacteria in Oil-Bearing Deposits]: Ceskosl. Biol., 2, No. 6, pp. 341-346.

DOSTALEK, M., 1953b. Mikrobiologie v Naftovem Vyzkumu [Microbiology in Oil Prospecting]: Československ. Biol., 2, No. 5, pp. 312-317.

DOSTALEK, M., 1953c. Uglevodorodnyye Bakterii v Pochvakh Neftenosnykh Oblastey [Hydrocarbon Bacteria in the Soils of Oil-Bearing Regions]: Biologiya (Czechoslovakia), v. 2 (6).

DOSTALEK, M., 1954. Propanokislyayushchiye Bakterii [Propane-Oxidizing Bacteria]: Biologiya (Czechoslovakia), v. 3 (5).

DOSTALEK, M., and M. SPURNY, 1958. Bacterial Release of Oil. I. Preliminary Trials in an Oil Deposit: Folia Biol. (Poland), v. 4, No. 3, pp. 166-172.

DROBYSHEV, D., 1930. K Voprosu o Genezise Mestorozhdeniy Sery Gornogo Dagestana [On the Problem of the Genesis of the Sulfur Deposits in the Dagestan Mountain Country]: Materialy po Obshch. i Prikl. Geol., No. 152. Leningrad, Izd-vo Geolkom.

DUTOVA, Ye. N., 1959. Neftepoiskovoye Znacheniye Mikroflory Podzemnykh Vod Nekotorykh Rayonov Zapadnoy Chasti Sredney Azii [The Oil-Prospecting Significance of the Microflora in the Ground Waters of Certain Districts in the Western Part of Central Asia]: Inform. Sb. Vses. Geol. In-ta, No. 19, "Podzemnyye Vody" [Ground Waters], Leningrad.

EDWARDS, O. F., and L. F. RETTGER, 1937. The Relation of Certain Respiratory Enzymes to the Maximum Growth Temperatures of Bacteria: J. Bacteriol., v. 34, No. 5, p. 489.

EKZERTSEV, V. A., 1948. Opredeleniye Moshchnosti Mikrobiologicheski Aktivnogo Sloya Ilovykh Otlozheniy Nekotorykh Ozer [Determination of the Thickness of the Microbiologically Active Layer of the Ooze Deposits in Certain Lakes]: Mikrobiologiya, v. 17, No. 6.

EKZERTSEV, V. A., 1951. Mikroskopicheskiye Issledovaniya Bakterial'noy Flory v Neftenosnykh Fatsiyakh Vtorogo Baku [Microscopic Investigations of the Bacterial Flora in the Oil-Bearing Facies of the Vtoroye Baku Deposits]: Mikrobiologiya, v. 20, No. 4.

EKZERTSEV, V. A., 1956. Obrazovaniye Metana Mikroorganizmami v Neftyanykh Mestorozhdeniyakh [The Formation of Methane by Microorganisms in Oil Deposits]: Avtoref. Diss. Izd-vo AN SSSR.

EKZERTSEV, V. A., 1958. Izucheniye Protsessa Razrusheniya Nefti Mikroorganizmami v Anaerobnykh Usloviyakh [A Study of the Process of Oil Destruction by Microorganisms under Anaerobic Conditions]: Mikrobiologiya, v. 27, No. 5.

EKZERTSEV, V. A., 1960. Obrazovaniye Metana Mikroorganizmami v Neftyanykh Mestorozhdeniyakh [The Formation of Methane by Microorganisms in Oil Deposits]: Geokhimiya, No. 4.

EKZERTSEV, V. A., and S. I. KUZNETSOV, 1954. Issledovaniye Mikroflory Neftenosnykh Mestorozhdeniy Vtorogo Baku [An

Investigation of the Microflora in the Vtoroye Baku Oil-Bearing Deposits]: Mikrobiologiya, v. 23, No. 1.

ELLIS, D., 1914. Fossil Microorganisms from the Jurassic and Cretaceous Rocks of Great Britain: Proc. Roy. Soc. Edinburgh, v. 35, No. 1, pp. 110-133.

FERSMAN, A. Ye., 1926. Geokhimicheskiye Problemy Sernykh Bugrov v Pustyne Kara-Kumy [Geochemical Problems of the Sulfur Hummocks in the Kara-Kum Desert]: "Sera," Materialy Komissii Yest. Proisv. Sil. AN SSSR, No. 59, Leningrad.

FILATOV, K. V., 1947. K Voprosu Genezisa Podsemykh Gravitatsionnykh Vod Depressiy [On the Problem of the Genesis of the Underground Gravitational Waters in Depressions]: Materialy k Poznaniyu Geol. Stroyeniya SSSR, Novaya Seriya, No. 8(12).

FJERDINGSTAD, E., 1956. Bacteriological Investigations of Mine Water from Lignite Pits in Denmark: Schweiz. Z. Hydrol., 18, No. 2, p. 215.

GASANOV, M. V., 1961. Biogennoye Vosstanovleniye Sul'fatov v Plastovykh Usloviyakh pri Zavodnenii Mestorozhdeniy Morskoy Vodoy. Sb. "Geologicheskaya Deyatel'nost' Mikroorganizmov" [The Biogenic Reduction of Sulfates under the Conditions Within the Strata Upon the Flooding of a Deposit with Sea Water. In the symposium volume, "The Geologic Activity of Microorganisms"]: Trudy In-ta Mikrobiol. AN SSSR, No. 9.

GAYEVSKAYA, N. S., 1948. Trofologicheskoye Napravleniye v Gidrobiologii, Yego Ob"yekt, Nekotoryye Osnovnyye Problemy i Zadachi [The Trophological Aspect of Hydrobiology, Its Object of Study, and Some Fundamental Problems and Tasks]: Sb. "Pamyati Akad. S. A. Zernova" [In the symposium volume dedicated "To the Memory of Academician S. A. Zernov"]: Izd-vo AN SSSR.

GAYUN, K. G., 1956. Rezul'taty Gidrogeologicheskikh Issledovaniy Mineral'nykh Vod Kurorta Nemirov [The Results of Hydrogeological Studies of the Mineral Waters of the Nemirov Spa]: Tezisy Dokl. Proizv.-Tekhnich. Soveshch. po Itogam Gidrogeol. Issl. Min. Vod na Kurortakh SSSR. Pyatigorsk.

GAZIZOVA, K. S., 1957. Mednoye Mestorozhdeniye Kounrad [The Kounrad Copper Deposit]: Moscow, Gosgeolizdat.

GINZBURG-KARAGICHEVA, T. L., 1932. Ocherki po Mikrobiologii Nefti [Outlines of Oil Microbiology]: Moscow, Izd-vo ONTI.

GINZBURG-KARAGICHEVA, T. L., 1953. Prevrashcheniye Organicheskikh Veshchestv v Anaerobnykh Usloviyakh Bakteriyami Neftenosnykh Plastov i Issledovaniye Neftey Rasnogo Geologicheskogo Vozrasta [The Transformation of Organic Substances under Anaerobic Conditions by the Bacteria in Oil-Bearing Strata and a Study of Oils of Various Geologic

Ages]: Trudy Mosk. Filiala Vses. Neft. N.-I. Geol.-Razved. In-ta, No. 3.

GLAZOVSKAYA, G. M., 1950. Vliyaniye Mikroorganizmov na Protsessy Vyvetrivaniya Pervychnykh Mineralov [The Influence of Microorganisms on the Process of Weathering of Primary Minerals]: Izv. AN Kazakh SSR, No. 86, Seriya Pochv., No. 6, pp. 79-100.

GLEEN, H., 1950. Biological Oxidation of Iron in the Soil: Nature, v. 166, No. 4229.

GOLOLOBOV, Ya. K., 1955. O Biogennykh Elementakh v Vode Chernogo Morya i Prichinakh Izmeneniy Nekotorykh Srednikh Gidrokhimicheskikh Velichin v Troficheskom Sloye Vodnoy Tolschchi Morya [The Biogenic Elements in the Water of the Black Sea and the Causes of the Changes in Certain Average Hydrochemical Quantities in the Trophic Layer of the Sea's Water Depth]: Trudy Azovo-Chernomorsk. N.-I. In-ta Morsk. Rybn. Khoz-va i Okeanogr., v. 16.

GONZOVSKAYA-GOLEVA, G. A., 1957. Ob Osnovnykh Tipakh Podzemnykh Vod Yugo-Zapadnoy Okrainy Russkoy Platformy [The Chief Types of Underground Waters in the Southwestern Margin of the Russian Platform]: Dopov. ta Povid. L'vivs'k. Derzh. Un-tu, No. 6, part 3.

GUREVICH, M. S., 1958. Nekotoryye Faktory Biogennogo Metamorfizma Podzemnykh Vod [Some Factors in the Biogenic Metamorphism of Ground Waters]: Trudy Lab. Gidrogeol. Problem im. F. P. Savarenskogo, v. 16.

GUREVICH, M. S., 1961. Rol' Mikroorganizmov v Formirovanii Khimicheskogo Sostava Podzemnykh Vod. Sb. "Geologicheskaya Deyatel'nost' Mikroorganizmov" [The Role of Microorganisms in Forming the Chemical Composition of Ground Waters. In the symposium volume, "The Geological Activity of Microorganisms"]: Trudy In-ta Mikrobiol. AN SSSR, No. 9.

GUSEVA, K. A., 1955. O Dvukh Planktonnykh Mikroorganizmakh, Prinimayushchikh Uchastiye v Krugovorote Zheleza [Two Planktonic Microorganisms Taking Part in the Iron Cycle]: Trudy Biol. Stantsii "Borok," No. 2.

HODGE, W. W., 1937. Pollution of Streams by Coal Mine Drainage: Indust. and Eng. Chem., v. 29, p. 1048.

HOF, T., 1935. Investigations Concerning Bacterial Life in Strong Brines: Rec. Trav. Botan. Nederl., v. 32, pp. 92-173.

HUTTON, W. E., and C. E. ZoBELL, 1949. The Occurrence and Characteristics of Methane-Oxidizing Bacteria in Marine Sediments: J. Bacteriol., v. 58, No. 4.

INOSTRANTSEV, A. A., 1877. Geologicheskiy Ocherk Povenetskogo Uyezda [An Outline of the Geology of the Povenets Uyezd]: Materialy po Geologii Rossii, v. 7.

ISACHENKO, B. L., 1927. Mikrobiologicheskiye Issledovaniya nad Gryazevymi Ozerami [Microbiological Investigations of Mud Lakes]: Trudy Geol. Kom., Novaya Seriya, No. 143. See also: Izbr. Trudy Akad. B. L. Isachenko [Selected Writings of Academician B. L. Isachenko]: v. 2, Izd-vo AN SSSR, 1951.

ISACHENKO, B. L., 1946. Serobakterii iz Neftyanykh Skvazhin—Pigmentoobrazovaniye v Otsutstviye Sveta na Organicheskikh Sredakh [Sulfur Bacteria from Oil Wells—the Formation of Pigments in the Absence of Light in Organic Media]: Mikrobiologiya, v. 15, No. 6.

ISACHENKO, B. L., 1951. O Zadachakh Izucheniya Geologicheskoy Deyatel'nosti Mikrobov [On the Problems in the Study of the Geological Activity of Microbes]: Izbr. Trudy Akad. B. L. Isachenko, v. 2.

ISACHENKO, B. L., 1958. O Genezise Mestorozhdeniy Sery [On the Genesis of Sulfur Deposits]: Trudy In-ta Mikrobiol. AN SSSR, No. 5.

IVANOV, M. V., 1956. Primeneniye Izotopov dlya Izucheniya Protsessa Reduktsii Sul'fatov v Oz. Belovod' [The Use of Isotopes in Studying the Reduction of Sulfates in Lake Belovod']: Mikrobiologiya, v. 25, No. 3.

IVANOV, M. V., 1957a. Rol' Mikroorganizmov v Obrazovanii Otlozheniy Sery v Serovodorodnykh Istochnikakh Sergiyevskikh Mineral'nykh Vod [The Role of Microorganisms in the Formation of the Sulfur Deposits in the Hydrogen Sulfide Springs of the Sergiyev Mineral Waters]: Mikrobiologiya, v. 26, No. 3.

IVANOV, M. V., 1957b. Uchastiye Mikroorganizmov v Obrazovanii Otlozheniy Sery v Shor-Su [The Participation of Microorganisms in the Formation of the Sulfur Deposits at Shor-Su]: Mikrobiologiya, v. 26, No. 5.

IVANOV, M. V., 1957c. Rol' Mikroorganizmov v Obrazovanii i Razrushenii Mestorozhdeniy Samorodnoy Sery [The Role of Microorganisms in the Formation and Destruction of Native Sulfur Deposits]: Diss. Bibl-ka Otd. Biol. Nauk AN SSSR.

IVANOV, M. V., 1958. Primeneniye Izotopov dlya Izucheniya Roli Mikroorganizmov v Obrazovanii Sernogo Mestorozhdeniya Shor-Su [The Use of Isotopes to Study the Role Played by Microorganisms in the Formation of the Shor-Su Sulfur Deposit]: Trudy Vses. Nauchno-Tekhn. Konf. po Primeneniyu Radioaktivnykh i Stabil'nykh Izotopov v Narodn. Khoz-ve, Izd-vo AN SSSR.

IVANOV, M. V., 1959. Izucheniye Intensivnosti Protsessa Krugovorota Sery v Ozerakh pri Pomoshchi Radioaktivnoy Sery (S^{35}) [A Study of the Intensity of the Process of the Sulfur Cycle in Lakes, Using Radioactive Sulfur (S^{35})]: Trudy

VI Soveshch. po Problemam Biologii Vnutrennykh Vod. Moscow-Leningrad, Izd-vo AN SSSR.

IVANOV, M. V., 1960a. Rol' Mikroorganizmov v Genezise i Meta-morfizatsii Sernykh Mestorozhdeniy [The Role of Micro-organisms in the Genesis and Metamorphism of Sulfur Deposits]: Zhurn. Obshch. Biol., v. 21, No. 1.

IVANOV, M. V., 1960b. Mikrobiologicheskiye Issledovaniya Prikar-patskikh Sernykh Mestorozhdeniy. 1. Issledovaniye Nemi-rovskogo i Lyubenskogo Mestorozhdeniy [Microbiological Investigations of the Carpathian Sulfur Deposits. 1. A Study of the Nemirov and Lyubenskoye Deposits]: Mikrobiologiya, v. 29, No. 1.

IVANOV, M. V., 1960c. Mikrobiologicheskiye Issledovaniya Pri-karpatskikh Sernykh Mestorozhdeniy. 2. Izucheniye Mikrobiol-ogicheskogo Protsessa Vosstanovleniya Sul'fatov v Rozdol'skom Sernom Mestorozhdenii [Microbiological Investigations of the Carpathian Sulfur Deposits. 2. A Study of the Microbiological Reduction of the Sulfates in the Rozdol'skoye Sulfur Deposit]: Mikrobiologiya, v. 29, No. 2.

IVANOV, M. V., 1961. Rol' Mikroorganizmov v Obrazovanii i Raz-rushenii Mestorozhdeniy Sery. Sb. "Geologicheskaya Deyatel'-nost' Mikroorganizmov" [The Role of Microorganisms in the Formation and Destruction of Sulfur Deposits. In the symposium volume, "The Geological Activity of Microorganisms"]: Trudy In-ta Mikrobiol. AN SSSR, No. 9.

IVANOV, M. V., N. N. LYALIKOVA and S. I. KUZNETSOV, 1958. Rol' Tionovykh Bakteriy v Vyvetrivanii Gornykh Porod i Sul'fidnykh Rud [The Role of Thiobacteria in the Weathering of Rocks and Sulfide Ores]: Izvestiya AN SSSR, Seriya Bio-logicheskaya, No. 2.

IVANOV, M. V., and V. N. RYZHOVA, 1961. Mikrobiologicheskiye Issledovaniya Prikarpatskikh Sernykh Mestorozhdeniy. 4. Issle-dovaniye Usloviy Zhiznedeyatel'nosti Sul'fatredutsiruyushch-ikh Bakteriy v Podzemnykh Vodakh Rozdola [Microbiological Investigations of the Carpathian Sulfur Deposits. 4. A Study of the Conditions Governing the Vital Activities of the Sulfate-Reducing Bacteria in the Ground Waters of Rozdol]: Mikro-biologiya, v. 30, No. 2.

IVANOV, M. V., and L. S. TEREBKOVA, 1959a. Izucheniye Mikro-biologicheskikh Protsessov Obrazovaniya Serovodoroda v Sole-nom Ozere. [A Study of the Microbiological Formation of Hydrogen Sulfide in Lake Solenoye]. Soobshcheniye I. Mikro-biologiya, v. 28, No. 2.

IVANOV, M. V., and L. S. TEREBKOVA, 1959b. Izucheniye Mikro-biologicheskikh Protsessov Obrazovaniya Serovodoroda v Sol-enom Ozere [A Study of the Microbiological Formation of

Hydrogen Sulfide in Lake Solenoye]: Soobshcheniye II. Mikrobiologiya, v. 28, No. 3.

IYA, K. K., and M. SRENIVASAYA, 1944. A Preliminary Study
of the Bacterial Flora Associated with Sulphur Deposits
on the East Coast (Masulipatam): Current Science, v. 13,
No. 12.

IYA, K. K., and M. SRENIVASAYA, 1945a. Studies in the Formation of Sulphur at Kona (Masulipatam), Pt. I: Current Science,
v. 14, No. 9.

IYA, K. K., and M. SRENIVASAYA, 1945b. Studies in the Formation of Sulphur at Kona (Masulipatam), Pt. II: Current Science,
v. 14, No. 10.

JANKOWSKI, G. I., and C. E. ZoBELL, 1944. Hydrocarbon Production by Sulfate-Reducing Bacteria: J. Bacteriol., v. 47, No. 5.

JOHNSON, F. H., 1957. The Action of Pressures and Temperature:
Microbiol. Ecology, Cambridge University Press.

JOSEPH, I. M., 1953. Microbiological Study of Acid Mine Waters,
Preliminary Report: Ohio J. Sci., v. 53, No. 2.

KALINENKO, V. O., 1946. Rol' Bakteriy v Formirovanii Zhelezo-
Margantsovykh Konkretsiy [The Role of Bacteria in the Forma-
tion of Iron-Manganese Concretions]: Mikrobiologiya, v. 15,
No. 5.

KALINENKO, V. O., 1949. Proiskhozhdeniye Zhelezo-Margantsov-
ykh Konkretsiy [The Origin of Iron-Manganese Concretions]:
Mikrobiologiya, v. 18, No. 6.

KALINENKO, V. O., 1952. Geokhimicheskaya Deyatel'nost'
Bakterial'noy Kolonii [The Geochemical Activity of a Bac-
terial Colony]: Izvestiya AN SSSR, Seriya Geologicheskaya,
No. 1.

KALININ, N. A., V. P. SAVCHENKO and V. G. VASIL'YEV, 1955.
K Itogam Soveshchaniya po Geokhimicheskim Metodam Poiskov
Nefti i Gaza [On the Results of the Conference on Geochemical Methods of Oil and Gas Prospecting]: Neftyan. Khoz-vo,
v. 33, No. 7.

KARAVAYKO, G. I., 1959. Znacheniye Biologicheskogo Faktora
v Okislenii Soyedineniy Sery Rozdol'skogo Mestorozhdeniya
[The Significance of the Biological Factor in the Oxidation
of Sulfur Compounds in the Rozdol'skoye Deposit]: Mikrobiologiya, v. 28, No. 6.

KARAVAYKO, G. I., 1961. O Mikrozonal'nom Rasprostranenii
Okislitel'nykh Protsessov v Sernoy Rude Rozdol'skogo Mes-
torozhdeniya [On the Microzonal Distribution of Oxidizing
Processes in the Sulfur Ore of the Rozdol'skoye Deposit]:
Mikrobiologiya, v. 30, No. 3.

KARAVAYKO, G. I., M. V. IVANOV and B. I. SREBRODOL'SKIY,
1962. Okisleniye Sernoy Rudy na Skladakh Rozdol'skogo

Kombinata [The Oxidation of the Sulfur Ore on the Folds of the Rozdol'skoye Combine]: Sovetskaya Geologiya.

KARZINKIN, G. S., and S. I. KUZNETSOV, 1931. Novyye Metody v Limnologii [New Methods in Limnology]: Trudy Limnol. Stantsii v Kosine, Nos. 13-14.

KEYS, A. E., E. H. CHRISTENSEN and A. KROGH, 1935. The Organic Metabolism of Sea Water With Special Reference to the Ultimate Food Cycle of the Sea: J. Marine Biol. Assoc. U. K., v. 20.

KHAIT, S. Z., 1924. Microspira desulfuricans Kuyal'nitskogo Limana [Microspira desulfuricans in the Kuyal'nitsa Estuary]: Zhurn. N.-I. Kafedr. v Odesse, v. 1, Nos. 10-11.

KHARTULARI, Ye. M., 1939. Bakteriologicheskiye i Khimicheskiye Issledovaniya Ryada Podmoskovnykh Ozer v Svyazi s Voprosom Razlozheniya Ila s Obrazovaniyem Gazov [Bacteriological and Chemical Studies of a Number of Lakes in the Moscow Basin From the Standpoint of the Problem of the Decomposition of Ooze with the Formation of Gases]: Trudy Limnol. Stantsii v Kosine, No. 22.

KHRAMOV, N. A., 1952. Poiski i Razvedka Ozokeritovykh Mestorozhdeniy [Prospecting and Exploration of Ozokerite Deposits]: Moscow, Gostoptekhizdat.

KIMATA, M., H. KADOTA, Y. HATA and T. TAJIMA, 1955. Studies on the Marine Sulfate-Reducing Bacteria. III. Influence of Various Environmental Factors Upon the Sulfate-Reducing Activity of Sulfate-Reducing Bacteria: Bull. Jap. Soc. Scient. Fish., v. 21, pp. 109-112.

KOLESNIK, Z. A., 1955. Mikroflora Vodyi Nefty Rayonov Vtorogo Baku [The Microflora of the Water and Oils in the Vtoroye Baku Districts]: Trudy Vses. Neft. N.-I. Geol.-Razved. In-ta, No. 82.

KORSHUNOVA, Yu. I., and S. Ye. PRYANISHNIKOV, 1935. Kvastsy Shor-Su. Sb. "Poleznyye Iskopayemyye Shor-Su" [The Alums of Shor-Su. In the collection, "The Economic Minerals of Shor-Su"]: Tashkent.

KOTOV, V. S., 1953. Opyt Primeneniya Glubinnoy Gazovoy S"yemki [An Experiment in the Use of Deep Gas Surveying]: Polevaya i Promyslovaya Geokhimiya, No. 1.

KOZLOV, A. L., 1950. Problemy Geokhimii Prirodnykh Gazov [Problems of the Geochemistry of Natural Gases]: Moscow, Gostoptekhizdat.

KRAMARENKO, L. Ye., 1956. Sostav i Raspredeleniye Mikroorganizmov v Podzemnykh Vodakh i Ikh Poiskovoye Znacheniye. Sb. "Voprosy Neftepoiskovoy Gidrogeologii" [The Composition and Distribution of Microorganisms in Ground Waters and Their Significance for Prospecting. In the collection, "Problems of Oil-Exploration Hydrogeology"]: Gosgeolizdat.

KRAMARENKO, L. Ye., 1962. Bakterial'nyye Biotsenozy v Pod-
zemnykh Vodakh Mestorozhdeniy Nekotorykh Poleznykh Isko-
payemykh i Ikh Geologicheskoye Znacheniye [Bacterial
Communities in the Ground Waters of Deposits of Certain
Economic Minerals and Their Geologic Significance]: Mikro-
biologiya.
KRAMARENKO, L. Ye., Ye. N. DUTOVA and I. I. PRIZRENOVA,
1956. Biokhimicheskiye Faktory Preobrazovaniya Podzemnykh
Vod [The Biochemical Factors in the Transformation of
Ground Waters]: Sb. Nauchno-Tekhn. Informatsii, No. 3.
Gosgeolizdat.
KRAMARENKO, L. Ye., I. I. PRIZRENOVA and R. I. TEBEN'KOVA,
1959. Rol' Biogennogo Faktora v Formirovanii Oreolov Ras-
seyaniya Molibdenovogo Mestorozhdeniya Shalgiya. Sb. "Geol-
ogiya i Poleznyye Iskopayemyye" [The Role of the Biogenic
Factor in the Formation of the Aureoles of Dispersed Molyb-
denum Mineralization in the Shalgiy Deposit. In the collection,
"Geology and Economic Minerals"]: Inform. Sb. No. 8, Vses.
Geol. In-ta, Leningrad.
KRASIL'NIKOV, N. A., 1949a. Rol' Mikroorganizmov v Vyvetrivanii
Gornykh Porod. I. Mikroflora Poverkhnostnogo Sloya Skal'nykh
Porod [The Role of Microorganisms in the Weathering of Rocks.
I. The Microflora in the Surface Layer of Rocks]: Mikro-
biologiya, v. 18, No. 4.
KRASIL'NIKOV, N. A., 1949b. Rol' Mikroorganizmov v Vyvetrivanii
Gornykh Porod. II. Ochagovoye Raspredeleniye Mikroorgan-
izmov na Poverkhnosti Skal'nykh Porod [The Role of Micro-
organisms in the Weathering of Rocks. II. The Nuclear
Distribution of the Microorganisms on the Surfaces of Rocks]:
Mikrobiologiya, v. 18, No. 6.
KRASIL'NIKOV, N. A., 1956. Mikroflora Vysokogornykh Skal'nykh
Porod i Azotfiksiruyushchaya Yeye Deyatel'nost' [The Micro-
flora of the Rocks in High Mountain Areas and Its Nitrogen-
Fixing Activity]: Usp. Sovr. Biol., v. 41, No. 2.
KRISS, A. Ye., 1953. Mikroorganizmy i Biologicheskaya Prod-
uktivnost' Vodoyemov [Microorganisms and the Biological
Productivity of Bodies of Water]: Priroda, No. 5.
KRISS, A. Ye., 1954. Rol' Mikroorganizmov v Biologicheskoy
Produktivnosti Chernogo Morya [The Role of Microorganisms
in the Biological Productivity of the Black Sea]: Usp. Sovr.
Biol., v. 38, No. 1 (4).
KRISS, A. Ye., 1958. Mikrobiologiya i Problemy Chernogo Morya
[Microbiology and Problems in the Study of the Black Sea]:
Priroda, No. 6.
KRISS, A. Ye., and M. N. LEBEDEVA, 1953. Vertikal'noye Ras-
predeleniye Chislennosti i Biomassy Mikroorganizmov v

Glubokovodnykh Oblastyakh Chernogo Morya [The Vertical Distribution of the Numbers and Biomass of Microorganisms in the Deep-Water Parts of the Black Sea]: Doklady AN SSSR, v. 89, No. 5.

KRISS, A. Ye., and Ye. M. MARKIANOVICH, 1954. Nablyudeniya za Skorost'yu Razmnozheniya Mikroorganizmov v Morskikh Glubinakh [Observations of the Rates of Multiplication of Microorganisms in the Depths of the Sea]: Mikrobiologiya, v. 23, No. 5.

KRISS, A. Ye., and Ye. A. RUKINA, 1949. O Proiskhozhdenii Serovodoroda v Chernom More [On the Origin of the Hydrogen Sulfide in the Black Sea]: Mikrobiologiya, v. 18, No. 4.

KRISS, A. Ye., and Ye. A. RUKINA, 1953. Purpurnyye Serobakterii v Serovodorodnykh Glubinakh Chernogo Morya [Purple Sulfur Bacteria in the Hydrogen Sulfide Depths of the Black Sea]: Doklady AN SSSR, v. 93, No. 6.

KUDRIN, L. N., 1953. K Voprosu o Genezise Serovodorodnykh Mineral'nykh Vod Yugo-Zapadnoy Okrainy Russkoy Platformy [On the Problem of the Genesis of the Hydrogen Sulfide Mineral Waters on the Southwestern Margin of the Russian Platform]: Doklady AN SSSR, v. 93, No. 5.

KUDRIN, L. N., 1957. Do Geologiy Rozdol'skogo Rodovishcha Sirki (Zakhidn. Oblasti URSR) [On the Geology of the Rozdol'-skoye Sulfur Deposit (in the Zakhidn. Oblast' of the Ukrainian SSR)]: Geol. Zhurn. URSR, v. 17, No. 4. [In Ukrainian].

KUDRYASHOV, V. V., 1924. Osnovnyye Momenty Istorii Kosinskikh Ozer [The Chief Milestones in the History of the Kosinskian Lakes]: Trudy Kosniskoy Biol. Stantsii, v. 1, No. 1.

KURBATOVA-BELIKOVA, N. M., 1951. Zakonomernost' Raspredeleniya Mikroorganizmov v Nizinnykh Torfyanikakh [The Regularities Characterizing the Distribution of Microorganisms in Lowland Peat Bogs]: Trudy In-ta Torfa AN BSSR, No. 1.

KURBATOVA-BELIKOVA, N. M., 1954. Itogi Izucheniya Mikrobiologicheskoy Deyatel'nosti v Yestestvennykh Torfyanykh Zalezhakh [The Results of a Study of the Microbiological Activity in Natural Peat Bog Deposits]: Trudy In-ta Torfa AN BSSR, No. 3.

KUZNETSOV, S. I., 1938a. Kolichestvennyy Uchet Mikroflory v Svyazi s Razrabotkoy Mikrozonal'nogo Pokazatelya Gryazey [A Quantitative Calculation of the Microflora in Connection with the Development of a Microzonal Criterion for Muds]: Mikrobiologiya, v. 7, No. 1.

KUZNETSOV, S. I., 1938b. Sravnitel'naya Kharakteristika Mikroflory Vody Matsestinskikh i Agurskikh Istochnikov [A Comparative Characterization of the Microflora in the Waters of the Matsestinskian and Agurskian Springs]: Mikrobiologiya, v. 7, No. 3.

KUZNETSOV, S. I., 1949a. Osnovnyye Itogi i Ocherednyye Zadachi Mikrobiologicheskikh Issledovaniy Ilovykh Ozernykh Otlozheniy [The Principal Results and the Successive Tasks of the Microbiological Investigation of Lake Ooze Deposits]: Trudy Vses. Gidrobiol. Ob-va, v. 1.

KUZNETSOV, S. I., 1949b. Primeneniye Mikrobiologicheskikh Metodov k Izucheniyu Organicheskogo Veshchestva v Vodoyemakh [The Application of Microbiological Methods to the Study of the Organic Matter in Bodies of Water]: Mikrobiologiya, v. 18, No. 3.

KUZNETSOV, S. I., 1950a. Mikrobiologicheskiye Issledovaniya Ozer Kokchetavskoy, Kurganskoy i Tyumenskoy Oblastey. Soobshcheniye 2-ye. Mikrobiologicheskaya Kharakteristika Protsessov Raspada Organicheskogo Veshchestva v Ilovykh Otlozheniyakh [Microbiological Investigations of the Lakes in the Kokchetav, Kurgan and Tyumen Oblasts. Article 2. A Microbiological Description of the Processes Involved in the Decay of the Organic Matter in Ooze Deposits]: Trudy Lab. Sapropelevykh Otlozheniy, No. 4.

KUZNETSOV, S. I., 1950b. Izucheniye Vozmozhnosti Sovremennogo Obrazovaniya Metana v Gazoneftenosnykh Fatsiyakh Rayona Saratova i Buguruslana [A Study of the Possible Current Formation of Methane in the Gas- and Oil-Bearing Facies of the Saratov and Buguruslan Districts]: Mikrobiologiya, v. 19, No. 3.

KUZNETSOV, S. I., 1952. Rol' Mikroorganizmov v Krugovorote Veshchestv v Ozerakh [The Role of Microorganisms in the Cycle of Organic Substances in Lakes]: Izd-vo AN SSSR.

KUZNETSOV, S. I., 1955a. Razrabotka Metodov Mikrobiologicheskogo Vozdeystviya na Plast s Tsel'yu Intensifikatsii Neftedobychi i Uvelicheniya Nefteotdachi. Sb. "Metody Uvelicheniya Nefteotdachi Plastov" [The Development of Methods of Microbiological Reaction Upon a Stratum in Order to Intensify the Extraction and Increase the Yield of Oil. In the symposium volume, "Methods of Increasing the Oil Yield of Strata"]: Materialy Vses. Soveshchaniya Ministerstva Neft. Prom. SSSR.

KUZNETSOV, S. I., 1955b. Ispol'zovaniye Radioaktivnoy Uglekisloty C^{14} dlya Opredeleniya Sravnitel'noy Velichiny Fotosinteza i Khemosinteza v Ryade Ozer Razlichnykh Tipov. Sb. "Izotopy v Mikrobiologii." Trudy Soveshchaniya po Primeneniyu Mechenykh Atomov v Mikrobiologii [The Use of Radioactive Carbon Dioxide Containing C^{14} to Determine the Comparative Rates of Photosynthesis and Chemosynthesis in a Number of Lakes of Different Types. In the symposium volume, "Isotopes in Microbiology". Transactions of the Conference on the Use of Tagged Atoms in Microbiology]: Izd-vo AN SSSR.

KUZNETSOV, S. I., 1955c. Primeneniye Radioaktivnykh Izotopov k Izucheniyu Protsessov Fotosinteza i Khemosinteza v Vodo-yemakh. Dokl. Sovetskoy Delegatsii na Mezhdunar. Kongresse po Mirnomu Ispol'z. Atomnoy Energii [The Use of Radio-active Isotopes in Studying the Processes of Photosynthesis and Chemosynthesis in Bodies of Water. Report of the Soviet Delegation to the International Congress on the Peaceful Uses of Atomic Energy]: Geneva.

KUZNETSOV, S. I., 1956. K Voprosu o Vozmozhnosti "Radio-sinteza" [On the Question of the Possibility of "Radiosyn-thesis"]: Mikrobiologiya, v. 25, No. 4.

KUZNETSOV, S. I., 1957a. Osnovnyye Itogi po Issledovaniyu Mikroflory Neftyanykh Mestorozhdeniy [The Chief Results of an Investigation of the Microflora of Oil Deposits]: Mikro-biologiya, v. 26, No. 6.

KUZNETSOV, S. I., 1957b. Znacheniye Bakteriy, Vosstanavlivayu-shchikh Sul'faty pri Korrozii Metallicheskogo Oborudovaniya [The Importance of Sulfate-Reducing Bacteria in the Cor-rosion of Metal Equipment]: Trudy Konf. po Korrozii pri In-te Fiz. Khimii AN SSSR.

KUZNETSOV, S. I., 1959a. Geologicheskaya Deyatel'nost' Mikro-organizmov (Oznovnyye Rezul'taty i Zadachi Issledovaniya) [The Geological Activity of Microorganisms (the Chief Re-sults and Future Tasks of Research)]: Vest. AN SSSR, No. 2, 30-33.

KUZNETSOV, S. I., 1959b. Obosnovaniya Mikrobiologicheskogo Metoda Poiskov Neftyanykh i Gazovykh Mestorozhdeniy. Trudy Konferentsii "Geokhimicheskiye Metody Poiskov Neftyanykh i Gazovykh Mestorozhdeniy" [The Scientific Basis of the Microbiological Method of Prospecting for Oil and Gas De-posits. Transactions of the Conference on "Geochemical Methods of Prospecting for Oil and Gas Deposits"].

KUZNETSOV, S. I., 1961. Osnovnyye Napravleniya Issledovaniy Geologicheskoy Deyatel'nosti Mikroorganizmov. Sb. "Geol-ogicheskaya Deyatel'nost' Mikroorganizmov" [The Main As-pects of Research in the Geological Activity of Microorganisms. In the symposium volume, "The Geological Activity of Micro-organisms"]: Trudy In-ta Mikrobiol. AN SSSR, No. 9.

KUZNETSOV, S. I., and Ye. M. KHARTULARI, 1941. Mikrobiologich-eskaya Kharakteristika Protsessov Anaerobnogo Raspada Organicheskogo Veshchestva Ila Belogo Ozera v Kosine [A Microbiological Description of the Processes of Decomposition of the Organic Matter in the Ooze of Lake Beloye at Kosino]: Mikrobiologiya, v. 10, Nos. 7-8.

KUZNETSOV, S. I., V. A. KUZNETSOVA and Z. S. SMIRNOVA, 1947. Izucheniye Protsessov Bakterial'nogo Okisleniya

Uglevodorodnykh Gazov v Usloviyakh Ikh Diffuzii Cherez Osado-
chnyye Porody [A Study of the Bacterial Oxidation of Hydrogen
Sulfide Gases Under the Conditions of Their Diffusion Through
Sedimentary Rocks]: Izv. Glavn. Upravl. Geol. Fondov, No. 3.
KUZNETSOV, S. I., and G. A. SOKOLOVA, 1960. Nekotoryye
Dannyye po Fiziologii Thiobacillus thioparus [Some Data on
the Physiology of Thiobacillus thioparus]: Mikrobiologiya, v. 29,
No. 2.
KUZNETSOV, S. I., T. A. SPERANSKAYA and V. D. KONSHIN,
1939. Sostav Organicheskogo Veshchestva Ilovykh Otlozheniy
Razlichnykh Ozer [The Composition of the Organic Matter
in the Ooze Deposits of Various Lakes]: Trudy Limnol.
Stantsii v Kosine, No. 22.
KUZNETSOV, S. I., and Z. P. TELEGINA, 1957. Nekotoryye
Dannyye po Fiziologii Propanokislyayushchikh Bakteriy [Some
Data on the Physiology of Propane-Oxidizing Bacteria]: Mikro-
biologiya, v. 26, No. 5.
KUZNETSOVA, V. A., 1947. Bakteriodebetnyy Metod S"yemki.
Novosti Neftyanoy Tekhniki (Geologiya). Geomikrobiologich-
eskaya Razvedka [The Bacterial-Debit Method of Survey.
New Techniques in Oil Geology. Geomicrobiological Explora-
tion]: Izd. Byuro Tekhn.-Ekon. Inform. Tsimtneft'. Moscow.
KUZNETSOVA, V. A., 1960. Rasprostraneniye Sul'fatvosstanav-
livayushchikh Bakteriy v Neftyanykh Mestorozhdeniyakh Kuy-
byshevskoy Obl. v Svyazi s Solevym Sostavom Plastovykh
Vod [The Propagation of Sulfate-Reducing Bacteria in the Oil
Deposits of the Kuybyshev Oblast' in Connection with the
Salt Composition of the Stratal Waters]: Mikrobiologiya,
v. 29, No. 3.
KUZNETSOVA, V. A., K. B. ASHIROV, V. A. GROMOVICH, I. V.
OVCHINNIKOVA and S. I. KUZNETSOV, 1957. Opyt Pod-
avleniya Razvitiya Vosstanavlivayushchikh Sul'faty Bakteriy
v Neftyanom Plaste Kalinovskogo Mestorozhdeniya [An Ex-
periment in Suppressing the Development of the Sulfate-
Reducing Bacteria in the Oil Stratum of the Kalinovskoye
Deposit]: Mikrobiologiya, v. 26, No. 3.
KUZNETSOVA, Z. I., 1957. Izucheniye Kolichestvennogo Soder-
zhaniya Bakteriy v Podzemnykh Vodakh Neftyanykh Mes-
torozhdeniy [A Study of the Quantitative Content of Bacteria
in the Ground Waters of Oil Deposits]: Mikrobiologiya, v. 26,
No. 2.
KUZNETSOVA, Z. I., 1959. Raspredeleniye Desul'furiruyushchikh
Bakteriy po Padeniyu Vodonosnogo Plasta (Tersko-Dagestan-
skaya Neftenosnaya Provintsiya). Sb. "Voprosy Gidrogeol.
i Inzhenern. Geol." [The Distribution of the Desulfurizing
Bacteria along the Dip of the Oil-Bearing Stratum in the

Terek-Dagestan Oil Province. In the symposium volume, "Problems of Hydrogeology and Engineering Geology"]: Trudy Vses. N.-I. In-ta Gidrol. i Inzhenern. Geol. (VSEGINGEO). No. 18.

KUZNETSOVA, Z. I., 1961. Raspredeleniye i Ekologiya Mikroorganizmov v Glubokikh Podzemnykh Vodakh Nekotorykh Territoriy SSSR. Sb. "Geologicheskaya Deyatel'nost' Mikroorganizmov" [The Distribution and Ecology of the Microorganisms in the Deep Ground Waters of Certain Territories of the USSR. In the symposium volume, "The Geological Activity of Microorganisms"]: Trudy In-ta Mikrobiol. AN SSSR, No. 9.

LAZAREVA, M. F., 1953. Pryamoy Schët Bakteriy pri Reshenii Zadachi Tekhnicheskoy Mikrobiologii [The Direct Counting of Bacteria in the Solution of Problems in Applied Microbiology]: Inform. Mat-ly, No. 1 Lab. Biologich. Ochistki Stochnykh Vod. Moscow, Izd-vo VODGEO.

LEATHEN, W. W., and S. A. BRALEY, 1955. Interpretation of Reaction in Acid Thiosulfate Media: J. Bacteriol., v. 69, p. 481.

LEATHEN, W. W., S. A. BRALEY and L. D. McINTYRE, 1953. The Role of Bacteria in the Formation of Acid: Appl. Microbiol., v. 1, No. 2.

LEATHEN, W. W., N. KINSEL and S. A. BRALEY, 1956. Ferrobacillus ferrooxidans, a Chemosynthetic Autotrophic Bacterium: J. Bacteriol., v. 72, No. 5.

LEATHEN, W. W., L. D. McINTYRE and S. A. BRALEY, 1951. A Medium for the Study of the Bacterial Oxidation of Ferrous Iron: Science, v. 114, p. 280.

LINDTROP, N. T., 1947. Neftyanyye Promysly i Razvedochnyye Ploshchadi Fergany [The Oil Fields and Exploration Areas of the Fergana Region]: Trudy Vses. N.-I. Geol.-Razved. Inst., Novaya Seriya, No. 24.

LIS, G., 1958. Biokhimiya Avtotrofnykh Bakteriy [The Biochemistry of the Autotrophic Bacteria]: IL.

LUCHTEROWA, A., 1953a. Prospecting of Oil by the Microbiological Method: Nafta (Poland), v. 9, pp. 217-220.

LUCHTEROWA, A., 1953b. Geomikrobiologia w Przemysle Naftowym [Geomicrobiology in the Oil Industry]: Acta Microbiol. Polon., v. 2, Nos. 2-3.

LUNDQVIST, G., 1927. Bodenablagerungen und Entwicklungstypen der Seen: Die Binnengewässer, v. II, Stuttgart.

LYALIKOVA, N. N., 1955. Nekotoryye Svoystva Mikroflory Ilovykh Otlozheniy, Vliyayushchey na Bal'neologicheskiye Kachestva Ila [Some Properties of the Microflora in Ooze Deposits that Affect the Balneological Quality of the Ooze]: Trudy In-ta Mikrobiol. AN SSSR, No. 4.

LYALIKOVA, N. N., 1958. Izucheniye Protsessa Khemosinteza u Thiobacillus ferrooxidans [A Study of the Process of Chemosynthesis in Thiobacillus ferrooxidans]: Mikrobiologiya, v. 27, No. 5.

LYALIKOVA, N. N., 1959. Fiziologiya i Ekologiya Thiobacillus ferrooxidans v Svyazi s Yego Rol'yu v Okislenii Sul'fidnykh Rud [The Physiology and Ecology of Thiobacillus ferrooxidans in Relation to Its Role in the Oxidation of Sulfide Ores]: Diss. Bibl-ka Otd. Biol. Nauk AN SSSR.

LYALIKOVA, N. N., 1960. Uchastiye Thiobacillus ferrooxidans v Okislenii Sul'fidnykh Rud na Kolchedannykh Mestorozhdeniyakh Srednego Urala [The Part Played by Thiobacillus ferrooxidans in Oxidizing the Sulfide Ores in the Copper Pyrite Deposits of the Middle Urals]: Mikrobiologiya, v. 29, No. 3.

LYALIKOVA, N. N., 1961a. Rol' Bakteriy v Okislenii Sul'fidnykh Rud Medno-Nikelevykh Mestorozhdeniy Kol'skogo Poluostrova [The Role of Bacteria in the Oxidation of the Sulfide Ores in the Copper-Nickel Deposits of the Kola Peninsula]: Mikrobiologiya, v. 30, No. 1.

LYALIKOVA, N. N., 1961b. Rol' Bakteriy v Okislenii Sul'fidnykh Rud [The Role of Bacteria in the Oxidation of Sulfide Ores]: Tr. In-ta Mikrobiol. AN SSSR, No. 9.

LYALIKOVA, N. N., and G. A. SOKOLOVA, 1962. Mikrobiologicheskoye Obsledovaniye Nekotorykh Rudnykh Mestorozhdeniy Tsentral'nogo Kazakhstana [A Microbiological Study of Some Ore Deposits of Central Kazakhstan].

MACKENZIE, K., 1952. The Metabolism of Vibrio desulfuricans in Anaerobic Petroliferous Formations: Biochem. J., v. 51, pp. 24-25.

MALYSHEK, V. T., and M. V. GASANOV, 1959. Izucheniye Protsessa Vosstanovleniya Sul'fatov v Smesyakh Morskoy i Shchelochnoy Plastovoy Vody. Sb. "Vopr. Geol. i Geokhim." [A Study of the Reduction of Sulfates in Mixtures of Marine and Alkaline Stratal Waters. In the symposium volume, "Problems of Geology and Geochemistry"]: Trudy Azerbaydzh. Nauchn. In-ta po Dobyche Nefti, No. 8.

MALYSHEK, V. T., and A. A. MALIYANTS, 1932. Serobakterii v Plastovykh "Rozovykh" Vodakh Surakhanskogo Neftyanogo Mestorozhdeniya i Ikh Znacheniye v Geokhimii Vod [The Sulfur Bacteria in the "Pink" Stratal Waters of the Surakhan Oil Deposit and Their Significance in the Geochemistry of the Waters]: Doklady AN SSSR, v. III, No. 5.

MAZURIN, K. P., 1955. Novyye Dannyye o Strukture Mestorozhdeniya im. III Internatsionala [New Data on the Structure of the "Third International" Deposit]: Razvedka i Okhrana Nedr, No. 1.

MEEHAM, W. J., and L. BAAS BECKING, 1927. Iron Organisms: Science, v. 66, p. 42.

MEKHTIYEVA, V. L., 1956. Izucheniye Mikroflora Otlozheniy Sovremennogo i Drevnego Kaspiya. Sb. "Nakopleniye i Pre-obrazovaniye Organicheskogo Veshchestva v Sovremennykh Morskikh Osadkakh" [A Study of the Microflora in the Deposits of the Modern and Ancient Caspian Sea. In the symposium volume, "The Accumulation and Transformation of Organic Matter in Modern Marine Deposits"]: Moscow, Gostoptekhizdat.

MEKHTIYEVA, V. L., 1961. Rasprostraneniye Mikroorganizmov v Sovremennykh i Drevnikh Glinisto-Alevrolitovykh Osadkakh. Sb. "Geologicheskaya Deyatel'nost' Mikroorganizmov" [The Propagation of Microorganisms in Modern and Ancient Clay-Silt Sediments. In the symposium volume, "The Geological Activity of Microorganisms"]: Trudy In-ta Mikrobiol. AN SSSR, No. 9.

MEKHTIYEVA, V. L., and S. B. MALKOVA, 1958. Materialy po Mikrobiologicheskoy Kharakteristike Tretichnykh i Chetvert-ichnykh Otlozheniy Severnogo Predkavkaz'ya. Sb. "Rezul'taty Geokhimicheskikh Issledovaniy" [Materials for a Microbio-logical Characterization of the Tertiary and Quaternary Deposits of the Northern Caucasus Foothills. In the symposium volume, "The Results of Geochemical Investigations"]: Trudy Vses. N.-I. Geol.-Razved. Neft. In-ta, No. 11.

MESHKOV, A. N., 1958. Primeneniye Metoda Pryamogo Scheta Bakteriy dlya Izucheniya Mikroflory Nefti [The Application of the Method of Direct Bacterial Count to the Study of Oil Microflora]: Mikrobiologiya, v. 27, No. 3.

MESSINEVA, M. A., 1947. Sovremennyye Vzglyady na Proiskh-ozhdeniye Nefti. Sb. "Proiskhozhdeniye Nefti i Prirodnogo Gaza" [Current Views of the Origin of Oil. In the symposium volume, "The Origin of Oil and Natural Gas"]: Byuro Tekhn.-Ekon. Inform. Tsimtneft'.

MESSINEVA, M. A., 1950. Nachal'nyye Stadii Preobrazovaniya Organicheskogo Veshchestva Vodnykh Rasteniy. Sb. "K Poznaniyu Sovremennykh Analogov Neftenosnykh Fatsiy" [The Initial Stages in the Transformation of the Organic Matter of Aquatic Plants. In the symposium volume, "On the Rec-ognition of Modern Analogues of Oil-Bearing Facies"]: Gos. Nauchn.-Tekh. Izd-vo Neft. i Gorn. Top. Lit-ry. Mos-cow.

MESSINEVA, M. A., 1955. Eksperimental'nyye Dokazatel'stva Vo-zmozhnosti Obrazovaniya Nefti iz Organicheskogo Veshchestva (Vystupleniye v Preniyakh). Materialy Diskussii po Pro-iskhozhdeniyu i Migratsii Nefti [Experimental Proofs of the Possibility of the Formation of Oil From Organic Matter

(Initiation of a Debate). Materials for a Discussion of the Origin and Migration of Oil]: Izd-vo AN Ukr. SSR.

MESSINEVA, M. A., 1961. Geologicheskaya Deyatel'nost' Bakteriy i Yeye Vliyaniye na Geokhimicheskiye Protsessy. Sb. "Geologicheskaya Deyatel'nost' Mikroorganizmov" [The Geological Activity of Bacteria and Its Influence on Geochemical Processes. In the symposium volume, "The Geological Activity of Microorganisms"]: Trudy In-ta Mikrobiol. AN SSSR, No. 9.

MESSINEVA, M. A., and A. I. GORBUNOVA, 1946. Protsess Razlozheniya Makrofitov Presnovodnykh Ozer i Uchastiye Ikh Ostatkov v Formirovanii Ozernykh Otlozheniy [The Process of Decomposition of the Macrophytes in Fresh-Water Lakes and the Part Played by Their Remains in the Formation of Lacustrine Deposits]: Izvestiya AN SSSR, Seriya Biologicheskaya, No. 5.

MESSINEVA, M. A., and V. Ya. PANKRATOVA, 1941. Razlozheniye Fitoplanktona i Rol' Mikroorganizmov v Etom Protsesse [The Decomposition of Phytoplankton and the Role of Microorganisms in This Process]: Trudy Lab. Genezisa Sapropelya In-ta Goryuchikh Iskopayemykh AN SSSR, No. 2.

MOGILEVSKIY, G. A., 1938. Mikrobiologicheskiye Issledovaniya v Svyazi s Gazovoy S"yemkoy [Microbiological Investigation in Connection With Gas Surveying]: Razvedka Nedr, Nos. 8-9.

MOGILEVSKIY, G. A., 1940. Bakterial'nyy Metod Razvedki na Neft' i Prirodnyye Gazy [The Bacterial Method of Prospecting for Oil and Natural Gases]: Razvedka Nedr, No. 12.

MOGILEVSKIY, G. A., 1953. Mikrobiologicheskiy Metod Poiskov Gazovykh i Neftyanykh Zalezhey [The Microbiological Method of Prospecting Gas and Oil Occurrences]: Byuro Tekhn.-Ekon. Inform. Tsemtnefti. Gostoptekhizdat.

MOGILEVSKIY, G. A., 1957. Rol' Bakteriy v Poiskakh Nefti i Gaza [The Role of Bacteria in the Search for Oil and Gas]: Priroda, No. 9.

MOLISCH, H., 1892. Die Pflanze in Ihren Beziehungen zum Eisen: Jena.

MOLISCH, H., 1910. Die Eisenbakterien: Jena.

MÜLLER, A., and W. SCHWARTZ, 1955. Über das Vorkommen von Mikroorganismen in Salzlagerstätten. Geomikrobiologische Untersuchungen, III: Z. Deutsch. Geol. Gesellsch., v. 105, pt. 4.

MÜNZ, E., 1915. Zur Physiologie der Methanbakterien: Inaugural Dissertation, Halle.

MURDOCK, H. R., 1953. Industrial Wastes: Indust. and Eng. Chem. (Industr.), v. 45, No. 2.

MURRAY, J., and A. F. RENARD, 1891. Reports on the Deep Sea Deposits: Sci. Res. of "Challenger," p. 240.

MURZAYEV, P. M., [MURSAIEV, P. M.] 1937. The Genesis of
Some Sulphur Deposits of the USSR: Economic Geology, v. 32,
No. 1.

MURZAYEV, P. M., 1939. Kratkiy Obzor Teoriy i Nekotoryye
Soobrazheniya o Genezise Plastovykh Mestorozhdeniy Sery
[A Brief Survey of the Theory and Some Remarks on the
Genesis of Sheet Deposits of Sulfur]: Trudy   Voronezhsk.
Fos. Un-ta, v. 11, Geol.-Pochv. Otd., No. 3.

MURZAYEV, P. M., 1950. O Vozmozhnykh Metodakh Uskoreniya
Prirodnykh Protsessov Obrazovaniya i Nakopleniya Samorodnoy
Sery [Possible Methods of Accelerating the Natural Proc-
esses of Formation and Accumulation of Native Sulfur]:
Doklady AN SSSR, v. 72, No. 2.

NADSON, G. A., 1903. Mikroorganizmy kak Geologicheskiye Deyateli
[Microorganisms as Geologic Agents]: Trudy Komissii Issl.
Min. Vod g. Slavyanska, St. Petersburg.

NALIVKIN, D. V., 1956. Ucheniye o Fatsiyakh [The Theory of
Facies]: Izd-vo AN SSSR.

NAUMANN, E., 1922. Über die See- und Sumpferze Süd- und
Mittelschwedens: Sver. Geol. Ündersökn., v. 13.

NAUMANN, E., 1927. Tsel' i Osnovnyye Problemy Regional'noy
Limnologii [The Purpose and the Basic Problems of Regional
Limnology]: Trudy Kosinskoy Biol. Stantsii, No. 6 (Trans-
lated from the German).

NAUMOVA, A. N., 1933. Metody Neposredstvennogo Schëta Mikroorganizmov v Pochve i Kharakteristika Otdel'nykh Pochv
Soyuza [Methods of Direct Count of the Microorganisms
in the Soil and a Characterization of the Individual Soils
of the Soviet Union]: Trudy Nauchn. In-ta Udobreniy, No.
108.

NECHAYEVA, N. B., 1949. Dva Vida Mikrobakteriy, Okislyayushchikh Metan [Two Species of Methane-Oxidizing Bacteria]:
Mikrobiologiya, v. 18, No. 4.

NEKRASOV, N. I., 1934. Fiziko-khimicheskiye Osnovy Opredeleniya
Okislitel'no-Vosstanovitel'nogo Potentsiala i Yego Znacheniya
v Biologii [The Physicochemical Basis for Determining the
Redox Potential and Its Significance in Biology]: Usp. Biol.
Khim., No. 10.

NEOFITOVA, V. K., 1953. Gribnaya Flora Verkhney Neosushennoy
Zalezhi Torfa i Yeyë Rol' v Protsesse Torfoobrazovaniya
[The Mycoflora of the Upper, Undrained Peat Layers and
Its Role in the Process of Peat Formation]: Vestn. Leningr.
Gos. Un-ta, No. 10.

NOVOBRANTSEV, P. V., 1937. Razvitiye Bakteriy v Ozerakh v
Zavisimosti ot Nalichiya Legkousvoyayemogo Organicheskogo
Veshchestva [The Growth of Bacteria in Lakes in Relation

to the Presence of Readily Assimilable Organic Matter]: Mikrobiologiya, v. 6, No. 1.

NOVOGRUDSKIY, D. M., 1946a. Mikrobiologicheskiye Protsessy v Pochvakh Polupustyn'. I. Pochvennyye Mikroorganizmy i Gigroskopicheskaya Pochvennaya Vlaga [Microbiological Processes in the Soils of Semidesert Areas. I. Soil Microorganisms and the Hygroscopic Soil Moisture]: Mikrobiologiya, v. 15, No. 1.

NOVOGRUDSKIY, D. M., 1946b. Mikrobiologicheskiye Protsessy v Pochvakh Polupustyn'. II. Nizhniy Predel Pochvennoy Vlagi dlya Zhiznedeyatel'nosti Bakteriy [Microbiological Processes in the Soils of Semidesert Areas. II. The Lower Limit of the Soil Moisture for the Vital Activities of Bacteria]: Mikrobiologiya, v. 15, No. 6.

NOVOGRUDSKIY, D. M., 1956. Pochvennaya Mikrobiologiya [Soil Microbiology]: Alma-Ata, Izd-vo AN Kazakh. SSR.

OMELYANSKIY, V. L., 1927. Rol' Mikroorganizmov v Vyvetrivanii Gornykh Porod. Yub. Sb., Posvyashch. I. P. Borodinu [The Role of Microorganisms in Rock Weathering. Jubilee Symposium Volume Presented to I. P. Borodin]; see also "Izbr. Tr." ["Selected Writings"]: v. I, p. 523, Izd-vo AN SSSR, 1953.

OPPENHEIMER, C. H., 1958. Evidence of Fossil Bacteria in Phosphate Rocks: Pub. Inst. Mar. Sci., v. 5, pp. 156–159.

OSNITSKAYA, L. K., 1942. Prevrashcheniye Naftenovykh Kislot Mikroorganizmami [The Transformation of Naphthenic Acids by Microorganisms]: Mikrobiologiya, v. 11, No. 3.

OSNITSKAYA, L. K., 1948. Okisleniye Mikroorganizmami Naftenovykh Kislot i Naftenovykh Uglevodorodov [The Oxidation of Naphthenic Acids and Naphthenic Hydrocarbons by Microorganisms]: Doklady AN SSSR, v. 58, No. 1.

OZEROV, S. A., 1915. Mytishchinskaya Voda i Prichina Uvelicheniya Yeyë Zhestkosti [Runoff Water and the Causes of the Increase in Its Hardness]: Trudy Komissii Mosk. Gorodsk. Upravy.

PEL'SH, A. D., 1939. O Neodnorodnosti Zhidkoy Fazy Ila (Gidrokhimicheskaya Rol' Mikroorganizmov) [On the Nonhomogeneity of the Liquid Phase of Ooze (the Hydrochemical Role of Microorganisms)]: Uch. Zap. Leningr. Gos. Un-ta, No. 30; and Trudy Borodinskoy Biol. Stantsii, No. 8.

PERFIL'YEV, B. V., 1926. Novyye Dannyye o Roli Mikrobov v Rudoobrazovanii [New Data on the Role of Microbes in Ore Formation]: Izvestiya Geol. Komiteta, v. 45, No. 7.

PERFIL'YEV, B. V., 1927. K Metodike Izucheniya Ilovykh Otlozheniy [On the Methods of Studying Ooze Deposits]: Trudy Borodinskoy Biol. Stantsii, No. 5.

PERFIL'YEV, B. V., 1952. Izucheniye Zaileniya Vodoyemov i Absolyutnaya Geokhronologiya [Absolute Geochronology and the Study of Ooze Deposition in Bodies of Water]: Izv. Vses. Geogr. Ob-va, v. 84 (4).

PERFIL'YEV, B. V., and D. R. GABE, 1961. Kapillyarnyye Metody Izucheniya Mikroorganizmov [Capillary Methods of Studying Microorganisms]: Moscow—Leningrad, Izd-vo AN SSSR.

PESHKOV, M. A., 1948. Polienergichnyye Stadii Razvitiya Bakteriy v Svyazi s Izmeneniyem Ikh Yadernogo Apparata [The High-Energy Stages in the Development of Bacteria in Connection With the Study of Changes in the Structure of Their Nuclei]: Trudy In-ta Tsit., Gistol. i Embriol. AN SSSR, v. 1, No. 2.

PIA, J., 1928. Die vorzeitliche Spaltpilze und ihre Lebensspuren. Paleobiologica, v. 1, Nos. 5-7, pp. 457-474.

PLÖCHINGER, B., 1952. Fossile Bakterien in den Tennengebirge Manganschiefern: Mikroskopie, v. 7, Nos. 5-6, pp. 197-201.

PLUMMER, F. B., and I. W. WALLING, 1946. Laboratory Investigations of Chemical Changes in East Texas Oil Field Water Affecting Its Injection Into Subsurface Sands: Amer. Inst. Mining Met. Engrs., Contrib. Petroleum Division, v. 165, pp. 64-77.

POKROVSKIY, V. A., 1961. O Nizhney Granitse Biosfery na Territorii Yevropeyskoy Chasti SSSR, po Dannym Regional'nykh Geotermicheskikh Issledovaniy. Sb. "Geologicheskaya Deyatel'nost' Mikroorganizmov" [On the Lower Boundary of the Biosphere in the European Part of the USSR, On the Basis of Regional Geothermal Investigations. In the symposium volume, "The Geological Activity of Microorganisms"]: Trudy In-ta Mikrobiol. AN SSSR, No. 9.

PORFIR'YEV, V. B., 1949. K Voprosu o Genezise Ozokeritovykh Mestorozhdeniy. Trudy Nauchn. Soveshchaniya po Nefti, Ozokeritu i Goryuchim Gazam USSR [On the Genesis of Mineral Wax Deposits. Transactions of the Scientific Conference on Oil, Ozokerite and Combustible Gases in the Ukrainian SSR]: Izd-vo AN Ukr. SSR.

PORFIR'YEV, V. B., 1960. O Prirode Nefti. Sb. "Problema Proiskhozhdeniya Nefti i Gaza i Usloviya Formirovaniya Ikh Zalezhey" [On the Nature of Oil. In the symposium volume, "The Problem of the Origin of Oil and Gas and of the Conditions Governing the Formation of Their Deposits"]: Moscow, Gostoptekhizdat.

PORFIR'YEV, V. B., and I. V. GRINBERG, 1957. O Roli Vody v Protsessakh Preobrazovaniya Organicheskogo Veshchestva v Iskopayemom Sostoyanii [On the Role of Water in the Transformation of Organic Matter in the Fossil State]: Geol. Sbornik L'vovsk. Geol. Ob-va, No. 4.

PORTER, J. R., 1946. Bacterial Chemistry and Physiology: New York, John Wiley & Co.

POSTGATE, J., 1959. Sulphate Reduction by Bacteria: Annual Rev. Microbiol., v. 13, pp. 505–520.

PRECHT, H., 1879. (Cited in V. I. Vernadskiy, 1927).

PRINGSHEIM, E., 1949. Iron Bacteria: Biol. Rev., Cambridge Philos. Soc., v. 24, No. 2.

PUSTOVALOV, L. V., 1940. Petrografiya Osadochnykh Porod [Sedimentary Petrography]: Gostoptekhizdat.

RABINOWICH, E., 1951. Fotosintez [Photosynthesis]: IL.

RABOTNOVA, I. L., 1957. Rol' Fiziko-Khimicheskikh Usloviy (pH i rH₂) v Zhiznedeyatel'nosti Mikroorganizmov [The Role of the Physicochemical Environment (pH and rH₂) in the Vital Activities of Microorganisms]: Izd-vo AN SSSR.

RAHN, O., 1934. Salt, a Study of Its Bacterial Content: The National Provisioner.

RAVICH-SHCHERBO, Yu. A., 1928. O Roli Mikroorganizmov v Vyvetrivanii Gornykh Porod [The Role of Microorganisms in Rock Weathering]: Arkhiv. Biol. Nauk, v. 28, No. 3.

RAZUMOV, A. S., 1932. Pryamoy Metod Ucheta Bakteriy v Vode [A Direct Method of Counting Bacteria in Water]: Mikrobiologiya, v. 1, No. 2.

RAZUMOV, A. S., 1957. K Voprosu o Khemosinteze u Zhelezobakteriy [On the Question of Chemosynthesis by Iron Bacteria]: Mikrobiologiya, v. 26, No. 3.

REMEZOVA, T. S., 1950. Mikrobiologicheskaya Kharakteristika Donnykh Otlozheniy Vodoyemov Tamanskogo Poluostrova. Sb. "K Poznaniyu Sovremennykh Analogov Neftenosnykh Fatsiy" [A Microbiological Characterization of the Bottom Deposits of the Bodies of Water on the Taman' Peninsula. In the symposium volume, "On the Identification of Modern Analogues of Oil-Bearing Facies"]: Moscow, Gostoptekhizdat.

RENAULT, B., 1895. Sur Quelques Bactéries des Temps Primaires. Bull: du Mus. Nat. d'Histoire Natur., Pt. 1, pp. 168–172.

RHYANEN, 1958. Einwirkung einer Kupfergrube auf einen dystrophen See: Verhandl. Internat. Verein. Limnolog., v. 13, pp. 596–602.

RILEY, G. A., 1938. Plankton Studies. I. A Preliminary Investigation of the Plankton of the Tortugas Region: J. Marine Res., v. 1, pp. 335–352.

RILEY, G. A., 1939. Correlations in Aquatic Ecology With an Example of Their Application to Problems of Plankton Productivity: J. Marine Res., v. 2, pp. 56–73.

RILEY, G. A., 1941. Plankton Studies. V. Regional Summary: J. Marine Res., v. 4, pp. 162–171.

RIPPEL, A., 1935. Fossile Mikroorganismen in einem permischen Salzlager: Arch. Mikrobiol., v. 6, No. 4.

RODINA, A. G., 1951. O Roli Otdel'nykh Grupp Bakteriy v Produktivnosti Vodoyemov. Sb. "Problemy Gidrobiol. Vnutrennykh Vod" [On the Role of the Individual Groups of Bacteria in the Productivity of Bodies of Water. In the symposium volume, "Problems of the Hydrobiology of Inland Waters"]: Trudy Probl. i Temat. Soveshchaniya Zool. Inst. AN SSSR, No. 1.

ROMANENKO, V. I., 1959. Uchët Metanokislyayushchikh Bakteriy v Vode Metodom Radioavtografii Koloniy s Membrannykh Fil'trov [Counting Methane-Oxidizing Bacteria in Water by the Method of Radioautography of Colonies with Membrane Filters]: Byull. In-ta Biol. Vodokhran., No. 5.

RUBENCHIK, L. I., 1947. Sul'fatredutsiruyushchiye Bakterii [Sulfate-Reducing Bacteria]: Izd-vo AN SSSR.

RUBENCHIK, L. I., and D. G. GOYKHERMAN, 1939. K Mikrobiologii Bioanizotropnykh Solenykh Vodoyemov. Issledovaniye Slavyanskikh Ozer [On the Microbiology of Bioanisotropic Saline Bodies of Water. A Study of the Slavyansk Lakes]: Mikrobiologiya, v. 8, No. 5.

RYBAKOVA, S. G., 1957. Mikroflora Glubokikh Neftey Tretichnogo Vozrasta Apsheronskogo Poluostrova [The Microflora of the Deep Oils of Tertiary Age in the Apsheron Peninsula]: Doklady AN SSSR, v. 105, No. 4.

RYZHOVA, V. N., and M. V. IVANOV, 1961. Mikrobiologicheskiye Issledovaniya Prikarpatskikh Sernykh Mestorozhdeniy. Soobshcheniye 6. Ispol'zovaniye Rasseyanogo Organicheskogo Veshchestva Gornykh Porod dlya Protsessa Sul'fatreduktsii [Microbiological Investigations of the Carpathian Sulfur Deposits. Article 6. The Use of the Organic Matter Disseminated in Rocks for the Process of Sulfate Reduction]: Mikrobiologiya, v. 30, No. 6.

SAAKYAN, P. S., 1960. O Rudoobrazuyushchikh Flyuidakh i Rastvorakh. Sb. "Geneticheskiye Problemy Rud" [Mineralizing Fluids and Solutions. In the symposium volume, "Problems of Ore Genesis"]: Mezhdunar. Geol. Kongr., XXI Sessiya, Dokl. Sov. Geol.

SAMOYLOV, Ya. V., and A. G. TITOV, 1917-1918. Zhelezo-Margantsevyye Konkretsii so Dna Chernogo, Baltiyskogo i Barentsova Morey [Iron-Manganese Concretions from the Bottoms of the Black, Baltic and Barents Seas]: Trudy Geol. i Mineral. Muzeya AN SSSR, v. 3, No. 2.

SAMSONOV, P. F., and T. F. MERZHANOVA, 1932. K Voprosu ob Uchastii Mikroorganizmov v Protsesse Okisleniya Sery Otvalov Rudy Shor-Su [On the Question of the Participation of Microorganisms in the Oxidation of the Sulfur in the

Shor-Su Ore Dumps]: Osvedomit. Byull. N.-I. Rabot Sredaz-geokhimrazvedka, No. 2.

SANDERSON, R. T., 1953. Treatment of Shale: US Patent No. 2,641,565, Assigned to the Texaco Development Corporation.

SAPOZHNIKOV, D. G., 1951. Sovremennyye Osadki i Geologiya Oz. Balkhash [The Modern Sediments and the Geology of Lake Balkhash]: Trudy In-ta Geol. Nauk AN SSSR, Issue 132, Seriya Geol., No. 53.

SASLAWSKY, A. S., 1928. Zur Frage der Wirkung hoher Salz-konzentrationen auf die biochemischen Prozesse im Liman-schlamm: Zbl. Bakteriol., Abt. II, v. 73, pp. 18-27.

SAYDAKOVSKIY, S. Z., 1955. O Formirovanii Serovodorodnykh Vod Yugo-Zapadnoy Okrainy Russkoy Platformy [The Formation of the Hydrogen Sulfide Waters of the Southwestern Margin of the Russian Platform]: Doklady AN SSSR, v. 103, No. 2.

SAZONOVA, I. V., 1961. Rezul'taty Izucheniya Plastovoy Mikro-flory Neftyanykh Mestorozhdeniy Kuybyshevskoy Oblasti. Sb. "Geologicheskaya Deyatel'nost' Mikroorganizmov" [The Re-sults of a Study of the Stratal Microflora in the Oil Deposits of the Kuybyshev Region. In the symposium volume, "The Geological Activity of Microorganisms"]: Trudy In-ta Mikro-biologii AN SSSR, No. 9.

SCHWARTZ, W., and A. MÜLLER, 1958. Methoden der Geomikro-biologie: Freiberger Forschungshefte C 48, Angewandte Natur-wissenschaften.

SEMENOVICH, N. I., 1958. Limnologicheskiye Usloviya Nakopleniya Zhelezistykh Osadkov v Ozerakh [The Limnological Conditions Governing the Accumulation of Ferruginous Sediments in Lakes]: Trudy Lab. Ozeroved. AN SSSR, v. 6 (Trudy Limnol. Stantsii na Oz. Punnus-Yarvi, No. 1).

SHEYKO, V., 1901. Opyt Bakteriologicheskogo Issledovaniya Neftey [An Attempt at a Bacteriological Study of Oils]: Neft. Delo, No. 7.

SHILOVTSEV, S. P., 1952. Predisloviye k "Trudam Kurorta Ser-giyevskiye Mineral'nyye Vody" [Foreword to the "Publications of the 'Sergiyev Mineral Waters' Spa"]: v. I.

SHTURM, L. D., 1950a. Mikroskopicheskoye Issledovaniye Neft-yanykh Plastovykh Vod [A Microscopic Investigation of Oil Stratal Waters]: Mikrobiologiya, v. 19, No. 1.

SHTURM, L. D., 1950b. Materialy po Mikrobiologicheskomu Iss-ledovaniyu Neftyanykh Mestorozhdeniy Vtorogo Baku [Ma-terials for a Microbiological Investigation of the Vtoroye Baku Oil Deposits]: Trudy In-ta Nefti AN SSSR, v. 1 (3).

SHTURM, L. D., 1958. Issledovaniya po Assimilyatsii Uglevodorodov Mikroorganizmami (Obzor) [Investigations of the Assimilation of Carbons by Microorganisms (a Survey)]: Mikrobiologiya, v. 27, No. 6.

SHTURM, L. D., and T. L. SIMAKOVA, 1928. O Mikrobiologicheskom Issledovanii Obraztsov Sery iz Krymskikh i Turkestanskikh Mestorozhdeniy [A Microbiological Study of Samples of Sulfur From Deposits in the Crimea and Turkestan]: Doklady AN SSSR, Ser. A, No. (8).

SILVERMAN, M., and D. LUNDGREN, 1959a. Studies on the Chemoautotrophic Iron Bacterium Ferrobacillus ferrooxidans. I. An Improved Medium and a Harvesting Procedure for Securing High Cell Yields: J. Bacteriol., v. 77, No. 5.

SILVERMAN, M., and D. LUNDGREN, 1959b. Studies on the Chemoautotrophic Iron Bacterium Ferrobacillus ferrooxidans. II. Manometric Studies: J. Bacteriol., v. 78, No. 3.

SIMAKOVA, T. L., A. I. GORSKAYA, Z. A. KOLESNIK, O. P. BOLOTSKAYA, N. I. SHMONOVA and N. V. STRIGALEVA, 1958. Kharakter Izmeneniya Neftey v Anaerobnykh Usloviyakh pod Vliyaniyem Biogennogo Faktora. Sb. "Voprosy Obrazovaniya Nefti" [The Nature of the Changes in Oils under Anaerobic Conditions Through the Effect of the Biogenic Factor. In the symposium volume, "Questions of Oil Formation"]: Trudy Vses. N.-I. Geol.-Razv. In-ta, No. 128.

SIMAKOVA, T. L., and M. A. LOMOVA, 1958. K Izucheniyu Mikroflory Neftyanykh Mestorozhdeniy Vtorogo Baku. Sb. "O Proiskhozhdenii Nefti v Kamennougol'nykh i Permskikh Otlozheniyakh Volgo-Ural'skoy Oblasti" [On the Study of the Microflora in the Vtoroye Baku Oil Deposits. In the symposium volume, "On the Origin of the Oil in the Carboniferous and Permian Deposits of the Volga-Urals Region"]: Trudy Vses. N.-I. Geol.-Razved. In-ta, No. 117.

SLAVNINA, G. P., 1958. Geobiokhimicheskiye Issledovaniya Podzemnykh Vod Podmoskov'ya. Sb. Statey po Rezul'tatam Geokhimich. Issl. [Geobiochemical Studies of the Ground Waters of the Moscow Basin. Collection of Articles on the Results of Geochemical Investigations]: Trudy Vses. N.-I. Geol.-Razv. In-ta, No. 10. Gostoptekhizdat.

SMIRNOV, S. S., 1955. Zona Okisleniya Sul'fidnykh Mestorozhdeniy [The Oxide Zone of Sulfide Deposits]: Moscow—Leningrad, Izd-vo AN SSSR.

SMIRNOVA, Z. S., 1957. Opredeleniye Granitsy Proniknoveniya Bakteriy iz Glinistogo Rastvora v Kerny Razlichnykh Porod [The Determination of the Boundary of Penetration of Bacteria from a Clay Solution into the Cores of Various Kinds of Rocks]: Mikrobiologiya, v. 26, No. 6.

SOKOLOV, A. S., 1958. Osnovnyye Zakonomernosti Geologicheskogo Stroyeniya i Razmeshcheniya Osadochnykh Mestorozhdeniy Samorodnoy Sery [The Principal Regularities Characterizing the Geologic Structure and the Emplacement of

Sedimentary Deposits of Native Sulfur]: Sovetskaya Geologiya, No. 5.

SOKOLOV, V. A., 1948. Ocherki Genezisa Nefti [Outlines of the Genesis of Oil]: Moscow, Gostoptekhizdat.

SOKOLOVA, G. A., 1959. Zhelezobakterii Ozera Glubokogo [The Iron Bacteria of Lake Glubokoye]: Mikrobiologiya, v. 28, No. 2.

SOKOLOVA, G. A., 1961a. Rol' Zhelezobakteriy v Dinamike Zheleza v Glubokom Ozere [The Role of the Iron Bacteria in the Iron Cycle of Lake Glubokoye]: Trudy Vses. Gidrobiol. Ob-va, v. 11.

SOKOLOVA, G. A., 1961b. Zakonomernosti Rasprostraneniya Thiobacillus thioparus v Podzemnykh Vodakh [The Laws Governing the Propagation of Thiobacillus thioparus in Ground Waters]: Mikrobiologiya, v. 30, No. 3.

SOROKIN, Yu. I., 1952. Novyye Priyemy Vydeleniya Sul'fatvosstanavlivayushchikh Bakteriy [New Methods of Separating Sulfate-Reducing Bacteria]: Trudy In-ta Mikrobiol. AN SSSR, No. 2.

SOROKIN, Yu. I., 1956. K Teorii Khemoavtotrofii [On the Theory of Autotrophic Chemosynthesis]: Mikrobiologiya, v. 25, No. 3.

SOROKIN, Yu. I., 1957. K Voprosu o Sposobnosti Sul'fatvosstanavlivayushchikh Bakteriy Ispol'zovat' Metan dlya Vosstanovleniya Sul'fatov do Serovodoroda [On the Question of the Ability of the Sulfate-Reducing Bacteria to Use Methane in Reducing Sulfates to Hydrogen Sulfide]: Doklady AN SSSR, v. 115, No. 4.

SOROKIN, Yu. I., 1958. Rol' Khemosinteza v Produktsii Organicheskogo Veshchestva v Vodokhranilishchakh. III. Produktivnost' Khemosinteza v Vodnoy Tolshche v Letniy Period [The Role of Chemosynthesis in the Production of Organic Matter in Reservoirs. III. The Productivity of Chemosynthesis in the Water Layer During the Summer Period]: Mikrobiologiya, v. 27, No. 3.

SOROKIN, Yu. I., 1959. Opredeleniye Produktivnosti Fotosinteza Fitoplanktona v Vodnoy Tolshche s Pomoshch'yu C^{14} [Determination of the Productivity of Photosynthesis of Phytoplankton in the Water Layer by Means of C^{14}]: Fiziologiya Rasteniy, v. 6 (1).

SPERANSKAYA, T. A., 1935. Dannyye po Izucheniyu Organicheskogo Veshchestva Ilovykh Ozernykh Otlozheniy [Data on the Study of the Organic Matter in Lake Ooze Deposits]: Trudy Limnol. Stantsii v Kosine, No. 20.

STADNIKOV, G. L., 1935. Iskopayemyye Ugli, Goryuchiye Slantsy, Asfal'tovyye Porody, Asfal'ty i Neft' [Fossil Coals, Combustible Shales, Asphalt Rocks, Asphalts and Oil]: ONTI.

STARKEY, R., and S. WAKSMAN, 1943. Fungi Tolerant to Extreme Acidity and High Concentrations of Copper Sulfate: J. Bacteriol., v. 45, No. 2.

STARKEY, R. L., 1950. Relations of Microorganisms to the Transformation of Sulphur in Soil: Soil Sci., v. 70, No. 1.

STEEMANN NIELSEN, E., 1952. The Use of Radioactive Carbon (C^{14}) for Measuring Organic Production in the Sea: J. Conseil Perman. Internat. Explorat. Mer, v. 18, No. 2, p. 117.

STEEMANN NIELSEN, E., 1955. The Production of Antibiotics by Plankton Algae and Its Effect Upon Bacterial Activities in the Sea: Deep-Sea Res., Suppl. 3, pp. 281-286.

STEEMANN NIELSEN, E., 1958. A Survey of Recent Danish Measurements of the Organic Productivity in the Sea: Rapp. et Procès-verbaux Réunions Conseil Perman. Internat. Explorat. Mer, v. 144, pp. 38-46.

STEPANYANTS, O. S., 1938. Akhtal'skoye Polimetallicheskoye Mestorozhdeniye [The Akhtal' Polymetallic Deposit]: Yerevan, Izd-vo AN Arm. SSR.

STRAKHOV, N. M., 1947a. Karbonaty v Sovremennykh Lagunnykh Vodoyemakh i Ikh Znacheniye dlya Problemy Dolomitoobrazovaniya [The Carbonates in Modern Lagoons and their Significance for the Problem of Dolomite Formation]: Byull. Mosk. Ob-va Ispyt. Prirody, Otd. Geol., No. 4.

STRAKHOV, N. M., 1947b. Zhelezorudnyye Fatsii i Ikh Analogi v Istorii Zemli [Iron-Ore Facies and Their Analogues in the History of the Earth]: Trudy In-ta Geol. Nauk AN SSSR, No. 73, Seriya Geologicheskaya, No. 22.

STRAKHOV, N. M., 1960. Osnovy Teorii Litogeneza [Foundations of the Theory of Lithogenesis]: v. I. Izd-vo AN SSSR.

STRUGGER, S., 1948. Fluorescence-Microscope Examination of Bacteria in Soil: J. Amer. Chem. Soc., v. 55.

SULIN, V. A., 1948. Gidrogeologiya Neftyanykh Mestorozhdeniy [The Hydrogeology of Oil Deposits]: Moscow, Gostoptekhizdat.

TAGEYEVA, N. V., 1955. Eksperimental'nyye Issledovaniya po Izucheniyu Proiskhozhdeniya Plastovykh Khloridnykh Shchelochnozemel'no-Natriyevykh Rassolov. Sb. "Voprosy Izucheniya Podzemnykh Vod i Inzh.-Geol. Protsessov" [Experimental Researches Into the Origin of Stratal Alkaline-Earth—Sodium Chloride Brines. In the symposium volume, "Problems of the Study of Ground Waters and Processes Important to Engineering Geology"]: Izd-vo AN SSSR.

TAUSON, V. O., 1925. K Voprosu ob Usvoyenii Parafina Mikroorganizmami [On the Question of the Utilization of Paraffin by Microorganisms]: Zhurn. Russk. Bot. Ob-va, v. 9.

TAUSON, V. O., 1928a. Bakterial'noye Okisleniye Syrykh Neftey [The Bacterial Oxidation of Crude Oils]: "Neft. Khoz-vo," v. 14.

TAUSON, V. O., 1928b. K Voprosu ob Okislenii Voskov Mikroorganizmami [On the Question of the Oxidation of Waxes by Microorganisms]: Zhurn. Russk. Bot. Ob-va, v. 13.

TAUSON, V. O., 1928c. Naftalin kak Istochnik Ugleroda dlya Bakteriy [Naphthalene as a Source of Carbon for Bacteria]: Trudy Otd. Fiz.-Khim. Osnov Zhizni, Seriya 1-aya, No. 2. Izdvo Gos. Timiryazevsk. In-ta.

TAUSON, V. O., 1928d. Okisleniye Fenantrena Bakteriyami [The Oxidation of Phenanthrene by Bacteria]: Trudy Otd. Fiz.Khim. Osnov Zhizni, Seriya 1-aya, No. 3. Izd-vo Gos. Timiryazevsk. In-ta.

TAUSON, V. O., 1947. Nasledstvo Mikrobov [The Inheritance of Microbes]: Izd-vo AN SSSR.

TAUSON, V. O., 1948. Velikiye Dela Malen'kikh Sushchestv [The Great Deeds of Small Creatures]: Izd-vo AN SSSR.

TAUSON, V. O., and V. I. ALESHINA, 1932. O Vosstanovlenii Sul'fatov Bakteriyami v Prisutstvii Uglevodorodov [The Bacterial Reduction of Sulfates in the Presence of Hydrocarbons]: Mikrobiologiya, v. 1, No. 3.

TAUSON, V. O., and S. L. SHAPIRO, 1950. Obshcheye Napravleniye Protsessa Okisleniya Nefti Bakteriyami. Sb. "Osnovnyye Polozheniya Rastitel'noy Bioenergetiki" [The General Trend of the Process of Oxidation of Oil by Bacteria. In the symposium volume, "The Fundamental Principles of the Science of Biological Energy"]: Izd-vo AN SSSR.

TAUSON, V. O., and I. Ya. VESELOV, 1934. O Bakterial'nom Razlozhenii Tsiklicheskikh Soyedineniy pri Vosstanovlenii Sul'fatov [The Bacterial Decomposition of Cyclical Compounds in the Reduction of Sulfates]: Mikrobiologiya, v. 3, No. 3.

TAYLOR, E. W., 1958. The Examination of Water and Water Supplies: London, J. A. Churchill.

TEMPLE, K., and A. COLMER, 1951. The Autotrophic Oxidation of Iron by a New Bacterium, Thiobacillus ferrooxidans: J. Bacteriol., v. 62, No. 5.

TEMPLE, K., and E. DELCHAMPS, 1953. Autotrophic Bacteria and the Formation of Acid in Bituminous Coal Mines: Appl. Microbiol., v. 1, No. 5.

THODE, H. G., R. K. WANLESS and WALLOUCH, 1954. The Origin of Native Sulphur Deposits From Isotope Fractionation Studies: Geochim. et Cosmochim. Acta, v. 5, No. 6.

TOKAREV, V. A., 1947. Serobakterii na Pomoshch' Neftyanoy Promyshlennosti [Sulfur Bacteria as an Aid to the Oil Industry]: Priroda, No. 9.

TROFIMOV, B. A., 1954. Zhizn' v Geologicheskikh Epokhakh [Life in Geologic Epochs]: Priroda, No. 6.

UKLONSKIY, A. S., 1940. Paragenezis Sery i Nefti [The Para-
    genesis of Sulfur and Oil]: Tashkent, Izd-vo Uzbeksk. Filiala
    AN SSSR.
UPDEGRAFF, D. M., and G. B. WREN, 1953. Secondary Recovery
    of Petroleum Oil by Desulfovibrio: US Patent No. 2,660,550,
    Assigned to Socony Vacuum Oil Company.
UPDEGRAFF, D. N., and G. B. WREN, 1954. The Release of
    Oil From Petroleum-Bearing Materials by Sulfate-Reducing
    Bacteria: Appl. Microbiol., v. 2, No. 6.
USPENSKAYA, V. I., 1939. Proniknoveniye Krasok i Medi v Kletki
    Vodorosley v Svyazi s pH i rH2 vnutri Kletok i v Srede
    [The Penetration of Stains and Copper Into the Cells of Algae
    in Relation to the pH and the rH2 Within the Cells and in the
    Medium]: Mikrobiologiya, v. 8, No. 8.
UPSENSKIY, Ye. Ye., 1936. K Energetike Zhiznennykh Protsessov.
    Sb. "Dokl. i Mat. Sessii Biol. In-ta im. Timiryazeva,
    Posvyashch. 15-letiyu Dnya Smerti K. A. Timiryazeva" [On
    the Energy of Life Processes.   In the symposium volume,
    "Reports and Materials of the Session of the Timiryazev
    Biological Institute Held on the Fifteenth Anniversary of the
    Death of K. A. Timiryazev"]: Moscow.
VAN DELDEN, A., 1904. Beitrag zur Kenntnis des Sulfatreduktion
    durch Bakterien: Zbl. Bakteriol., Abt. II, v. 11.
VARSANOF'YEVA, V. A., 1945. Razvitiye Zhizni na Zemle [The
    Development of Life on the Earth]: Nauka i Zhizn', Nos. 8-9
    and No. 10.
VASSOYEVICH, N. B., 1955. O Proiskhozhdenii Nefti [On the
    Origin of Oil]: Trudy VNIGRI, Novaya Seriya, No. 83, Geol.
    Sb. No. 1.
VASSOYEVICH, N. B., and G. A. AMOSOV, 1953. Izmeneniye Neftey
    v Zemnoy Kore [The Alteration of Oils Within the Earth's
    Crust]: Geol. Sb. NITO pri VNIGRI, v. 11.
VEBER, V. V., 1955. Voprosy Nefteobrazovaniya po Dannym Izuch-
    eniya Sovremennykh Morskikh Osadkov [Aspects of the Forma-
    tion of Oil From the Standpoint of the Study of Modern Marine
    Sediments]: "Sovetskaya Geologiya," Sb. 46.
VERNADSKIY, V. I., 1912-1922. Opyt Opisatel'noy Mineralogii,
    t. I [A Proposed Descriptive Mineralogy, Vol. I]. See also
    Izbr. Soch. [Selected Writings]: v. II, pp. 300, 450, Izd-vo
    AN SSSR, 1955.
VERNADSKIY, V. I., 1912-1922. Opyt Opisatel'noy Mineralogii,
    t. II [A Proposed Descriptive Mineralogy, Vol. II]. See
    also Izbr. Soch. [Selected Writings]: v. III, Izd-vo AN SSSR,
    1959.
VERNADSKIY, V. I., 1923. Zhivoye Veshchestvo i Khimiya Morya
    [Living Matter and the Chemistry of the Sea]: 2nd ed.

VERNADSKIY, V. I., 1927. Istoriya Mineralov Zemnoy Kory [History of the Minerals in the Earth's Crust]: v. I, No. 2, Leningrad. See also Izbr. Soch. [Selected Writings]: v. IV, book 1, Izd-vo AN SSSR, 1959.

VERNADSKIY, V. I., 1933. Istoriya Mineralov Zemnoy Kory, t. II. Istoriya Prirodnykh Vod, ch. 1 [History of the Minerals in the Earth's Crust, Vol. II. History of Natural Waters, Part 1]: Leningrad, Goskhimtekhizdat. See also Izbr. Soch. [Selected Writings]: v. IV, book 2, Izd-vo AN SSSR, 1960.

VINBERG, G. G., 1948. Bioticheskiy Balans Chërnogo Ozera [The Biotic Equilibrium of Lake Chernoye]: Byull. Mosk. Ob-va Ispyt. Prirody, Otd. Biol., v. 53.

VINBERG, G. G., 1960. Pervichnaya Produktsiya Vodoyemov [The Primary Production of Bodies of Water]: Izd-vo AN BSSR, Minsk.

* VINOGRADSKIY, S. N., 1888. Über Eisenbakterien: Bot. Ztg., v. 46.

* VINOGRADSKIY, S. N., 1922. Eisenbakterien als Anorgoxydanten: Zblt. Bak., Abt. II, v. 57.

* VINOGRADSKIY, S. N., 1924. Sur l'Etude Microscopique du Sol: Compt. Rend. Ac. Sci. Paris, v. 179.

VINOGRADSKIY, S. N., 1952. Mikrobiologiya Pochvy [Soil Microbiology]: Izd-vo AN SSSR.

VISHNIAC, W., and M. SANTER, 1957. The Thiobacilli: Bacteriol. Revs, v. 21, No. 3.

VOLKOVA, O. Yu., and A. D. TASHINSKAYA, 1961. O Biogennom Obrazovanii Serovodoroda v Podzemnykh Vodakh Pyatigorskogo i Nekotorykh Drugikh Mestorozhdeniy [On the Biogenic Formation of Hydrogen Sulfide in the Waters of the Pyatigorsk and Certain Other Deposits]: Mikrobiologiya, v. 30, No. 4.

VOLODIN, N. A., 1935. Burovyye Vody Promysla Imeni Ordzhonikidze, Okrashennyye v Rozovyy Tsvet [The Pink-Colored Waters in the Workings of the Ordzhonikidze Mine]: Azerbaydzh. Neft. Khozyaystvo, No. 6.

VOLOGDIN, A. G., 1947. Geologicheskaya Deyatel'nost' Mikroorganismov [The Geologic Activity of Microorganisms]: Izvestiya AN SSSR, Seriya Geologicheskaya, No. 3.

VOLOGDIN, A. G., 1962. Zhizn' Zemli [Life on the Earth]: Izd-vo AN SSSR.

VOROSHILOVA, A. A., and YE. V. DIANOVA, 1950. O Bakterial'nom Okislenii Nefti i Yeyë Migratsii v Prirodnykh Vodoyemakh

---

*The asterisks indicate papers by S. N. Vinogradskiy which were published in Russian translation in his book, "Mikrobiologiya Pochvy" ["Soil Microbiology"]: Izd-vo AN SSSR, 1952.

[The Bacterial Oxidation of Oil and Its Migration in Natural Bodies of Water]: Mikrobiologiya, v. 19, No. 3.

VOROSHILOVA, A. A., and Ye. V. DIANOVA, 1952. Okislyayu-shchiye Neft' Bakterii—Pokazateli Intensivnosti Biologiches-kogo Okisleniya Nefti v Prirodnykh Usloviyakh [Oil-Oxidizing Bacteria—Indicators of the Intensity of the Biological Oxidation of Oil Under the Conditions of Nature]: Mikrobiologiya, v. 21, No. 4.

WAKSMAN, S. A., and J. S. JOFFE, 1921. Acid Production by a New Sulfur-Oxidizing Bacterium: Science, n.s., v. 53, p. 216.

WAKSMAN, S. A., and J. S. JOFFE, 1922. Microorganisms Concerned in the Oxidation of Sulphur in the Soil. II. Thiobacillus thiooxidans, a New Sulphur-Oxidizing Organism Isolated From the Soil: J. Bacteriol., v. 7, pp. 239-256.

WALTER, H., 1931. Die Hydratur der Pflanze: Jena.

WEED, K. C., 1956. Cananeas Program for Leaching in Place: Mining Eng., v. 8, p. 721.

WINOGRADSKY, See VINOGRADSKIY.

YAROSLAVTSEV, I. N., 1952. Biologicheskiye Faktory Vyvetriv-aniya v Vysokogor'yakh [The Biological Factors Affecting Weathering in High Mountain Areas]: Priroda, No. 12.

YENIKEYEV, P. B., and I. S. SINDAROVSKIY, 1947. Razrabotka Pozharnogo Uchastka Glavnoy Linii na Krasnogvardeyskom Rudnike [Development of the Fire Area of the Main Line in the "Red Guard" Mine]: Gorn. Zhurn., No. 6.

YUROVSKIY, A. Z., 1948. Sera Kamennykh Ugley [The Sulfur in Rock Coals]: Moscow, Ugletekhizdat.

ZARUBINA, Z. M., N. N. LYALIKOVA and Ye. I. SHMUK, 1959. Issledovaniye Mikrobiologicheskogo Okisleniya Pirita Uglya [A Study of the Microbiological Oxidation of the Pyrite in Coal]: Izvestiya AN SSSR, Seriya Tekhnicheskaya, No. 1.

ZAVARITSKIY, A. N., 1950. Metamorfizm i Metasomatoz Kolchedan-nykh Mestorozhdeniy. Kolchedannyye Mestorozhdeniya Urala [The Metamorphism and Metasomatism of Copper-Pyrite Deposits. The Copper-Pyrite Deposits of the Urals]: Izd-vo AN SSSR.

ZAVARZINA, N. B., 1955. Izucheniye Prichin, Zaderzhivayushchikh Razvitiye Mikroorganizmov v Tolshche Ilovykh Otlozheniy Ozera Biserova [A Study of the Causes Inhibiting the Growth of Microorganisms in the Ooze Deposits of Lake Biserovo]: Mikrobiologiya, v. 24, No. 5.

ZIMMERLEY, S., D. WILSON and J. PRATER, 1958. Cyclic Leaching Process Employing Iron-Oxidizing Bacteria: US Patent No. 2,829,964, Assigned to Kennecott Copper Corp.

ZoBELL, C. E., 1943. Bacteria as a Geological Agent, With Particular Reference to Petroleum: Petrol. World, v. 40, pp. 30-43.

ZoBELL, C. E., 1946a. Function of Bacteria in the Formation and Accumulation of Petroleum: Oil Weekly, v. 120, pp. 30-36.

ZoBELL, C. E., 1946b. Bacteriological Process for Treatment of Fluid-Bearing Earth Formations: US Patent No. 2,413,278, Assigned to the American Petroleum Institute.

ZoBELL, C. E., 1946c. Action of Microorganisms on Hydrocarbons: Bacteriol. Rev., v. 10, No. 1.

ZoBELL, C. E., 1947a. Bacterial Release of Oil From Oil-Bearing Materials, I, II: World Oil, v. 126, No. 13, pp. 36-44; v. 127, No. 1, pp. 35-40.

ZoBELL, C. E., 1947b. Microbial Transformation of Molecular Hydrogen in Marine Sediments, With Particular Reference to Petroleum: Bull. Amer. Assoc. Petrol. Geol., v. 31.

ZoBELL, C. E., 1958. Ecology of Sulfate-Reducing Bacteria: Producer's Monthly, v. 22, No. 7.

ZoBELL, C. E., and C. W. GRANT, 1942. Bacterial Activity in Dilute Nutrient Solutions: Science, v. 96, p. 189.

ZoBELL, C. E., C. W. GRANT and H. F. HAAS, 1943. Marine Microorganisms Which Oxidize Petroleum Hydrocarbons: Bull. Amer. Assoc. Petrol. Geol., v. 27, p. 1175.

ZoBELL, C. E., and F. H. JOHNSON, 1949. The Influence of Hydrostatic Pressure on the Growth and Viability of Terrestrial and Marine Bacteria: J. Bacteriol., v. 57, No. 2.

ZoBELL, C. E., and C. H. OPPENHEIMER, 1950. Some Effects of Hydrostatic Pressure on the Multiplication and Morphology of Marine Bacteria: J. Bacteriol., v. 60, pp. 771-781.

Index

A

Acid, formation of, in coal-mine waters, 140, 141, 203-205
Acid in mine waters, preventing formation of, 205
Actinomyces balotrichis, 35
Aerobic oxidation of oil and gas, 92
Alpine geosynclinal cycle, 2
Anaerobic decomposition of oil, 84-92
Argon, absence of, in gases as criterion of anaerobic oil decomposition, 90

B

Bacillus, various species, 32, 33
Bacteria, critical hydrostatic pressure for growth of, in rocks, 34
  destruction of oil by, with formation of gas in stratum, 191, 192
  distribution of, by groups in oil stratal waters, 87
  factors determining distribution of, in oil deposits, 45-50
  fossil, in iron ores, 51, 54
    in phosphorites, 53, 58
    in rock salt, 57
    in salt domes, 51, 53
    methods of studying, 50-54
  hydrocarbon-oxidizing, areal distribution of, in natural gas deposit, 98
    list of species of, 97
  iron-oxidizing, use of, in removing sulfur from coal, 205, 206
  positive and negative roles of, in mine and river waters, 203, 204
  methane-forming, distribution of, in oil and gas deposits, 85
  presence of, in oil and gas deposits, 66, 67
  nitrogen, presence of, in ground waters, 65
  numbers of, in oil stratal waters, 49, 50
    in petroliferous and nonpetroliferous rocks, 47
    in waters from various sources, 42
  oligocarbophilic, 43
  optimum temperature for life of, in lithosphere, 31

  physiological groups of, in rocks and ground waters, 64-68
  presence of, in oil and oil stratal waters, 44, 45
    in sulfide ore deposits, 209, 210
  proteolytic, relative to albumin in sediments, 27
  purple sulfur, presence of, in ground waters, 65
  role of, in biogenesis of oil, 82, 83
    in decomposition of vegetation, 83
    in weathering processes, 69, 70
  saprophytic, numbers of, in ground waters, 64
  spore-forming, maximum temperature for active life processes of, 32
  sulfate-reducing, activity of, in Carpathian sulfur deposits, 199, 200
    as agents of anaerobic oil decomposition, 91
    effect of salt concentrations in oil stratal waters on development of, 38
    inhibiting development of, in oil deposits, 196-197
    occurrence of, in oil stratal waters, 65, 66, 85
    resistance of, to salt concentration and composition, 37
    role of, in deposition of molecular sulfur in lakes, 108
    in formation of hydrogen sulfide in ground waters, 179-183
    use of, for increasing secondary extraction of oil, 190, 191
    vertical distribution of, in lakes, 110
  temperature limits for activity of, in lithosphere, 31-35
  thermophilic, in lithosphere, 32-33
  use of, in extraction of copper from low-grade ores, 207-209
    in ground waters to locate ore deposits, 209-210
  (*See also* Microorganisms, Thiobacteria)
Bacterial chemosynthesis, 72
  as a source of organic matter in Black Sea, 73
  relationship of, to oil genesis, 73, 74